GCSE Higher Mathematics ②

B V Hony, D A Turner, I A Potts and W R J Waite

Longman

Pearson Education Limited
Edinburgh Gate
Harlow
Essex
CM20 2JE
England

First published 2002
Third impression 2003
ISBN 0 582 50357 4

Editorial by First Class Publishing Ltd, Surrey GU21 2YW
Cover design by Moondisks Limited
Typeset by TechSet Ltd, Gateshead, Tyne and Wear.

Printed in Great Britain by Scotprint, Haddington.

The publisher's policy is to use paper manufactured from sustainable forests.

Acknowledgements

We are grateful for permission to reproduce copyright material: Australian Associated Press for permission to reproduce an extract from 'What Australia Drinks' published in *The Mercury* on 23 May 1995; QA Photos for the photographs of the Channel tunnel on pages 170 and 171; and Miriam Rothschild for permission to reproduce a photograph taken by her with the assistance of Dr Kim Parker.

We are also grateful to Edexcel, NEAB and OCR for permission to reproduce copyright examination questions. Edexcel, NEAB and OCR can accept no responsibility whatsoever for the accuracy or method of working in the answers, where given.

Contents

* Each section of Unit 4 starts with a summary of topics covered in *Book 1*.
The revision exercises then test *all* topics of *Book 1* and Units 1–3 of *Book 2*.

Course Structure

iv

Preface

This 2-book series is written for students following the GCSE Higher tier specification for all examination boards. It comprises a Student's Book for each year of the course with fully integrated ICT activities available on a companion website.

The course has been structured to enable these two books to be used in a sequential manner, both in the classroom and by students working on their own.

Each book contains five units of work. Each unit contains five sections in the topic areas:
Number, Algebra, Sequences & Graphs, Shape & Space and Handling Data

In each unit, there are concise explanations and worked examples, plus numerous exercises that will help students to build up confidence.

Paired questions, with answers to the odd numbered questions at the end of the Student's Book, allow students to check their answers and monitor their own progress. More difficult questions, to stretch the more able student, appear at the end of some exercises, and are identified by blue question numbers.

Non-calculator questions are clearly marked giving consistent practice at numerical skills.

Parallel exercises are provided allowing students to consolidate basic principles before being challenged with more difficult questions.

♦ **Non-starred exercises** are designed for students working towards GCSE grades B/C.
  These could be used by students working towards the Intermediate tier specifications.

♦ **Starred exercises** are designed to challenge students working towards GCSE grades A/A*.

Real data has been used where possible and ICT links are identified by the icon 🖥 to give opportunities for students to investigate topics further using these skills. Both within the sections and at the end of each unit, challenges and investigations encourage students to think for themselves.

♦ **Challenges** provide questions applying the basic principles in unusual situations.

♦ **Investigations** prepare students for the coursework component of GCSE examinations.
  Students can refer to the 'How to Tackle Investigations' section at the end of Book 1 before embarking on any of these investigations.

Consolidation is a recurring theme throughout the course and general skills are reinforced at the end of each unit.

♦ **Pairs of parallel revision exercises** appear at the end of each of the five sections within each unit.

♦ **Numeracy practice exercises** provide opportunities for students to flex their basic arithmetic and algebraic skills.

♦ **Fact-finders** test numerical comprehension of real data. Students use the information supplied to answer thought-provoking questions. The shaded questions are more challenging.

♦ **Summaries** précis the major points of each unit.

♦ **Examination practice papers** (calculator and non-calculator) test students' understanding of material and terminate each of the units in Book 1 and the first 4 units of Book 2.

Revision is vital to the success of every student and has been covered in Unit 4 of Book 2:

♦ Summaries of all topics in Book 1 plus ten Revision exercises

♦ Six examination exercises covering the entire syllabus with cross-referencing to the text for students who might require assistance

Advanced preparation is provided in the final unit of the series, Unit 5 of Book 2, to allow the student who wishes to prepare for Advanced Level material exposure to some of the foundation stones of higher-level mathematics: modelling, algebra, areas under graphs, rates of change and standard deviation.

Number 1

Inverse proportion

An example of **direct proportion** is: when one quantity doubles, the other quantity also doubles.

For example, if 2 kg of apples cost £3, then 4 kg of the same type of apple costs £6.

This relationship produces a straight line graph through the origin.

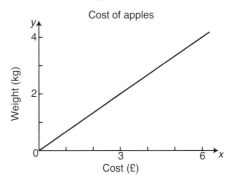

However, with **inverse proportion**, when one quantity doubles, the other quantity is halved.

For example, if one machine produces 100 lamp shades in one hour, then it will take two machines half an hour to produce the same number of identical lamp shades.

This relationship produces a **hyperbola**.

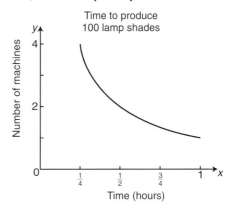

Activity 1

For a distance of x km, a train travels at a constant speed of 80 km/hour for 2 hours. Clearly, if the speed were halved, the same journey would take twice as long. This is an example of **inverse proportion**. This can be written as:

It takes 2 hours to travel x km at 80 km/hour

$\therefore$ It takes 4 hours to travel x km at 40 km/hour

♦ Copy and complete this table for the train journey over x km:

Time (hours)	1	2	4	6	7	8
Speed (km/hour)		80	40			

To find the speed for 6 and 7 hours, look at the product of the speed and time for the other entries.

♦ Plot the points on a suitable graph of speed against time. Join the points with a *smooth curve*. Comment on the shape of the curve.

Example 1

Last year, a farmer used 3 ploughs to plough a field and it took 17 hours. This year the same job must be done in less than 5 hours. How many ploughs will be needed?

It took 17 hours to plough with 3 ploughs

∴ in 1 hour it will require 3×17 ploughs

∴ in 5 hours it will require $\dfrac{3 \times 17}{5}$ ploughs

$$= 10.2 \text{ ploughs}$$

Therefore to plough the field in *less* than 5 hours the farmer will need to use 11 ploughs.

Exercise 1

1 It takes 1 person 8 days to dig a trench. To dig a similar trench, how long would it take with

   a 2 people?   **b** 4 people?   **c** 3 people?

2 It takes 2 people 12 days to build a wall. To build a similar wall, how long would it take with:

   a 1 person?   **b** 4 people?   **c** 5 people?

3 Using the facts in Question 1, how many people are required to dig a similar trench in

   a 1 day?   **b** half a day?   **c** quarter of a day?

4 Using the facts in Question 2, how many people are required to build a similar wall in

   a 2 days?   **b** 3 days?   **c** 4 days?

5 It has been estimated that it took 4000 men 30 years to build the largest pyramid, at Giza, in Egypt, over four and a half thousand years ago. How long would it have taken with

   a 2000 men?   **b** 8000 men?   **c** 100 men?

6 Using the facts in Question 5, how many men would have been required to build it in

   a 3 years?   **b** 6 years?   **c** 300 years?

7 Over a given distance, a train travels at a constant speed of 120 km/hour for 3 hours.

   a Over the same distance, how long will it take a train travelling at 30 km/hour?

   b Find the speed of another train that takes 5 hours to travel the same distance.

8 A car's average fuel consumption is 40 mpg (miles per gallon) and, over a certain distance, it uses 4 gallons of fuel.

   a Over the same distance, another car uses 5 gallons. Find its mpg.

   b The fuel consumption of another car is 8 mpg. How much fuel did this car use to travel the same distance?

Exercise 1★

1 In an exam room, the total power of all the light bulbs has to be 3000 watts.

a Copy and complete this table.

Number of light bulbs (N)	Power of each bulb (P)
6	
	600
2	
	100
N	P

b Write down the relationship between N and P.

2 The construction of the Channel Tunnel created about 100 000 man-years of employment in the UK. In theory, this meant that it could have been built by 20 000 men in 5 years.

a Copy and complete this table.

Number of years (N)	Number of men (M)
1	
	50 000
4	
	10 000
N	M

b Write down the relationship between N and M.

3 In a scientific experiment three different substances, A, B and C, *each of the same mass*, are used. Substance A has a density of $4\,\text{g/cm}^3$ and a volume of $3\,\text{cm}^3$.

a Find the density of $1\,\text{cm}^3$ of substance B.

b Find the volume of substance C with a density of $8\,\text{g/cm}^3$.

4 A water tank is filled in 8 minutes with a rate of flow of 40 litres/minute.

a How long will it take to fill at 32 litres/minute?

b What rate of flow will fill it in 25 minutes?

5 Using the facts for Question 2, copy and complete this table.

Number of men	Number of tunnels	Time in years
100 000	4	
100 000		2
20 000	8	
	2	0.5

6 One mosquito can produce 9 million young in 500 hours. Copy and complete this table.

Number of mosquitoes	Number of young	Time
1	18 000	
1		1 second
	9 million	1 hour
500		500 hours

7 One cow belches 200 g of methane in a day. Copy and complete these statements.

a 1 cow belches 1 kg of methane in ... days.

b ... cows belch 1000 kg of methane in 5 days.

c 3100 million cows belch ... tonnes of methane in 365 days.

(It is estimated that there are about 3100 million cows in the world.)

8 During the University Boat Race, a commentator said, 'every member of the crew does the equivalent amount of work as someone who lifts a 25 kg sack of potatoes, from the floor to shoulder height, 36 times a minute for 18 minutes'.

a What total mass is 'lifted' by one crew member during the 18 minute race?
Give your answer to 2 significant figures.

b A lorry is to be loaded with sacks of potatoes each of mass 25 kg.
Work out, correct to 1 significant figure, how long it should take

(i) 1 crew member to load 4 tonnes

(ii) 8 crew members to load 4 tonnes

(iii) 4 crew members to load 4 tonnes

(iv) 8 crew members to load 1 tonne

Recurring decimals

Remember

♦ All fractions can be written as decimals which either *terminate* or produce a set of *recurring* digits.

♦ Fractions that produce terminating decimals have, in their simplest form, denominators with only 2 or 5 as factors. This is because 2 and 5 are the only factors of 10 (*decimal* system).

♦ The dot notation is used to indicate which digits recur.
For example 0.2323... = 0.2̇3̇, 0.056056... = 0.0̇56̇.

Example 2

Change $0.\dot{5}$ to a fraction.

$x = 0.5555555\ldots$	(Multiply both sides by 10)
$10 \times x = 5.5555555\ldots$	(Subtract the top from the bottom)
$9 \times x = 5$	(Divide both sides by 9)
$x = \frac{5}{9}$	

Example 3

Change $0.\dot{7}\dot{9}$ to a fraction.

$x = 0.797979\ldots$	(Multiply both sides by 100)
$100 \times x = 79.797979\ldots$	(Subtract the top from the bottom)
$99 \times x = 79$	(Divide both sides by 99)
$x = \frac{79}{99}$	

Example 4

Change $0.\dot{1}2\dot{3}$ to a fraction.

$x = 0.123123\ldots$	(Multiply both sides by 1000)
$1000 \times x = 123.123123\ldots$	(Subtract the top from the bottom)
$999 \times x = 123$	(Divide both sides by 999)
$x = \frac{123}{999}$	

Key Point

To change a simple recurring decimal to a fraction

No. of repeating digits	First, multiply by	Last, divide by
1	10	9
2	100	99
3	1000	999

Exercise 2

For Questions 1–6, change the fraction to a terminating decimal.

1 $\frac{3}{8}$ **2** $\frac{1}{20}$ **3** $\frac{2}{25}$ **4** $\frac{3}{16}$ **5** $\frac{9}{32}$ **6** $\frac{11}{80}$

For Questions 7–14, change the fraction to a recurring decimal, writing your answers using the dot notation.

7 $\frac{2}{9}$ **8** $\frac{5}{9}$ **9** $\frac{2}{11}$ **10** $\frac{4}{11}$

11 $\frac{4}{15}$ **12** $\frac{8}{15}$ **13** $\frac{7}{18}$ **14** $\frac{17}{18}$

For Questions 15–18, *without* doing any calculation, write down the fractions that produce terminating decimals.

15 $\frac{5}{11}$, $\frac{9}{16}$, $\frac{2}{3}$, $\frac{5}{6}$, $\frac{2}{15}$

16 $\frac{5}{7}$, $\frac{4}{33}$, $\frac{5}{32}$, $\frac{7}{30}$, $\frac{3}{8}$

17 $\frac{2}{19}$, $\frac{3}{20}$, $\frac{5}{48}$, $\frac{5}{64}$, $\frac{13}{22}$

18 $\frac{3}{40}$, $\frac{5}{17}$, $\frac{7}{80}$, $\frac{9}{25}$, $\frac{9}{24}$

For Questions 19–30, change each of these recurring decimals to a fraction in its simplest form.

19 $0.\dot{3}$ **20** $0.\dot{4}$ **21** $0.\dot{5}$ **22** $0.\dot{6}$ **23** $0.\dot{7}$ **24** $0.\dot{9}$

25 $0.0\dot{7}$ **26** $0.0\dot{1}$ **27** $0.0\dot{3}$ **28** $0.0\dot{2}$ **29** $0.0\dot{5}$ **30** $0.0\dot{6}$

Exercise 2★

For Questions 1–8, change each fraction to a recurring decimal, writing your answers using the dot notation.

1 $\frac{7}{15}$ **2** $\frac{11}{18}$ **3** $\frac{7}{150}$ **4** $\frac{11}{180}$

5 $2\frac{10}{33}$ **6** $4\frac{4}{33}$ **7** $\frac{149}{495}$ **8** $\frac{139}{495}$

For Questions 9–12, *without* doing any calculation, write down the fractions that produce terminating decimals.

9 $\frac{7}{17}$, $\frac{11}{16}$, $\frac{2}{3}$, $\frac{7}{40}$, $\frac{3}{15}$

10 $\frac{2}{7}$, $\frac{7}{40}$, $\frac{5}{32}$, $\frac{1}{30}$, $\frac{7}{8}$

11 $\frac{3}{17}$, $\frac{19}{20}$, $\frac{3}{25}$, $\frac{5}{64}$, $\frac{13}{24}$

12 $\frac{11}{125}$, $\frac{5.5}{128}$, $\frac{7}{81}$, $\frac{9}{512}$, $\frac{9}{48}$

For Questions 13–24, change each of these recurring decimals to a fraction in its simplest form.

13 $0.\dot{2}\dot{4}$ **14** $0.\dot{3}\dot{8}$ **15** $0.\dot{3}0$ **16** $0.9\dot{3}$ **17** $9.0\dot{1}\dot{9}$ **18** $8.0\dot{2}\dot{9}$

19 $0.0\dot{2}\dot{7}$ **20** $0.0\dot{3}\dot{6}$ **21** $0.\dot{4}1\dot{2}$ **22** $0.\dot{1}0\dot{1}$ **23** $0.\dot{3}8\dot{4}$ **24** $0.\dot{4}7\dot{4}$

For Questions 25–28, change each recurring decimal to a fraction.

25 $0.1\dot{2}$ **26** $0.8\dot{6}$ **27** $0.05\dot{6}$ **28** $0.15\dot{6}$

For Questions 29–30, write each answer as a recurring decimal.

29 $0.7\dot{3} \times 0.0\dot{5}$ **30** $0.0\dot{7} \times 0.\dot{2}14285\dot{7}$

Exercise 3 (Revision)

1 A rounders field can be cut with 2 mowers in 3 hours.

   a How long would it take to cut the field with 3 mowers?

   b How many mowers would be required to cut the field in 1 hour?

2 A car's average fuel consumption is 60 mpg (miles per gallon) and, over a certain distance, it uses 3 gallons of fuel.

   a Over the same distance, another car uses 12 gallons. Find its mpg.

   b The fuel consumption of another car is 25 mpg. How much fuel did this car use to travel the same distance?

3 Write these fractions as terminating decimals.

   a $\frac{1}{5}$ **b** $\frac{1}{8}$ **c** $\frac{1}{20}$

4 Change these fractions to recurring decimals, writing your answers using the dot notation.

   a $\frac{1}{6}$ **b** $\frac{4}{9}$ **c** $\frac{3}{7}$

5 Change these recurring decimals to fractions.

   a $0.\dot{2}$ **b** $0.0\dot{7}$ **c** $0.\dot{2}\dot{3}$

Exercise 3★ (Revision)

1 The average fuel consumption of Mrs Singh's car is 15 km/litre. On a particular journey, she used 48 litres of fuel.

   a If she had used 45 litres, find her fuel consumption.

   b If the fuel consumption had been 18 km/litre, how much fuel would she have used?

2 One honey bee has to travel 75 000 km to produce 500 g of honey.
Copy and complete these statements.

   a ... honey bees would each have to travel 3000 km to produce a total of 500 g.

   b 25 honey bees would each have to travel 60 km to produce a total of ... g.

   c 25 honey bees would each have to travel ... km to produce a total of 1 tonne.

3 Given that $\frac{1}{13} = 0.\dot{0}7692\dot{3}$, write $\frac{2}{13}$ as a recurring decimal.

4 Which of these produce terminating decimals? $\frac{11}{25}$, $\frac{5}{12}$, $\frac{7}{256}$, $\frac{9}{500}$, $\frac{9}{15}$

5 Write these recurring decimals as fractions in their simplest form.

   a $0.\dot{2}$ **b** $0.0\dot{1}$ **c** $0.6\dot{7}$ **d** $3.0\dot{4}\dot{5}$

6 Change $\frac{11}{90}$ to a recurring decimal.

Algebra 1

Proportion

If two quantities are related to each other, given enough information, it is possible to write a formula describing this relationship.

Activity 2

Copy and complete this table to show which paired items are directly related.

Variables	Related? Y/N
Area of a circle (A) and its radius (r)	Y
Circumference of a circle (C) and its diameter (d)	
Volume of water in a tank (V) and its weight (w)	
Distance travelled (D) at constant speed and time taken (t)	
Number of pages in a book (N) and its thickness (t)	
Mathematical ability (M) and a person's height (h)	
Wave height in the sea (W) and wind speed (s)	
Grill temperature (T) and time to toast bread (t)	

Direct proportion

Linear relationships

When water is poured into an empty fish tank, each litre poured in increases the depth by a fixed amount.

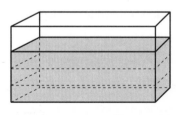
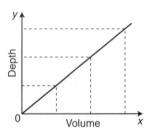

A graph of depth, y, against volume, x, is a straight line through the origin showing a linear relationship.

In this case, y is **directly proportional** to x. If y is doubled, so is x. If y is halved, so is x, etc.

This relationship can be expressed in *any* of these ways.

◆ *y* is directly proportional to *x*.

◆ *y* varies directly with *x*.

◆ *y* varies as *x*.

All these statements mean the same.

In symbols, direct proportion relationships can be written as $y \propto x$. The $\propto$ sign can then be replaced by '$= k$' to give $y = kx$, where k is the **constant of proportionality**. The graph of $y = kx$ is the equation of a straight line through the origin, with slope k.

Key Point

y is directly proportional to x
is written as $y \propto x$
and this means $y = kx$, for some fixed value k.

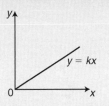

Example 1

The extension, y cm, of a spring is directly proportional to the mass, x kg, hanging from it.
If $y = 12$ cm when $x = 3$ kg, find

a the formula for y in terms of x

b the extension y cm when a 7 kg mass is attached

c the mass x kg that produces a 20 cm extension

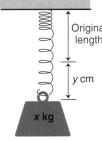

a y is proportional to x, so $y \propto x$ $y = kx$

$y = 12$ when $x = 3$ $12 = k \times 3$

                                  $k = 4$

The formula is therefore $y = 4x$.

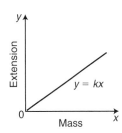

b When $x = 7$ $y = 4 \times 7$

The extension produced from a 7 kg mass is 28 cm.

c When $y = 20$ cm $20 = 4x$

                                 $x = 5$

The extension produced from a 5 kg mass is 20 cm.

Exercise 4

1   y is directly proportional to x. If $y = 10$ when $x = 2$, find

  a the formula for y in terms of x

  b y when $x = 6$

  c x when $y = 25$

2   d is directly proportional to t. If $d = 100$ when $t = 25$, find

  a the formula for d in terms of t

  b d when $t = 15$

  c t when $d = 180$

3   An elastic string's extension y cm varies as the mass x kg that hangs from it.
The string extends 4 cm when a 2 kg mass is attached.

  a Find the formula for y in terms of x.

  b Find y when $x = 5$.

  c Find x when $y = 15$.

4   A bungee jumping rope's extension e m varies as the mass M kg of the person attached to
it. If $e = 4$ m when $M = 80$ kg, find

  a the formula for e in terms of M

  b the extension for a person with a mass of 100 kg

  c the mass of a person with extension 6 m

5   An ice-cream seller discovers that, on any particular day, the number of sales (I) is directly
proportional to the temperature ($t\,^\circ$C). 1500 sales are made when the temperature is 20 °C.
How many sales might be expected on a day with a temperature forecast of 26 °C?

6   The number of people in a swimming pool (N) varies as the daily temperature ($t\,^\circ$C).
175 people swim when the temperature is 25 °C. The pool's capacity is 200 people.
Will people have to queue and wait if the temperature reaches 30 °C?

Exercise 4★

1   The speed of a stone, v m/s, falling off a cliff is directly proportional to the time, t seconds,
after release. Its speed is 4.9 m/s after 0.5 s.

  a Find the formula for v in terms of t

  b What is the speed after 5 s?

  c At what time is the speed is 24.5 m/s?

2   The cost, c pence, of a tin of salmon varies directly with its mass, m g. The cost of a
450 g tin is 150 p.

  a Find the formula for c in terms of m.

  b How much does a 750 g tin cost?

  c What is the mass of a tin costing £2?

3 The distance a honey bee travels, d km, is directly proportional to the mass of honey, m g, it produces. A bee travels 150 000 km to produce 1 kg of honey.

    a Find the formula for d in terms of m.

    b What distance is travelled by a bee to produce 10 g of honey?

    c What mass of honey is produced by a bee travelling once around the world, a distance of 40 000 km?

4 The mass of sugar m g used in making oat-meal cookies varies directly as the number of cookies, n. 3.25 kg are used to make 500 cookies.

    a Find the formula for m in terms of n.

    b What mass of sugar is needed for 150 cookies?

    c How many cookies can be made using 10 kg of sugar?

5 The height of a tree, h m, varies directly with its age, y years. A 9 m tree is 6 years old.

    a Find the formula for h in terms of y.

    b What height is a tree that is 6 months old?

    c What is the age of a tree that is 50 cm tall?

6 The yearly profit (£P million) made by an Internet company, 'Line-On', is directly proportional to the annual amount spent (£x million) on its advertising on TV, radio, newspapers and the Internet. Its profit in one year from TV advertising alone amounts to £6 million at a cost of £1.5 million.

    a Copy and complete this table.

Advertising medium	£x million	£P million
TV	1.5	6
Radio	0.5	
Newspapers		5
Internet	0.1	

    b How much total profit was made by 'Line-On' in this particular year?

    c What was the total amount spent by the company on advertising itself in this year?

    d Express x as a percentage of P. Comment on your answer.

Nonlinear relationships

Water is poured into an empty inverted cone. Each litre poured in will result in a different depth increase.

A graph of volume, y, against depth, x, will illustrate a direct **nonlinear relationship**.

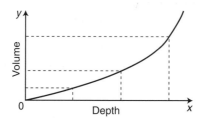

This relationship can be expressed in *either* of these ways.

◆ y is directly proportional to x cubed.
◆ y varies as x cubed.

Both these statements mean the same.

In symbols, this relationship is written as $y \propto x^3$.
The $\propto$ sign can then be replaced by '$= k$' so $y = kx^3$,
where k is the constant of proportionality.

Key Point

y varies as x squared is written as $y \propto x^2$ and this means $y = kx^2$, for some fixed value, k.

Example 2

Express these relationships as equations with constants of proportionality

a y is directly proportional to x squared. $\qquad\qquad y \propto x^2 \quad \Rightarrow \quad y = kx^2$

b m varies directly with the cube of n. $\qquad\qquad m \propto n^3 \quad \Rightarrow \quad m = kn^3$

c s is directly proportional to the square root of t. $\qquad s \propto \sqrt{t} \quad \Rightarrow \quad s = k\sqrt{t}$

d v squared varies as the cube of w. $\qquad\qquad v^2 \propto w^3 \quad \Rightarrow \quad v^2 = kw^3$

Example 3

The cost of Luciano's take-away pizzas (C pence) is directly proportional to the square of the diameter (d cm) of the pizza. A 30 cm pizza costs 675 p.

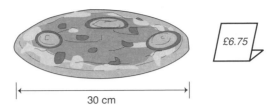

£6.75

|←——————— 30 cm ———————→|

a What is the price of a 20 cm pizza?
b What size of pizza should you expect for £4.50?

a C is proportional to d^2, so $C \propto d^2$ $C = kd^2$
$C = 675$ when $d = 30$ $675 = k(30)^2$
$$k = 0.75$$

The formula is therefore $C = 0.75d^2$.
When $d = 20$ $C = 0.75(20)^2$
$$C = 300$$

The cost of a 20 cm pizza is £3.

b When $C = 450$ $450 = 0.75d^2$
$$d^2 = 600$$
$$d = \sqrt{600} = 24.5 \text{ (3 s.f.)}$$

A £4.50 pizza should be 24.5 cm in diameter.

Exercise 5

1 y is directly proportional to the square of x. If $y = 100$ when $x = 5$, find
  a the formula for y in terms of x **b** y when $x = 6$
  c x when $y = 64$

2 p varies directly as the square of q. If $p = 72$ when $q = 6$, find
  a the formula for p in terms of q **b** p when $q = 3$
  c q when $p = 98$

3 v is directly proportional to the cube of w. If $v = 16$ when $w = 2$, find
  a the formula for v in terms of w **b** v when $w = 3$
  c w when $v = 128$

4 m varies directly as the square root of n. If $m = 10$ when $n = 1$, find
  a the formula for m in terms of n **b** m when $n = 4$
  c n when $m = 50$

5 The distance fallen by a parachutist, y m, is directly proportional to the square of the time taken, t secs. If 20 m are fallen in 2 s, find

  a the formula relating y in terms of t b the distance fallen through in 3 s

  c the time taken to fall 100 m

6 'Espirit' perfume is available in bottles of different volumes of similar shapes.
 The price £P is directly proportional to the cube of the bottle height h cm.
 A 10 cm high bottle is £50. Find

  a the formula of P in terms of h b the price of a 12 cm high bottle

  c the height of a bottle of 'Espirit' costing £25.60

Exercise 5★

1 If f is directly proportional to g^2, copy and complete this table.

g	2	4	
f	12		108

2 If m is directly proportional to n^3, copy and complete this table.

n	1		5
m	4	32	

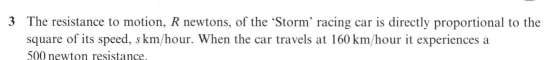

3 The resistance to motion, R newtons, of the 'Storm' racing car is directly proportional to the square of its speed, s km/hour. When the car travels at 160 km/hour it experiences a 500 newton resistance.

  a Find the formula for R in terms of s.

  b What is the car's speed when it has a resistance of 250 newtons?

4 The height of Giants, H metres, is directly proportional to the cube root of their age, y years. An 8-year-old Giant is 3 m tall.

  a Find the formula for H in terms of y.

  b What age is a 12 m tall Giant?

5 The surface area of a sphere is directly proportional to the square of its radius.
 A sphere of radius 10 cm must be increased to x cm if its surface area is to be doubled. Find x.

6 The mass of spherical cannon balls is directly proportional to the cube of their diameter.
 A cannon ball of diameter 100 cm must be decreased to y cm if its mass is to be halved. Find y.

Activity 3

The German astronomer, Kepler (1571–1630) devised three astronomical laws.
Kepler's third law gives the relationship between the orbital period, t days, of a planet around the Sun, and its mean distance, d km, from the Sun.

In simple terms, this law states that t^2 is directly proportional to d^3.

◆ Find a formula relating t and d given that the Earth is 150 million km from the Sun.

◆ Copy and complete this table.

Planet	d (million km)	Orbital period around Sun t (earth days)
Mercury	57.9	
Jupiter		4315

◆ Try to find the values of d and t for other planets in the Solar System, and see if they fit the same relationship.

Inverse proportion

The temperature of a cup of coffee decreases as time increases.

A graph of temperature (T) against time (t) shows an **inverse relationship**.

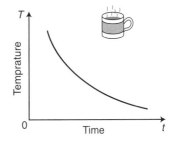

This can be expressed as: 'T is inversely proportional to t.'
In symbols, this is written as

$$T \propto \frac{1}{t}$$

The $\propto$ sign can then be replaced by '$= k$', so

$$T = \frac{k}{t}$$

where k is the constant of proportionality.

Key Point

If y is inversely proportional to x, the graph of y plotted against x looks like this.

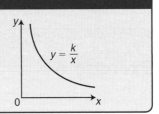

Example 4

Express these equations as relationships with constants of proportionality.

a y is inversely proportional to x squared.

$$y \propto \frac{1}{x^2} \quad \Rightarrow \quad y = \frac{k}{x^2}$$

b m varies inversely as the cube of n.

$$m \propto \frac{1}{n^3} \quad \Rightarrow \quad m = \frac{k}{n^3}$$

c s is inversely proportional to the square root of t.

$$s \propto \frac{1}{\sqrt{t}} \quad \Rightarrow \quad s = \frac{k}{\sqrt{t}}$$

d v squared varies inversely as the cube of w.

$$v^2 \propto \frac{1}{w^3} \quad \Rightarrow \quad v^2 = \frac{k}{w^3}$$

Example 5

Sound intensity, I dB (decibels), is inversely proportional to the square of the distance, d m, from the source. At a music festival, it is 110 dB, 3 m away from a loudspeaker.

a Find the formula relating I and d.

I is inversely proportional to d^2 $\qquad I = \dfrac{k}{d^2}$

$I = 110$ when $d = 3$ $\qquad\qquad 110 = \dfrac{k}{3^2}$

$\qquad\qquad\qquad\qquad\qquad\qquad k = 990$

The formula is therefore $I = \dfrac{990}{d^2}$.

b Calculate the sound intensity 2 m away from the speaker.

When $d = 2$ $\qquad\qquad\qquad I = \dfrac{990}{2^2} = 247.5$

The sound intensity is 247.5 dB, 2 m away (enough to cause deafness).

c At what distance away from the speakers is the sound intensity 50 dB?

When $I = 50$ $\qquad\qquad\qquad 50 = \dfrac{990}{d^2}$

$\qquad\qquad\qquad\qquad\qquad d^2 = 19.8$

$\qquad\qquad\qquad\qquad\qquad d = 4.45$ (3 s.f.)

The sound intensity is 50 dB, 4.45 m away from the speakers.

Exercise 6

1 y is inversely proportional to x. If $y = 4$ when $x = 3$, find

    a the formula for y in terms of x **b** y when $x = 2$ **c** x when $y = 3$

2 d varies inversely with t. If $d = 10$ when $t = 25$, find

    a the formula for d in terms of t **b** d when $t = 2$.   **c** t when $d = 50$

3 *m* varies inversely with the square of *n*. If $m = 4$ when $n = 3$, find

    a the formula for *m* in terms of *n*

    b *m* when $n = 2$ **c** *n* when $m = 1$

4 *V* varies inversely with the cube of *w*. If $V = 12.5$ when $w = 2$, find

    a the formula for *V* in terms of *w*

    b *V* when $w = 1$ **c** *w* when $V = 0.8$

5 Light intensity, *I* candle-power, from a lighthouse is inversely proportional to the square of the distance, *d* m, of an object from this light source. If $I = 10^5$ when $d = 2$ m, find

    a the formula for *I* in terms of *d*   **b** the light intensity at 2 km

6 The life-expectancy, *L* days, of a cockroach varies inversely with the square of the density, *d* people/m², of the human population near its habitat. If $L = 100$ when $d = 0.05$, find

    a the formula for *L* in terms of *d*

    b the life-expectancy of a cockroach in an area where the human population density is 0.1 people/m²

Exercise 6★

1 If *a* is inversely proportional to b^2, copy and complete this table.

b	2	5	
a	50		2

2 A scientist gathers this data.

t	1	4		10
r	20		4	2

    a Which of these relationships describes the collected data?

$$r \propto \frac{1}{\sqrt{t}} \qquad r \propto \frac{1}{t} \qquad r \propto \frac{1}{t^2}$$

    b Copy and complete the table.

3 The electrical resistance, *R* ohm, of a fixed length of wire is inversely proportional to the square of its radius, *r* mm. If $R = 0.5$ when $r = 2$, find

    a the formula for *R* in terms of *r*

    b the resistance of a wire of 3 mm radius

4 The cost of Mrs Janus' electricity bill, £*C*, varies inversely with the average temperature, *t* °C, over the period of the bill. If the bill is £200 when the temperature is 25 °C, find

    a the formula relating *C* in terms of *t*

    b the bill when the temperature is 18 °C

    c the temperature generating a bill of £400

5 The number of people shopping at Harrison's Cornershop per day, N, varies inversely with the square root of the average outside temperature, $t\,°C$.

a Copy and complete this table.

Day	N	t
Mon	400	25
Tues		20
Wed	500	

b The remainder of the week (Thurs to Sat) has a hot spell with a constant daily average temperature of $30\,°C$. What is the average number of people per day who shop at Harrison's for that week? (The shop is closed on Sundays.)

6 The time for a pendulum to swing, $T\,s$, is inversely proportional to the square root of the acceleration due to gravity, $g\,m/s^2$. On Earth $g = 9.8$, but on the Moon, $g = 1.9$. Find the time of swing on the Moon of a pendulum whose time taken to swing on Earth is $2\,s$.

Activity 4

This graph shows an inverse relationship between the body mass, $M\,kg$, of mammals and their average heart pulse, P beats/min.

◆ Use the graph to complete this table.

	P (beats/min)	M (kg)
Hare		3
Dog	135	
Man		70
Horse	65	

◆ An unproven theory in Biology states that the hearts of all mammals beat the same number of beats in an average life-span.

▸ If man lives on average for 75 years, calculate the total number of heart beats in an average life-span.

▸ Test out this theory by calculating the expected life-span of the creatures in the table above.

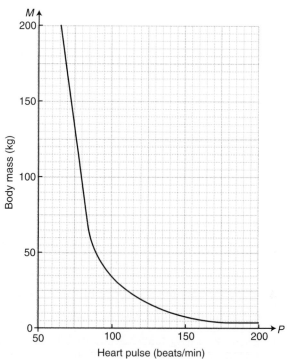

Body mass (kg)

Heart pulse (beats/min)

Exercise 7 (Revision)

1 y is directly proportional to x. If $y = 12$ when $x = 2$, find

    a the formula for y in terms of x **b** y when $x = 7$ **c** x when $y = 66$

2 p varies as the square of q. If $p = 20$ when $q = 2$, find

    a the formula for p in terms of q **b** p when $q = 10$ **c** q when $p = 605$

3 The cost, £c, of laying floor tiles is directly proportional to the square of the area, $a\,\mathrm{m}^2$, to be covered. If a $40\,\mathrm{m}^2$ kitchen floor costs £1200 to tile, find

    a the formula for c in terms of a

    b the cost of tiling a floor of area $30\,\mathrm{m}^2$

    c the area of floor covered by these tiles costing £600

4 The time taken, t hours, to make a set of 20 curtains is inversely proportional to the number of people, n, who work on them. One person would take 80 hours to finish the task. Copy and complete this table.

n	1	2	4	
t	80			10

Exercise 7★ (Revision)

1 y squared varies as z cubed. If $y = 20$ when $z = 2$, find

    a the formula relating y to z

    b y when $z = 4$

    c z when $y = 100$

2 m is inversely proportional to the square root of n.
If $m = 2.5 \times 10^7$ when $n = 1.25 \times 10^{-7}$, find

    a the formula for m in terms of n

    b m when $n = 7.5 \times 10^{-4}$

    c n when m is one million

3 The frequency of radio waves, f MHz, varies inversely as their wavelengths, μ metres. If Radio 1 has $f = 99$ and $\mu = 3$, what is the wavelength of the World Service on 198 kHz?

4 If y is inversely proportional to the nth power of x, copy and complete this table.

x	0.25	1	4	25
y		10	5	

Find a formula for y in terms of x.

Graphs 1

Perpendicular lines

> **Remember**
>
> A *positive* gradient looks like ╱   A *negative* gradient looks like ╲

Activity 5

♦ On graph paper, draw axes with the x-axis labelled from 0 to 10 and the y-axis labelled from 0 to 6. Use the same scale for both axes.

♦ Plot the points A(1, 0), B(3, 2) and C(0, 5). Join A to B and B to C.

♦ Measure the angle between the lines AB and BC.

♦ Find m_1, the gradient of AB, and m_2, the gradient of CB. Multiply the two gradients together and put your results in a copy of this table.

Point A	Point B	Point C	m_1	m_2	$m_1 \times m_2$
(1, 0)	(3, 2)	(0, 5)			
(5, 0)	(3, 4)	(5, 5)			
(10, 3)	(7, 2)	(6, 5)			

♦ Repeat for the two other sets of points in the table. Comment on your results.

♦ Investigate if your conclusion holds for other points.

♦ Copy and complete these statements.

Lines that are .... have the same gradient ($m_1 = m_2$).

Lines that are .... have $m_1 \times m_2 = -1$.

Example 1

a Find the gradient of a line perpendicular to a line of gradient -2.

$m_1 \times m_2 = -1$ for perpendicular lines. This can be rearranged as $m_2 = -\dfrac{1}{m_1}$.

$$m_2 = -\frac{1}{-2} = \frac{1}{2}$$

b Find the gradient of a line perpendicular to a line of gradient $\frac{1}{3}$.

$$m_2 = -\frac{1}{\frac{1}{3}} = -1 \times \frac{3}{1} = -3$$

Example 2

Show that the line joining A(−2, 5) to B(−1, 1) is perpendicular to the line joining P(1, 3) to Q(5, 4).

First draw a sketch diagram
and mark on the rise and run for each line.

The gradient of AB is $\dfrac{-4}{1} = -4$.

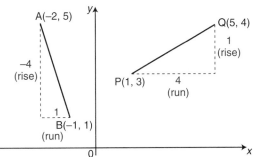

The gradient of PQ is $\dfrac{1}{4}$.

The product of the gradients

is $-4 \times \dfrac{1}{4} = -1$

so the lines are perpendicular.

Example 3

Find the equation of the straight line perpendicular to $y = 3x - 2$ that passes through (3, 1).

First, draw a sketch showing
what is required.

The gradient of $y = 3x - 2$ is 3.

Lines perpendicular to the given
line must have a gradient of $-\dfrac{1}{3}$,

because $3 \times \left(-\dfrac{1}{3}\right) = -1$.

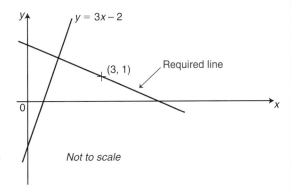

The required equation is $y = -\dfrac{1}{3}x + c$

$$= -\dfrac{x}{3} + c$$

(3, 1) is on the line, so to find c, substitute the values $x = 3$ and $y = 1$

$$1 = -\dfrac{3}{3} + c$$

$$c = 2$$

The required equation is $y = -\dfrac{x}{3} + 2$.

Exercise 8

For Questions 1–8, write down the gradients of the lines perpendicular to lines of the given gradient.

1 2

2 3

3 −3

4 −1

5 $-\dfrac{1}{3}$

6 $\dfrac{2}{3}$

7 $\dfrac{3}{2}$

8 $-\dfrac{1}{4}$

For Questions 9–12, find the gradients of lines parallel and perpendicular to AB.

9 A is (1, 1), B is (3, 2)

10 A is (1, 2), B is (2, 5)

11 A is (1, 4), B is (2, 1)

12 A is (0, 3), B is (2, 2)

For Questions 13–18, decide whether AB is parallel or perpendicular to PQ.

13 A(1, 4), B(2, 0), P(0, 1), Q(5, 2)

14 A(0, 0), B(−1, 3), P(1, 0), Q(4, 1)

15 A(3, 3), B(4, 6), P(4, 1), Q(6, 7)

16 A(1, 2), B(2, 7), P(4, 1), Q(5, 7)

17 A(0, 2), B(4, 1), P(4, 2), Q(5, 6)

18 A(1, 8), B(2, 6), P(3, 7), Q(5, 3)

19 Find the equation of the straight line perpendicular to $y = -2x + 1$ that passes through (4, 3).

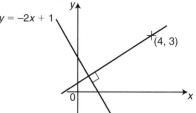

20 Find the equation of the straight line perpendicular to $y = \frac{1}{4}x + 7$ that passes through (1, 2).

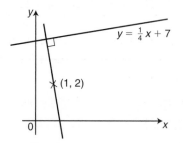

21 A mast for a lighting rig at an outdoor concert was held up during erection by wire ropes as shown in the diagram.

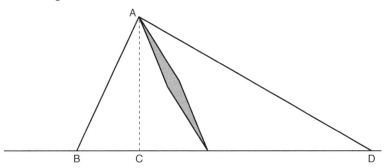

A is 6 m above the ground, C is vertically below A, BD is 15 m and BC is 3 m.

a Find the gradient of AB.

b Find the gradient of AD.

c Are AB and AD at right angles? Give a reason for your answer.

22 'Speedy Pot' Joe has been snookered. The situation is shown in the diagram, where corner A of the snooker table has been taken as the origin.

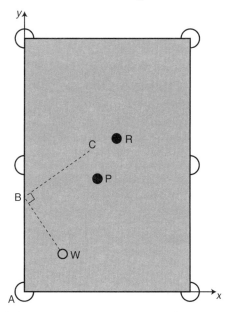

Joe wants to hit the red ball R at (5, 8) with the white ball W at (2, 2) but the pink ball P at (4, 6) is in the way. He aims the white ball at a point B (0, 5) on the cushion.

a What is the gradient of the line BW?

By playing one of his special trick shots, Joe makes the ball bounce off the cushion along the line BC, which is perpendicular to BW.

b What is the gradient of BC?

c What is the equation of the line BC?

d Does the white ball hit the red ball?

Exercise 8★

For Questions 1–8, write down the gradients of lines perpendicular to lines of the given gradient.

1 4

2 5

3 $-\dfrac{1}{5}$

4 $\dfrac{2}{5}$

5 $\dfrac{2}{3}$

6 $-\dfrac{3}{4}$

7 -6

8 -4

For Questions 9–12, find the gradients of lines parallel and perpendicular to AB.

9 A is $(-4, -1)$, B is $(4, 2)$

10 A is $(-2, 4)$, B is $(2, 1)$

11 A is $(-3, 1)$, B is $(1, 6)$

12 A is $(-3, 2)$, B is $(4, 4)$

13 Find the equation of the line that is perpendicular to $y = 8x - 14$ and passes through $(0, 8.4)$.

14 Find the equation of the line that is perpendicular to $9x - 5y = -3$ and passes through $(9, -3)$.

15 Find the equation of the perpendicular bisector of A$(4, 1)$ and B$(-2, -1)$.

16 Find the equation of the perpendicular bisector of A$(4, 0)$ and B$(-2, 4)$.

17 An architect is designing a roof on a building.
The cross-section is shown in the diagram.
The point D is vertically below A,
BC is 3 m and CD is 5 m.

   a The gradient of AB is 0.8.
   How high is A above D?

   b AF is at right angles to AB.
   What is the gradient of AF?

   c What is the width of the building?

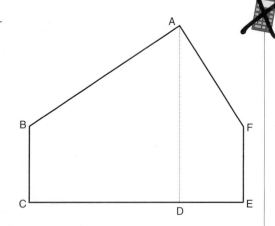

18 Rachael is designing the letter M for a project.
The point A is $(0, 0)$, the point E is $(7, 0)$ and B is $(2, 6)$.

   a ED and AB are parallel and the same length.
   Find the coordinates of D.

   b The gradient of BC is $-\dfrac{3}{2}$. Find the equation of BC.

   c CD is to be perpendicular to BC.
   Find the equation of CD.

   d Find the coordinates of C.

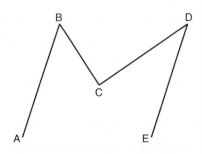

19 Find the gradients of lines perpendicular to lines of gradient

a $-\dfrac{b}{a}$ **b** $-\dfrac{1}{p}$ **c** m

20 Find b such that the line from the origin to $(3, 4b)$ is perpendicular to the line from the origin to $(3, -b)$.

21 The vertices of a triangle are A$(-2, 1)$, B$(6.1, 3.7)$ and C$(1, c)$.
Find the value of c so that angle ABC is a right angle.

22 Find the value of p if the line joining $(3, p)$ to $(7, -4p)$ is perpendicular to the line joining $(-1, -3)$ to $(3, 7)$.

Exponential functions

Exponential functions are of the form $y = a^x$ where a is some number.

As x grows, y grows very quickly indeed.

Activity 6

◆ Cut a piece of A4 paper in half. Place the pieces on top of each other and cut in half again, placing the pieces on top of each other. Keep repeating this, filling in a table like the one below. How many times can you do it before the pile becomes too thick to cut?

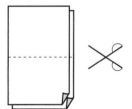

Number of cuts (c)	0	1	2	3	4	5	6
Number of pieces (p)	1	2					

◆ Find the formula giving the number of pieces p in terms of the number of cuts c.
Hint: It is an exponential function.

◆ Plot a graph of your results, with number of cuts along the horizontal axis and number of pieces along the vertical axis.

◆ *Guess* how thick the pile would be after 30 cuts, assuming you and your scissors are strong enough and your original piece of paper is large enough.

◆ Assuming the paper is 0.1 mm thick, work out how thick the pile is after 30 cuts.

Example 4

Plot the graph of the function $y = 3^x$ for $1 \leqslant x \leqslant 5$.

First make out a table of values.

x	1	2	3	4	5
y	3	9	27	81	243

The graph then looks like this.

The points can be joined up with a smooth curve because expressions like $3^{2.5}$ do have a meaning.

If you study mathematics beyond GCSE you will learn how to work out expressions like $3^{2.5}$.

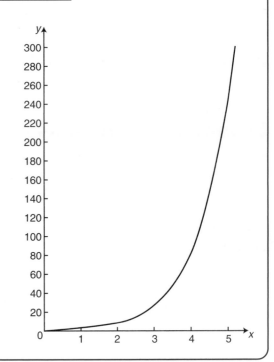

Example 5

Solve the equation $5^x = 125$.

Work out successive powers of 5: $5^1 = 5$, $5^2 = 25$, $5^3 = 125$, so $x = 3$.

Exercise 9

Solve these equations.

1 $2^x = 32$

2 $4^x = 64$

3 $3^x = 81$

4 $2^x = 16$

5 $3^x + 4^x = 25$

6 $2^x + 3^x = 13$

7 Plot the graph of the function $y = 2^x$ for $1 \leqslant x \leqslant 5$.

8 Plot the graph of the function $y = 4^x$ for $1 \leqslant x \leqslant 5$.

9 The number of people who know of a certain rumour is doubling every hour.
If 96 people know about the rumour after 5 hours, how many people started the rumour?

10 The population of mice in a laboratory is trebling every month. If there are 1458 mice after six months and none have died, how many were there at the start?

11 A colony of bacteria trebles in number every day. On the first day, there are three bacteria.

a Copy and complete this table to show the number of bacteria on each day.

Day number (d)	1	2	3	4	5	6
Number of bacteria (b)	3					

b Find a formula giving the number of bacteria in terms of the day number.

c After how many days will there be more than one million bacteria?

12 Mrs Exponential, a mathematics teacher, sets punishment essays if pupils are late to her class. If a pupil is one minute late, the essay is one page, and the length doubles for every further minute that the pupil is late.

a Copy and complete this table to show the number of pages for each minute late.

Minutes late (m)	1	2	3	4	5	6
Number of pages (p)	1	2				

b Find a formula giving the number of pages in terms of minutes late.

c John was 15 minutes late one day. How long was his essay? If it takes John 5 minutes to write one page, how long will it take him to write the essay?

Exercise 9★

Solve these equations.

1 $2^x = 512$

2 $3^x = 729$

3 $5^{2x} = 625$

4 $4^{2x} = 4096$

5 $3^x + 4^x = 91$

6 $2^x + 3^x = 35$

7 Plot the graph of the function $y = 5 \times 2^x$ for $1 \leqslant x \leqslant 5$.

8 Plot the graph of the function $y = 3 \times 4^x$ for $1 \leqslant x \leqslant 5$.

9 A famous story concerns the inventor of the game of chess. The Emperor of the time was so impressed that he asked the inventor to name his own reward. The inventor asked that one grain of rice be put on the first square of the chess board, two grains on the second square, four on the third and so on, the number doubling each time.

a Work out how many grains should be put on the fifth and seventh squares.

b Approximately how many grains should be put on the last square? (There are 64 squares on a chess board.)

c Assuming a grain of rice is a cuboid 5 mm by 1 mm by 1 mm, approximately what volume of rice should be put on the last square? Give your answer in km^3.

10 Jason has a holiday job with his uncle, and asks to be paid 1p for the first day, 2p for the second, 4p for the third and so on, the amount doubling each day.

a How much is Jason paid on the seventh day?

b If Jason works for 30 days, what will be his pay on the last day?

c If he receives his pay on the last day in £10 notes, and each note is 0.1 mm thick, how thick is Jason's pay packet?

11 A colony of bacteria quadruples in size every day. On the sixth day, there are 16 384 000 bacteria. How many were there on the first day?

12 On a TV quiz programme you receive £100 for answering the first question correctly, £200 for answering two questions correctly, and so on, the prize money doubling each time. If the maximum amount you can win is £204 800, how many questions are there?

Activity 7

◆ Draw the graph of $y = 2^x$ for $1 \leqslant x \leqslant 5$.

◆ Let the point with x coordinate 1 be A, the point with x coordinate 2 be B, and so on.

◆ Work out the gradient of the chords AB, BC, CD and DE.

◆ Predict the gradient of the next chord in the sequence.

◆ Try to find a formula for the gradient of the chord joining any two adjacent points. Try to prove your formula.

◆ Investigate chords joining A to C, B to D, etc., or other patterns of chords.

Investigate

Investigate chords on graphs of different exponential functions.

Exercise 10 (Revision)

1   Write down the gradients of lines perpendicular to

   a $y = 2x - 4$ **b** $y = -\dfrac{x}{3} + 2$ **c** $y = -2x + 4$

2   Find the gradients of the lines parallel and perpendicular to AB when

   a A is (1, 2),   B is (4, 4)   **b** A is (−2, 1),   B is (2, −1)

3   Find the equations of the lines that are

   a perpendicular to $y = 3x - 4$ passing through (0, 0)

   b perpendicular to $y = \dfrac{x}{2} - 5$ passing through (2, 1)

4   A(4, −3), B(6, 4), C(−1, 6) and D(−3, −1) are the four vertices of a quadrilateral.

   a Find the lengths of AB and BC.

   b Show that AB is parallel to CD and that AD is parallel to BC.

   c Show, by considering gradients, that AB is perpendicular to AD.

   d What kind of quadrilateral is ABCD?

5   Show, by considering gradients, that the points A(3, 0), B(12, 3) and C(1, 6) form a right-angled triangle.

6   Solve these equations.

   a $4^x = 256$ **b** $2^x = 64$

7   A large square piece of paper is cut into four smaller squares by making two cuts as shown by the dotted lines.

The four pieces are put on top of each other and the process repeated.

   a Copy and fill in the table showing the number of pieces of paper after each pair of cuts.

Number of pairs of cuts (c)	0	1	2	3	4	5
Number of pieces (p)	1	4				

   b Find a formula giving the number of pieces in terms the number of pairs of cuts.

   c After how many pairs of cuts will there be more than one million pieces of paper?

Exercise 10★ (Revision)

1 Find the gradients of the lines parallel and perpendicular to AB when

   a A is $(-2, -1)$ and B is $(4, 2)$ **b** A is $(-1, 4)$ and B is $(1, -1)$

2 Which of these lines are perpendicular?

   $4x + 3y = 12$ $3x + 4y = 12$ $3y = 4x - 1$ $4y = 3x + 7$

3 Find the equations of the lines passing through $(6, 4)$ that are parallel and perpendicular to $3y = x + 21$.

4 Show, by considering gradients, that the triangle $A(-2, -2)$, $B(-2.5, 3)$, $C(8, -1)$ is right-angled.

5 $A(0, -2)$, $B(11, 1)$, $C(4, 10)$, $D(-7, 7)$ are the four vertices of a quadrilateral.

   a Find the mid-points of AC and BD.

   b Show, by considering gradients, that AC and BD are perpendicular.

   c What kind of quadrilateral is ABCD?

6 Prove that the points $A(-2, 5)$, $B(-1, -2)$ and $C(6, -1)$ lie on three corners of a square. Find the coordinates of the fourth corner and the area of the square.

7 Solve these equations.

   a $6^x = 1296$ **b** $4^x = 4096$

8 Find both solutions of the equation $x^2 = 2^x$.

9 A simple game gives three different possible positions at each move.
Anna is trying to write a computer program to play the game.
Her program involves looking at all the possible positions after a certain number of moves.

   a How many possible positions are there after six moves?

   b Her computer can only store a maximum number of one million positions.
     How many moves ahead can the program look?

10 John is a chocoholic.

On Monday, he decides to buy a bar of chocolate, and every day after that to buy double what he bought before.

Nine days later, he has to stop because he should buy 25.6 kilograms of chocolate, which is more than he can carry.

How many kilograms of chocolate did he buy on the first day?

Shape and space 1

Congruence

If two figures are the same size and shape (one can be placed exactly on top of the other) they are **congruent**.

For example, an isosceles triangle ABC can be cut from a folded piece of paper.

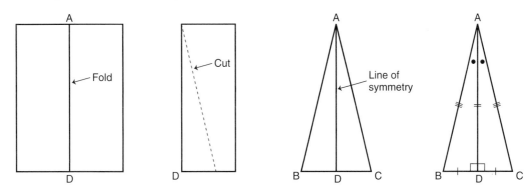

Because of the fold (line of symmetry), triangle ABD is exactly the same size and shape as triangle ACD. The triangles are congruent. Reversing this argument, $\triangle ABD \equiv \triangle ACD$ *because* of the line of symmetry.

Activity 8

♦ Use a pair of compasses and a protractor to construct the two triangles T_1 and T_2 below.

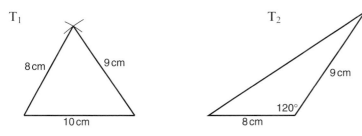

All triangles drawn from triangle T_1 should be exactly the same size and shape because three sides are given (SSS). This is one condition for congruency. In triangle T_2, two sides and the included angle are given (SAS), which is another condition for congruency.

♦ Triangle ABC is to be drawn where
$\angle CAB = 30°$ and AB = 10 cm.
Copy the figure below and investigate
all possible lengths of BC.
Comment on your results.

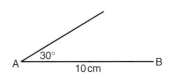

Key Point

For triangles to be **congruent** (the same size and shape), the corresponding sides and angles must be: **SSS**, **SAS**, **AAS** or **ASA** (in that order) or **RHS** (right angle, hypotenuse, side).

Example 1

Why are triangles ABC and XYZ congruent?

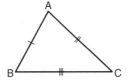 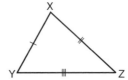

AB = XY
AC = XZ
BC = YZ

Triangles ABC and XYZ are congruent because the lengths of their corresponding sides are equal (SSS).

Remember

When trying to prove congruence, or calculate a length or angle using congruence:

◆ Only use the given facts.

◆ Draw a reasonably accurate and neat diagram to show all known facts.

◆ Give a reason for each statement in the proof.

Example 2

Triangles ABC and XYZ are congruent (SAS). Write down three deductions that follow from this fact.

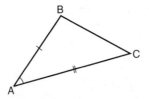 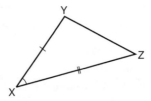

∠ACB = ∠XZY, BC = YZ, ∠ABC = ∠XYZ

Example 3

Triangles ABC and XYZ are congruent (RHS). Write down three deductions that follow from this fact.

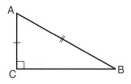 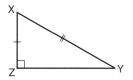

∠CAB = ∠ZXY, CB = ZY, ∠ABC = ∠XYZ

Example 4

Prove that the diagonals of a parallelogram bisect each other.

Draw a parallelogram.

(To prove that triangles ABX and CDX are congruent, show that one pair of corresponding sides are equal and two corresponding angles are equal.)

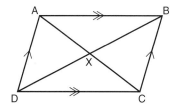

State the triangles that are to be proved to be congruent.

In triangles ABX and CDX

State the three conditions for congruency and give the reason in brackets in each case.

1   AB = CD   (Opp. sides of //gram)
2   ∠BAX = ∠DCX   (Alternate angles)
3   ∠AXB = ∠CXD   (Vertically opposite)

Write the conclusion.

∴   △ABX ≡ △CDX   (AAS)
∴   AX = CX

Exercise 11

For Questions 1–6, state whether pairs of triangles are congruent and give the condition, e.g. SSS, SAS.

1

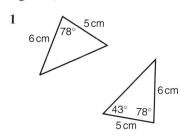

2

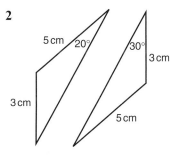

3

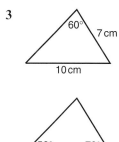

4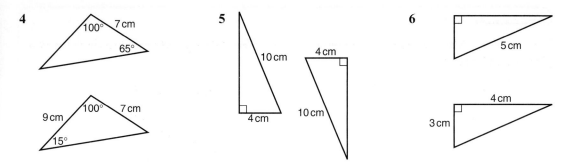

5

6

In Questions 7 and 8, the triangles ABC and XYZ are congruent. Write down three deductions about the sides and angles that follow from this fact.

7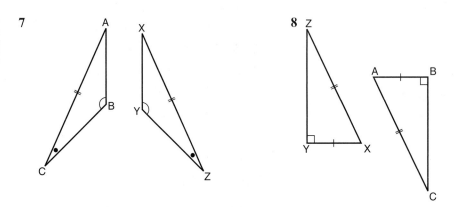

8

For Questions 9 and 10, copy and complete the workings (with SSS, SAS, etc.) to show the two given triangles are congruent.

9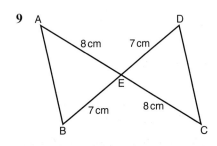

10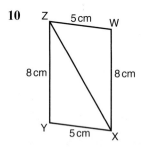

In triangles ABE and CDE

1 BE = DE   (Given)

2 AE = CE   (............)

3 ∠AEB = ∠CED   (............)

∴   △ABE ≡ △CDE   (............)

∴   ∠EDC = ...

     ∠ECD = ...

and   AB = ...

In triangles WXZ and YZX

1 WZ = YX   (............)

2 WX = YZ   (............)

3 Line XZ is common

∴   △WXZ ≡ △YZX   (............)

∴   ∠ZWX = ...

     ∠WZX = ...

and ∠XZY = ...

Exercise 11★

For Questions 1 and 2, copy and complete the workings (with SSS, SAS, etc.) to show the two given triangles are congruent.

1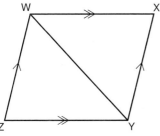

In triangles WXY and YZW

1 WX = YZ   (............)

2 WZ = YX   (............)

3 WY is common

∴   △WXY ≡ △YZW (............)

∴   ∠WXY = ...

    ∠XWY = ...

and ∠XYW = ...

2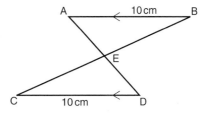

In triangles ABE and DCE

1 AB = DC   (Given)

2 ∠ABE = ∠DCE   (............)

3 ∠AEB = ∠DEC   (............)

∴   △ABE ≡ △DCE   (............)

∴   BE = ...

      AE = ...

and ∠BAE = ...

3 Prove that AD = BC.

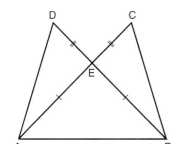

4 Prove that ∠XDC = ∠XCD.

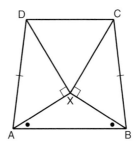

5 P is the mid-point of the side YZ of triangle XYZ. PA is the perpendicular from P to XY and PB is the perpendicular from P to XZ. If AP = BP prove that XY = XZ.

6 Triangle XYZ is isosceles where XY = XZ. A is a point on XY and B is a point on XZ such that AX = BX. Prove that AZ = BY.

7 The construction shows the angle bisector of ∠ABC where BM = BN and MO = NO. Use congruent triangles to prove that BX bisects ∠ABC.

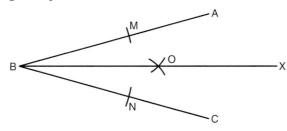

8 The construction shows the perpendicular from
P on to the line AB where PL = PM and LX = MX.
Use congruent triangles to prove that ∠PYB = 90°.

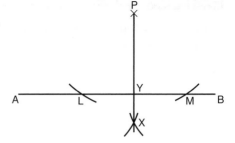

9 ABCD is a square, and the points E, F, G and H shown
are such that EB = FC = GD = HA.
Prove that EFGH is also a square.

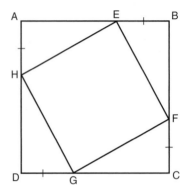

10 D is the mid-point of BC in the triangle ABC. BX and CY are perpendiculars.
Prove that CY = BX.

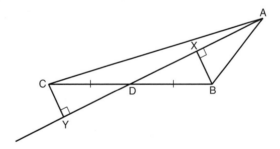

11 PX and PY are tangents to the circle, centre O. Prove that PX = PY.

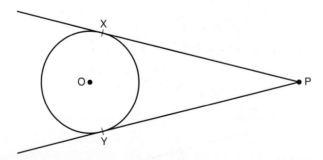

12 The perpendicular bisector of the chord AB passes through X.

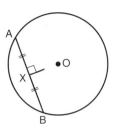

Prove that it also passes through the centre of the circle O.

13 AB and CD are two equal straight lines. The perpendicular bisectors of AC and BD meet at X. Prove that triangles AXB and CXD are congruent.

14 XYZ is an acute-angled triangle. On the sides XY and XZ equilateral triangles AXY and BXZ are drawn on the outside of triangle XYZ. Prove that triangles AXZ and YXB are congruent.

Practical surveying with a Silva compass

A Silva compass is used to measure a magnetic bearing, that is the angle between magnetic North and a given direction. For their own safety, all hill walkers should be able to use such a compass. In this surveying exercise, you will use a Silva compass to work out the length of a hedge from a distance.

How to use a Silva compass

♦ Point the compass in the required direction.

♦ Rotate the 'compass housing' so that the 'black arrow' lines up with the magnetic needle.

♦ Read off the bearing.

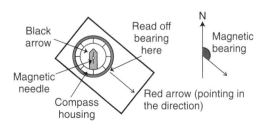

Finding the length of a hedge XY by scale drawing

A 'base-line' AB is marked with two posts 50 metres apart and positioned so that BA is pointing to magnetic North. (Your teacher will set this up.)

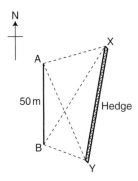

♦ Stand at A and measure the magnetic bearing of X and of Y. Record your results.

♦ Stand at B and measure the magnetic bearing of X and of Y. Record your results.

♦ Make a neat scale drawing and work out the length of the hedge XY.

♦ With a tape measure, measure the actual length of the hedge and calculate the percentage error in your answer by scale drawing.

Repeat, but this time the 50-metre long 'base line' AB is positioned so that BA is *not* pointing to magnetic North. In this case you must also measure the magnetic bearing of A from B.

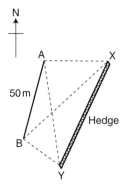

Investigate

Investigate the circumstances under which

a the length of the 'base line' and

b its position relative to the hedge

affect the accuracy of the method of calculating the length of a hedge in Activity 9.

Circles

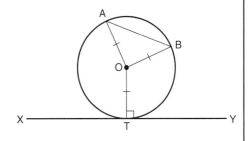

Remember

Radii, tangent, chord

- AB is a chord
- The letter O will always indicate the centre of a circle
- △OAB is isosceles
- XY is a tangent to the circle at T
- ∠YTO = 90°

Angle at centre is twice the angle at the circumference

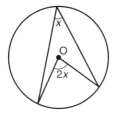
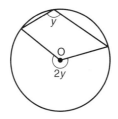
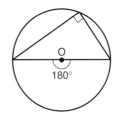

Opposite angles of a cyclic quadrilateral sum to 180°

$a° + b° = 180°$
$x° + y° = 180°$

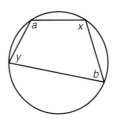

Angles in the same segment are equal

Activity 10

Use the diagram to prove that the angle at the centre is twice the angle at the circumference, and use this to prove that

- angles in the same segment are equal
- opposite angles of a cyclic quadrilateral sum to 180°.

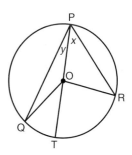

Remember

When trying to find angles or lengths in circles:

◆ Use the basic facts of geometry (as summarised on pages 39 and 287).

◆ A figure is **cyclic** if a circle can be drawn through its vertices. The vertices are **concyclic** points.

◆ Always draw a neat diagram, and include all the facts. Use a pair of compasses to draw all circles.

◆ Give a reason, in brackets, after each statement.

Example 5

Find ∠PNM.

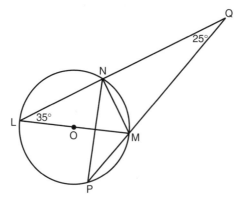

∠NPM = 35° (Angles in the same segment)

∠LNM = 90° (Angle at centre is 180°)

∠MNQ = 90° (△LMN is right-angled)

∴   ∠PNM = 30° (Angle sum of triangle PNQ)

Example 6

Prove that XY meets OZ at right angles.

∠OXY = 30° (Alternate to ∠ZYX)

∴   ∠OYX = 30° (△OXY is isosceles)

∠YZO = 60° (△YZO is isosceles)

∴   ∠ZNY = 90° (Angle sum of triangle ZNY)

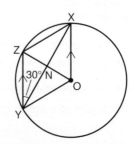

Exercise 12

For Questions 1–10, find the coloured angles, fully explaining your reasoning.

1
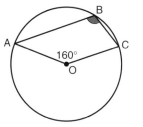

2
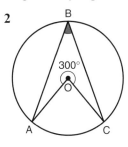

3
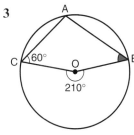

4

5
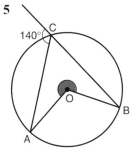

6
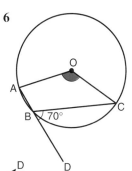

7

8
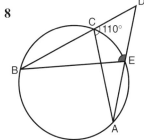

9

10
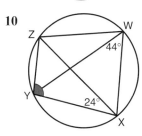

For Questions 11 and 12, prove that the points ACBD are concyclic.

11
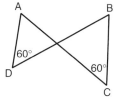

12
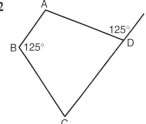

13 LK and MN are two equal chords of a circle. X and Y are their mid-points.
By considering the shape of LKMN, prove that XY makes equal angles with LK and MN.

14 Two circles of different radii and with centres P and Q intersect at X and Y.
By considering the shape of XPYQ, prove that XY meets PQ at right angles.

Exercise 12★

For Questions 1–8, find the coloured angles, fully explaining your reasoning.

1

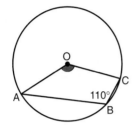

2

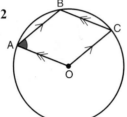

3

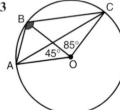

4

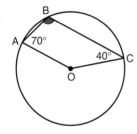

5

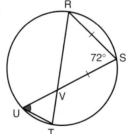

6

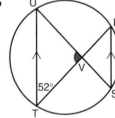

7

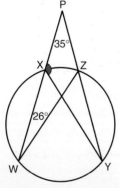

8

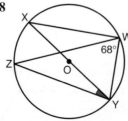

9 Find, in terms of x, $\angle$AOX.

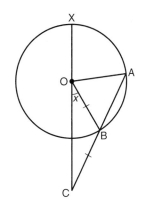

10 Find, in terms of x, $\angle$BCD.

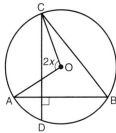

11 ABCD is a quadrilateral in which AB = AD and BD = CD.
Let $\angle$DBA = $x°$ and $\angle$DBC = $2x°$. Prove that A, B, C and D are concyclic.

12 ABCDEF is a hexagon inscribed in a circle. By joining AD, prove that
$\angle$ABC + $\angle$CDE + $\angle$EFA = 360°.

13 Prove that $\angle$CEA = $\angle$BDA.

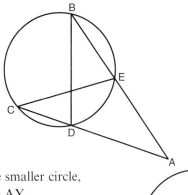

14 In the figure OX is the diameter of the smaller circle,
which cuts XY at A. Prove that AX = AY.

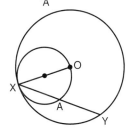

15 WXYZ is a cyclic quadrilateral. The sides XY and WZ produced meet at Q.
The sides XW and YZ produced meet at P. $\angle$WPZ = 30° and $\angle$YQZ = 20°.
Find the angles of the quadrilateral.

16 PQ and PR are any two chords of a circle, centre O. The diameter, perpendicular to PQ,
cuts PR at X. Prove that the points Q, O, X and R are concyclic.

Angles in the alternate segment

Activity 11

In the figure AB is the tangent to the circle, centre O.
Let $\angle QTB = x$.

Find in terms of x the angles OTQ, OQT and QOT,
and hence show that angle QPT = x.

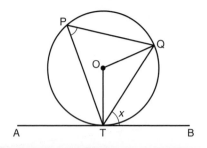

Key Point

Angles in the alternate segment are equal.

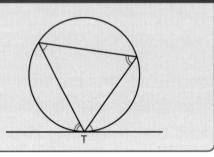

Exercise 13

In this exercise, O indicates the centre of a circle and T indicates a tangent to the circle.

For Questions 1–8, find the coloured angles, fully explaining your reasons.

1

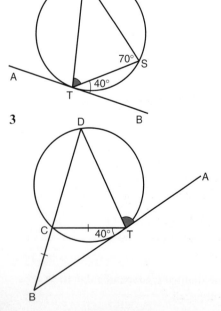

2

3

4

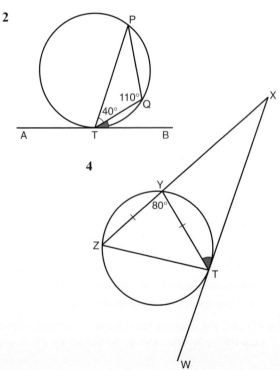

5

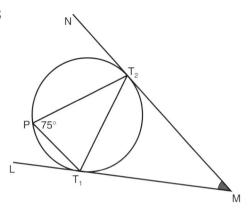

6

7

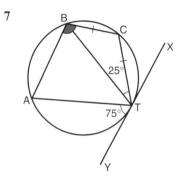

8

9 Find

   a ∠OTX **b** ∠TOB **c** ∠OBT **d** ∠ATY

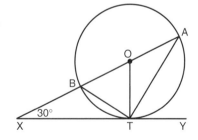

10 Find

   a ∠OTB **b** ∠OTC **c** ∠OCT **d** ∠DTA

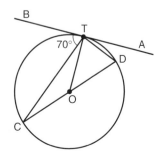

11 Copy and complete these two statements to prove ∠NPT = ∠PLT.

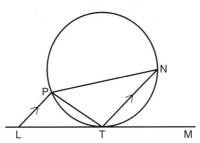

∠NTM = ... (Alternate segment)

∠PLT = ... (Corresponding angles)

12 Copy and complete these two statements to prove ∠ATF = ∠BAF.

∠ATF = ∠FDT (.....................)

∠FDT = ∠BAF (.....................)

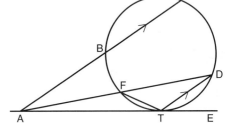

13 Copy and complete these two statements to prove ∠ATC = ∠BTD.

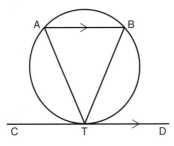

∠ATC = ... (Alternate segment)

∠ABT = ∠BTD (.....................)

14 Copy and complete these two statements to prove
that triangles BCT and TBD are similar.

∠DCT = ...° (Alternate segment)

.... is common.

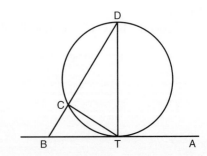

Exercise 13★

On all given diagrams, O indicates the centre of a circle and T indicates a tangent to the circle.

For Questions 1–4, find the coloured angles, fully explaining your reasons.

1

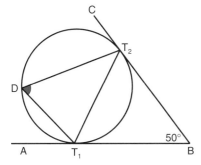

2

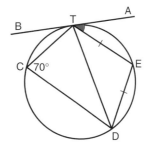

3

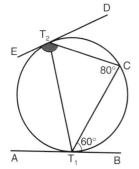

4

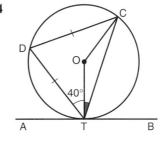

5 Prove that AB is the diameter.

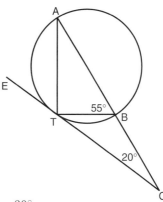

6 Given that $\angle BCT = \angle TCD$, prove that $\angle TBC = 90°$.

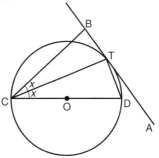

7 The inscribed circle of XYZ touches XY at A, YZ at B and XZ at C. If ∠ZXY = 68° and
   ∠ZYX = 44°, find

   a ∠ABC   **b** ∠ACB

8 PRY and PQX are tangents to the circle RSQ. If ∠SRY = 154° and ∠SQX = 136°, find

   a ∠RSQ   **b** ∠RPQ

9 Find

   a ∠DAE

   b ∠BED

   c Prove that triangle ACD is isosceles.

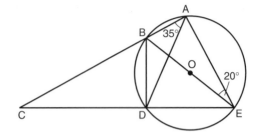

10 Find

   a ∠DTA

   b ∠BCT

   c Prove that triangles BCT and BTD are similar.

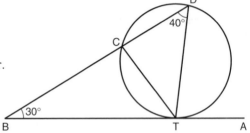

11 CD and AB are tangents at T. Find ∠ETF.

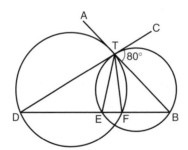

12 AB and CD are tangents at T and ∠DTB is less than 90°. Find ∠DEB.

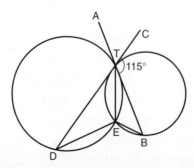

13 a Explain why ∠ACG = ∠ABF = 15°.

   b Prove that the points CFGB are concyclic.

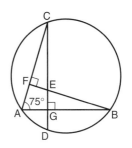

14 AB and DE are tangents to the circle, centre O.

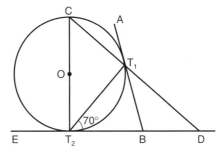

   a Write down all the angles equal to (i) 70° (ii) 20°

   b Prove that B is the mid-point of DT_2.

15 a Giving reasons, find, in terms of x, the angles EOC and CAE. Use your answers to show that triangle ABE is isosceles.

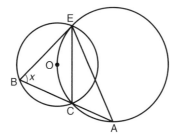

   b If BE = CE prove that BE will be the tangent to the larger circle at E.

16 BD is the tangent to the smaller circle at T_2 and AB is the tangent to the larger and smaller circles at T_1.

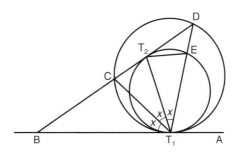

   a By finding all the angles of the figure in terms of x, write down three pairs of triangles that are similar.

   b Investigate the maximum and minimum value of x.

17 AB is a diameter of the circle shown in the figure. D is any point on the circle, and C is the point on AB produced such that DB = BC. The line DC cuts the circle at N. CT is a tangent to the circle at T. Copy the figure.

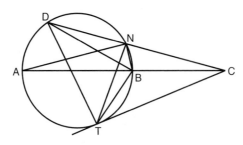

  a Prove that angle BCD = angle NTB.

  b Let angle BCD = $x°$. Express in terms of x the size of
    (i) angle ABD
    (ii) angle ABN

  c Give a reason why angle CTB = angle BNT.

  Let angle CTB = $y°$.
  Express in terms of x and y the size of angle NBT.

MEI

Exercise 14 (Revision)

In this exercise, O is the centre of a circle and T indicates a tangent to the circle.

1 Copy and complete the working to show that triangles ABE and CDE are congruent.

In triangles ABE and CDE

  1   DE = ... (Given)

  2   ∠BAE = ... (Alternate)

  3   ∠AEB = ∠CED   (...........)

  ∴ △ABE ≡ △CDE   (...........)

  ∴ ∠ABE = ...

      AB = ...

      AE = ...

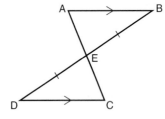

2 The construction shows the perpendicular bisector of the line AB.

Prove that triangles CBD and CAD are congruent.
Explain why this proves that AX = XB

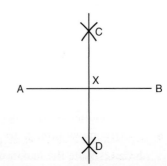

For Questions 3–6, find the marked angles, fully explaining your reasoning.

3

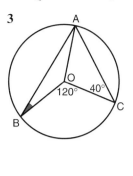

4

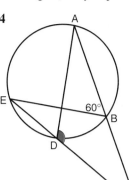

5

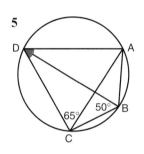

6

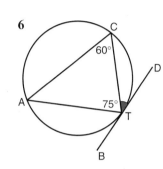

7 Find
  a ∠DCT
  b ∠TCB
  c ∠CTB
  d ∠TDC

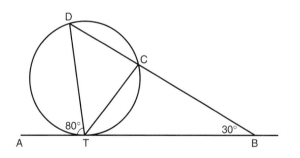

8 Find
  a ∠OBT₁
  b ∠T₁OB
  c ∠DT₁B
  d ∠T₁ET₂

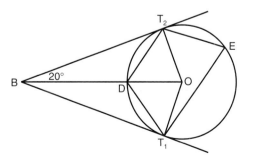

9 By drawing a suitable diagram, prove that the angle at the centre is twice the angle at the circumference.

Exercise 14★ (Revision)

1 The construction shows the perpendicular through W on AB. Prove that triangles ZXW and ZYW are congruent.

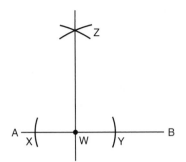

2 In the figure let $\angle ABO = x$.

  a Show that $\angle EAO = \angle BOC = 45° + x$.

  b Use congruent triangles to prove that $EA = OC$.

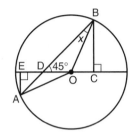

3 Find

  a $\angle ETD$

  b $\angle TEB$

  c Prove that EC is the diameter of the circle.

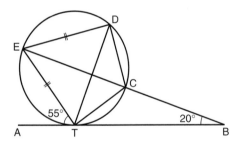

4 **a** Explain why triangles T_1ET_3, T_2DT_3 and T_1BT_2 are isosceles.

  b Find the angles of the triangle BDE.

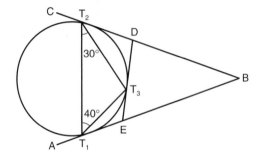

5 AB is the common tangent.

  a Find $\angle XZT$.

  b Find $\angle WVT$.

  c Prove that XZ is parallel to WV.

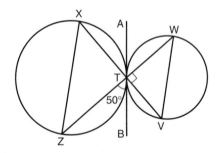

6 ABC is a triangle inscribed in a circle. The bisector of angle A meets CB at X and the circle at Y.

  a Prove that triangle BCY is isosceles.

  b Prove that $\angle ABY = \angle BXY$.

Handling data 1

Sampling

A **sample** is taken from a **population** when it is too time-consuming, or too expensive, or even impossible, to 'test' every 'member' of the population.

A **representative sample** has the same characteristics as the population it is taken from. It is **unbiased**. The statistics calculated from the sample will be approximately equal to those same statistics in the population. The distribution of the sample will be similar to the distribution of the population.

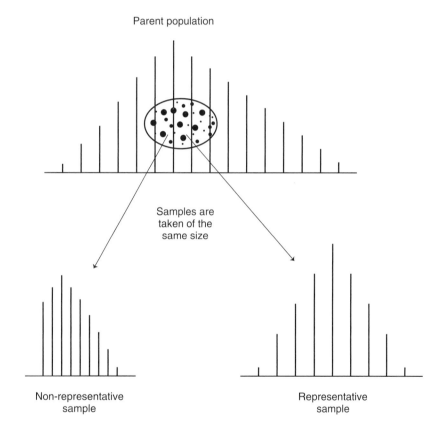

Parent population

Samples are
taken of the
same size

Non-representative
sample

Representative
sample

A **non-representative sample** is said to be **biased**. it will give a misleading impression of the population. A sample might be biased deliberately or accidentally.

Deliberate bias

♦ To stretch the truth

♦ To give a false impression

♦ To deceive and influence people

Accidental bias

♦ False conclusions may be drawn.

♦ Bad decisions may be made.

♦ In business, it could have serious financial consequences.

The statistician aims to design a sampling strategy which keeps the chance of accidental bias within acceptable limits while keeping the **sample size** as small as possible.

Larger sample
♦ Costs more to collect
♦ Takes more time to collect and analyse
♦ Less chance of accidental bias

Smaller sample
♦ Costs less to collect
♦ Takes less time to collect and analyse
♦ More chance of accidental bias

No matter how carefully a sample is selected, or how large the sample is, one can never be absolutely certain of the results.

Exercise 15

For each question, criticise, with reasons, the conclusion drawn.

1   The captain of a hockey team called 'heads' and won the toss at all six matches at a tournament. *Conclusion*: The captain is cheating and has a two-headed coin.

2   A gambler playing roulette at a casino won seven times in a row by betting on an even number. *Conclusion*: He must be cheating and the roulette wheel has been tampered with.

3   A researcher in a shopping mall found that only three out of the twenty people interviewed owned a mobile phone. *Conclusion*: Only 15% of the people in this town own a mobile phone. It is a good place to open a new store.

4   The first four customers who agreed to try out a new brand of hair dye at a salon stated that they preferred it to the traditional type. *Conclusion*: Cancel the order for the traditional type and order plenty of the new brand.

5   A Police Authority discovered that four out of ten car drivers involved in accidents between Christmas and the New year were over the alcohol limit. *Conclusion*: 40% of motorists are 'drinking and driving'. Plan £100 000 campaign for next year.

6   A Health Authority survey at a newsagent's shop revealed that 50% of teenage customers asked to buy cigarettes. *Conclusion*: The number of teenage smokers has increased to 50%. Plan new Health Education initiative in schools.

7   500 questionnaires were handed out to passengers on a commuter train and these results were obtained:

    64 responded
    29 were dissatisfied with the service
    35 were satisfied with the service

Conclusion: nearly half of the passengers are complaining of bad service. Appoint 'watchdog' to review working practices and to report to the Managing Director.

8   A Headteacher sent out a questionnaire to each pupil in the school enquiring about homework. The 'returns' revealed that 90% of the pupils were doing over two hours every evening. *Conclusion*: This is too much homework. Instruct the teachers to set less homework!

Methods of sampling
A random sample

In a random sample, each member of the population has an equal chance of being selected.

This is not as simple as it appears!

◆ Ask someone to write down a number at random between 1 and 10. They are more likely to select one from the middle.

◆ A researcher who is selecting people randomly in the street is unlikely to approach people who (s)he thinks might respond rudely or aggressively.

◆ Ask someone to pick ten books at random from the library. It is likely that all ten books are picked from shelves at 'eye-level'.

A scheme to produce a truly random sample must eliminate any form of human preference or selection.

Example 1

A random sample of 50 pupils from a school of 800 has to be selected to complete a survey on school meals. Devise a scheme.

Assign a unique number to each pupil and then use a random number generator on a calculator to select 50 numbers.

001	Abbott
002	Adobe
003	Andrews
004	Ata
⋮	⋮

The National Lottery

The National Lottery selects a random sample of six numbers from a population of forty-nine numbers! With such a lot of money at stake, it has to be *seen to be fair* and it also has to attract a television audience.

A stratified sample

A population often includes distinct groupings or **strata** which are considered to be important by the researcher. A stratified sample is divided into the *same* strata, in the *same* proportions as the population. (Smaller) random samples are taken from each grouping or strata and put together to form the complete sample.

Example 2

The manager of a theatre decides to canvass views from the audience about the theatre facilities. He employs a researcher to select a sample of 40 and obtain their views from a questionnaire. He obtains this information from the ticket office.

Children (under 18 years)	Young adults (aged 18–40 years)	Mature adults (over 40 years)	Total audience
87	290	203	580

Male	Female	Total audience
235	345	580

Plan two different schemes for a stratified sample.

First, note that 'age' is important, and calculate the proportions of each age-group in a calculation table.

	Children	Young adults	Mature adults	Total
Numbers	87	290	203	580
Proportions	$\frac{87}{580} = 0.15$	$\frac{290}{580} = 0.50$	$\frac{203}{580} = 0.35$	1
Strata size	$0.15 \times 40 = 6$	$0.50 \times 40 = 20$	$0.35 \times 40 = 14$	40

Choose strata of sizes 6, 20 and 14 respectively.

Then note that 'gender' is important.

	Male	Female	Total
Numbers	235	345	580
Proportions	$\frac{235}{580} = 0.405$	$\frac{345}{580} = 0.595$	1
Strata size	$0.405 \times 40 = 16.2$	$0.595 \times 40 = 23.8$	40

Round off to the nearest whole numbers and choose strata of size 16 and 24.

Example 3

The theatre manager in Example 2 realises that he could have collected his data in a better form.

	Children	Young adults	Mature adults	Totals
Male	18	130	87	235
Female	69	160	116	345
Totals	87	290	203	580

Design a stratified sample of 40 to take account of 'age' and 'gender' from the revised data table.

Calculate the proportions for each cell.

	Children	Young adults	Mature adults	Totals
Male	$\frac{18}{580} \times 40 = 1.24 \simeq 1$	$\frac{130}{580} \times 40 = 8.96 \simeq 9$	$\frac{87}{580} \times 40 = 6$	235 **16**
Female	$\frac{69}{580} \times 40 = 4.76 \simeq 5$	$\frac{160}{580} \times 40 = 11.04 \simeq 11$	$\frac{116}{580} \times 40 = 8$	345 **24**
Totals	87	290	203	580
Sample	**6**	**20**	**14**	**40**

So, for example, there would be 9 'male young adults' in the sample.

Exercise 16

1 In a school of 800 pupils, 60 are left-handed and the rest are right-handed. A stratified sample is designed with these two strata. How many left-handers and right-handers must there be in a sample of size

   a 40?   **b** 30?

2 The distribution of the ages of the drivers employed by a coach company is given in this table.
How many drivers of each category would there be in a stratified sample of size

   a 20?   **b** 35?   **c** 50?

Age	Number of drivers
20–34	96
35–49	84
50–65	60

3 The children on a school trip were seated on the buses according to the table. A sample of seven is to be selected.
Design a stratified sample taking account of

   a the buses   **b** gender

	Boys	Girls
Bus A	18	6
Bus B	22	10

4 The membership of a health and fitness club is described in this table. A sample of 30 is to be selected.

Members	Male	Female
Full-time	80	72
Part-time	24	64

Design a stratified sample taking account of

a gender

b full and part-time members

5 CIA statistics categorised the labour force in the UK, in 1999, according to this table.

Design a stratified sample of 40 to survey opinion on job opportunities. Group together Energy and Agriculture!

Services	64.3%
Manufacturing	16.1%
Government	10.5%
Energy	1.1%
Agriculture	1.0%
Unemployed	7.0%

6 This table shows the number of pupils in each year group at Creepton Manor School.

Year group	9	10	11	12	13
Number of pupils	305	285	220	240	150

Freddie is surveying the pupils' views on school dinners.

He decides to select a stratified sample of 50 pupils according to year group.

Calculate the number of pupils in his sample from each year group.

7 This table shows the number of ferry passengers using British ports and their country of origin for 1998.

Use the data to design a stratified sample of 100 to survey opinion on immigration facilities.

	(1000s)
France	4500
Irish Republic	900
Netherlands	300
Belgium	100
Spain and Portugal	100
Germany, Baltic and Scandinavia	100
All overseas routes	6000

8 The data show the number of convictions for burglary at a Magistrates Court in a three-month period. A criminal psychologist needs to choose a sample of 20 for research into criminal behaviour. Design a stratified sample.

Age	10–15	16–24	25–34	Over 35
Number convicted	44	69	19	8

Exercise 16★

1 Customer numbers at an Oxford Street store for a typical weekday are given in this table. A stratified sample of 60 customers is chosen to research 'customer satisfaction'. Calculate the number of customers in the sample from

a the '10:00–12:00' group

b the '14:00–16:00' group

Time	Number of customers
pre 10:00	200
10:00–12:00	500
12:00–14:00	800
14:00–16:00	700
16:00–18:00	300

2 The passenger list of a cruise liner is shown in this table. A stratified sample of 50 passengers is to be chosen to receive complimentary tickets for a future cruise. How many passengers will receive vouchers from

a third class?

b economy class?

Class	Number
Economy class	440
Third class	480
Second class	360
First class	150
Corporate	70

3 The data show the ages and gender of the patients at a London asthma clinic. A sample of 50 is to be selected to 'trial' a new treatment. Design a stratified sample to take account of

a age only

b gender only

c both age and gender

Age	Male	Female
Under 6	42	36
7–12	48	36
13–19	54	42
20–24	24	18

4 A supermarket orders soft drinks in these quantities. The Quality Control Department samples a stratified sample of 40 from each delivery. How many of these types should be tasted within each sample?

a Diet drinks   **b** Cola   **c** Regular squash

	Regular	Diet
Cola	680	400
6up	200	120
Squash	160	40

5 A stratified sample of 80, taken from an audience of 72 540 at a music festival, contained 31 women. Calculate a range for the number of women in the audience.

6 A stratified sample of 120 taken from the armed forces of a South American country contained 9 members of the Spearhead Unit. Government statistics show that there are 65 685 personnel in the armed forces. Calculate a range for the size of the Spearhead Unit.

7 This table gives the populations and parliamentary constituency of EU member states.

EU (in July 2000)	Population in millions	Number of MEPs	EU (in July 2000)	Population in millions	Number of MEPs
Austria	8	21	Luxembourg	0.4	6
Belgium	10.2	25	Netherlands	15.9	31
Denmark	5.3	16	Portugal	10.0	25
Finland	5.2	16	Rep. of Ireland	3.8	15
France	59.3	87	Spain	40.0	64
Germany	82.8	99	Sweden	8.9	22
Greece	10.6	25	UK	59.5	87
Italy	57.6	87	Totals	377.5	626

If the parliament was, instead, a stratified sample of the population of the EU, calculate how many MEPs there would be from

a UK   **b** Republic of Ireland

8 This data table shows the distribution of police officers, by rank and gender, in England and Wales for 1999.

	Males	Females	Totals
Chief Constable	47	2	49
Assistant Chief Constable	142	9	151
Superintendent	1156	57	1213
Chief Inspector	1511	93	1604
Inspector	5602	334	5936
Sergeant	17 196	1542	18 738
Constable	78 302	17 848	96 150
All ranks	103 956	19 885	123 841

A sample of 120 has to be selected. Design a stratified sample to take account of rank and gender. You may have to group together some categories.

9 A researcher is planning a survey of MPs elected at the last UK general election. A sample size of 50 is selected and it is decided that the sample should be stratified to represent the views of the different political parties. By referring to secondary data (from the Internet, or elsewhere), choose and calculate the size of the categories within the sample.

Activity 12

Read this newspaper extract from page 11 of *The Mercury* (Hobart, Australia, Tuesday 23 May, 1995).

What Australia Drinks?

WHAT Australia Drinks, a national survey released yesterday, showed men and women of the 90s are more likely to reach for a glass of milk or water than a can of beer or lager.

Beer scraped into the list of the top 10 most consumed drinks, ranking number nine.

The survey recorded the drinking habits of 1000 people in Melbourne, Sydney, Perth and Brisbane over a seven-day period.

It found that milk was the most popular drink among Australians, with 83% of respondents drinking it during the week, while 81% drank water.

The Australian trend towards healthier drinks was further evidenced by the growth in consumption of natural fruit juices.

While 49% of respondents drank fruit juice in 1993, the figure rose to 59% in 1995.

The trend was also supported by a decline in the consumption of sugared cola and spirits.

The survey also found the so-called new age drinks, including still-water, sports drinks, iced-teas, fruit-based drinks and clear fruit carbonates, were making a big impact on the beverage scene.

New age drinks were particularly popular in the youth market, with peak consumption occurring among 17- to 19-year-olds.

Among alcohol drinkers, the survey showed women were drinking more beer than in the past, up from 11% in 1993 to 16% in 1995.

Forty-nine per cent of men drank beer during the survey and also consumed more wine than in 1993.

Schweppes Cottees managing director Andrew Cosslett, which sponsored the survey, said it confirmed the company's long-held belief that drinking habits in Australia were changing rapidly.

'In particular, the search for a more balanced lifestyle is leading to a demand for healthier, more natural beverage options and we believe this trend will continue and accelerate here in Australia,' he said in a statement.

Discuss these questions.

◆ What is the *sample* and what is the *population*?

◆ How might the different climates of the four cities affect the findings?

◆ What time of year was the survey run? How might this affect the findings?

◆ How might the representation of different age groups affect the findings?

◆ Could the fact that the sponsor of the survey, Schweppes Cottees, manufacture soft drinks have *biased* the questions that were asked?

◆ How much do you think the survey might have cost?

◆ The results are interesting, but why would Schweppes Cottees have commissioned the survey and why would they have published the report in the Press?

Choose at least three factors that need to be considered and then design a stratified sample of a 1000 for this survey. Do you think that the sample size is large enough?

Activity 13

Plan and conduct a survey to investigate the drinking preferences of pupils in your school and write a report of your findings.

You will need to consider all these points before you begin.

♦ *Sample*: sample size, selecting groupings and designing a stratified sample
♦ *Questionnaire*: unbiased questions, simple to fill in, easy to extract and analyse data
♦ Which *statistics* to calculate and how to display your findings (include comparisons)
♦ *Conclusions*: how to report them so that people will take notice

Exercise 17 (Revision)

1 Comment on these conclusions.

 a A telephone poll, conducted by Capital Radio, revealed that contemporary music was five times more popular than classical music.

 b A survey, conducted in a shopping centre on a Friday morning, revealed that 75% of mothers with young children did not have a full- or part-time job.

2 Alison is conducting a survey of Year 12 opinion at Swatterton High School for the next School Council meeting. She has written a questionnaire and decided on a sample size of 30 from the 240 pupils in the Year. She selects the first 30 pupils from the dining room queue on a Tuesday as her random sample.

 a Comment briefly on whether this scheme will produce a good random sample.

 b Suggest a better scheme.

3 A stratified sample of size 40 is required from 215 examination candidates to survey 'exam technique'.

Grade	A	B	C	D	E
No.	43	77	56	25	14

 a How many A-grade candidates should there be?

 b How many C-grade candidates should there be?

4 A school pupil has classified the teachers according to age and gender.

	Male	Female
Young	23	26
Old	35	46

A questionnaire is to be issued to a stratified sample of 30 teachers.

Calculate how many there should be in each of the four groupings.

Exercise 17★ (Revision)

1 The Headteacher of Swatterton High School is concerned about pupils smoking at school, and decides to investigate this. He issues this questionnaire to each pupil in Year 10.

Swatterton High School – Year 10 Questionnaire

Section 1 **Personal details:**

Name [   ]   Class [   ]   Date of birth [/   /]

Section 2 **Smoking:** *Please answer all the questions by ticking the appropriate boxes*

1. How many people in your household smoke regularly?

   0 ☐   1 ☐   2 ☐   3 ☐   4 ☐   More than 4 ☐

2. How many cigarettes do you smoke per day?

   None ☐   1–5 ☐   6–10 ☐   More than 10 ☐

3. Do you smoke at home?   Never ☐   Rarely ☐   Often ☐

4. Do you smoke at school?   Never ☐   Rarely ☐   Often ☐

5. Do you smoke on the school bus?   Never ☐   Rarely ☐   Often ☐

The Headteacher is delighted when the results indicate that less than 2% of pupils smoke at school or on the school buses, and that, therefore, there is no problem at this school.

a What is the difference between a census and a sample?

b Comment on the likely accuracy of these results.

c Suggest what changes might be made to the questionnaire to obtain a better picture of 'smoking at Swatterton High School'.

2 Government data reveal the figures for 'asylum applications' in the UK in 1998. Design a scheme for a stratified sample of 100 so that views on the application process can be analysed.

Country of origin	Applications (1000s)
Europe	17.5
Africa	12.4
Asia	11.9
Middle East	2.8
Other	1.4
All regions	46

3 The membership of a sailing club is given in this table.

It has been decided to survey opinion on lakeside conditions by taking a stratified sample of 30 from the members.

Calculate the number required for each of the eight classes.

	Novice	Expert
Mirror	27	25
Enterprise	23	57
Laser	25	33
Scorpion	18	42

Numeracy practice 1

Skills practice

Number

Work out these.

1 0.67×100 **2** 0.7×100 **3** $5.8 \div 0.1$ **4** $93 \div 0.1$ **5** $34.6 + 3.46$ **6** $1.56 + 0.96$

7 $0.7 - 2.3$ **8** $0.5 - 1.85$ **9** 6.59×7 **10** 4.91×8 **11** $3.43 \div 7$ **12** $7.36 \div 8$

13 3×2^0 **14** 2×3^0 **15** $(3 \times 2)^3$ **16** $(3 + 2)^3$ **17** $10^3 \div 10^4$ **18** $10^2 \div 10^4$

19 $\sqrt{169}$ **20** $\sqrt{144}$ **21** $3\frac{3}{7} + 2\frac{4}{21}$ **22** $4\frac{5}{9} + 3\frac{1}{3}$ **23** $3\frac{3}{7} \div 4\frac{2}{3}$ **24** $2\frac{1}{7} \div 2\frac{1}{2}$

Give your answers to these in standard form.

25 $6 \times (4.5 \times 10^4)$ **26** $7 \times (3.8 \times 10^6)$

Correct these to 3 significant figures.

27 $0.046\,86$ **28** $0.035\,79$

What is the reciprocal of each of these?

29 6 **30** 8

Simplify and write each of these as a single fraction.

31 $\dfrac{1.5}{7.5}$ **32** $\dfrac{1.2}{2.8}$ **33** $6 \times \dfrac{0.5}{3.5}$ **34** $7 \times \dfrac{0.2}{3.6}$

Algebra

Simplify these.

1 $4x^2 + 2x^2$ **2** $3p^3 + 7p^3$ **3** $4x^2 \times 2x^2$ **4** $5x^2 \times 3x^2$

5 $\dfrac{4a^2}{2a}$ **6** $\dfrac{6a^2}{3a}$ **7** $x(x^2 - 2) - x$ **8** $p(p^3 + 3) + p$

Factorise these.

9 $4ab^2 - 6a^2b$ **10** $8a^3b + 4ab^2$ **11** $x^2 - x - 2$ **12** $x^2 - 5x + 6$

Solve each of these for x.

13 $\dfrac{92}{x} = 4$ **14** $\dfrac{112}{x} = 7$ **15** $8.7 - x = 7.8$ **16** $12.6 - x = 9.5$

17 $3x - 5 = 8 - x$ **18** $5x - 7 = 7 - 2x$ **19** $3x^2 + 5 = 17$ **20** $5x^2 - 10 = 35$

Substitute $a = 3$, $b = -2$ and $c = 1$ to find the value of each of these.

21 $a^2 - b + c$ **22** $a^3 - 2b - c$ **23** $\dfrac{a}{b^2} + 2b$ **24** $\dfrac{2a}{b^2} + b$

25 $(a - b)^2$ **26** $(b - a)^2$

Challenges

1 French Mathematician Marin Mersenne (1588–1648) discovered that some prime numbers (called Mersenne numbers) were given by

$$2^n - 1 \qquad \text{where } n \text{ is an integer, } n > 1$$

   a Find the first five Mersenne prime numbers.

   b What is the product of the first five Mersenne prime numbers?

2 Given that $a \triangle b = a^b$, find the value of

   a $2 \triangle 4$ **b** $(2 \triangle 2) \triangle 3$

3 Solve for x: $\sqrt{x^x} = 216$

4 ABCDEFGH is a square cuboid of side 10 cm. M and N are the mid-points of sides AB and AD respectively. Find the area of triangle MEN.

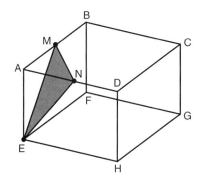

5 The pursuit of the true value of π has fascinated many people for many years. Investigate the approximations shown here and, where possible, rank them in order of accuracy.

Approximation of π	Source
3	*Bible* 1 Kings 7:23
$3\frac{1}{8}$	Babylon 2000 BC; found on a clay tablet in 1936
$256 \div 81$	Egypt 2000 BC; found on the 'Rhind Papyrus'
$22 \div 7$	Syracuse 250 BC; Archimedes
$377 \div 120$	Greece 140 BC; Hipparchus
$355 \div 113$	China AD 450; Tsu Chung-Chih
$\sqrt{10}$	India AD 625; Brahmagupta
$864 \div 275$	Italy AD 1225; Fibonacci
$\dfrac{2 \times 2 \times 2 \times 4 \times 4 \times 6 \times 6 \times 8 \times 8 \cdots}{1 \times 3 \times 3 \times 5 \times 5 \times 7 \times 7 \times 9 \cdots}$	England 1655 AD; Wallis
$\sqrt[4]{9^2 + \dfrac{19^2}{22}}$	India 1910 AD; Ramanujan

Fact finder: The Forth railway bridge

The Forth railway bridge was completed on 4 March 1890 and was nearly four times longer than the previous longest bridge, Robert Stephenson's Britannia Bridge over the Menai Strait in Wales.

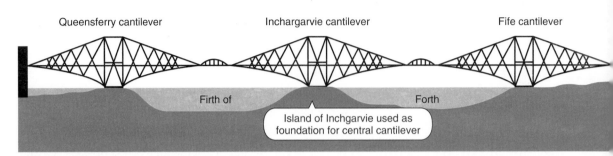

Queensferry cantilever   Inchargarvie cantilever   Fife cantilever

Firth of   Forth

Island of Inchgarvie used as foundation for central cantilever

It was the world's first cantilever bridge, and to inspire public confidence, after the Tay bridge disaster, two engineers demonstrated the cantilever principle.

Each end of the bridge had to be anchored down by a force of **1000 tonnes**. This was done by **600 bolts**, each **eight metres** long.

It was designed by Benjamin Baker who, before it was built, described its size in this way:

> Stand in Piccadilly and look towards Buckingham Palace and then consider that we have to span the entire distance across, be as high above the sea as the dome of the Albert Hall is above street level, and the structure will soar **200 feet** above that level, or as high as St Paul's.

The length between the anchorages is **1.6 kilometres** and the total mass of steel used was **51 000 tonnes**. It is held together with **6.5 million rivets** which weigh **4200 tonnes**. The main tubes are **3.7 m** in diameter and have, on average, **100 rivets per 300 mm** length, which were put in at the rate of about **860 per week**. It took **seven years** to build and cost **£1.6 million**. Today, it costs **£1 200 000** to maintain every year and is repainted once every **ten years**.

During the peak workforce, **4600 men** were employed and there were, on average, **518 minor accidents** each week. During its construction there were **53 fatal accidents**. Most accidents were caused by falling objects and, on one occasion, a spanner fell **100 m**, went straight through a workman's waistcoat pocket, and clean through **100 mm of timber**! Throughout the project, the rate of payment was between $4\frac{1}{2}$**d and 8 d per hour**. (In those days, there were **240 d** to the pound.)

Exercise

Where appropriate, give your answers correct to 3 significant figures.

1 How far is it from Piccadilly to Buckingham Palace?

2 Walking at 3 km/hour, how long, in minutes, would it take to cross the bridge?

3 If all the anchorage bolts were placed end to end, in a straight line, how far would they reach, in kilometres?

4 What is the force on each anchorage bolt?

5 How many minor accidents were there in the year of peak workforce?

6 Find the average mass, in kilograms, of each rivet.

7 Find the average cost per week to maintain the bridge today.

8 By measuring the length of the bridge in the picture, show that the scale is approximately 1 : 10 000.

9 Use the same scale to work out an estimate of the height of one of the towers above the water level.

10 Find the volume of one main tube of length 140 m.

11 What is the scale of the picture of the bridge?

12 Estimate the maximum depth of the Firth of Forth.

13 How long would the bridge be shown on an Ordnance Survey map of scale 1 : 25 000?

14 How long would you expect the bridge to have taken to build if a peak workforce of 5600 had been employed?

15 What percentage of the total mass of steel is made up of rivets?

16 What was the probability of a worker having a minor accident at the peak workforce time? Copy and complete: 'At peak workforce time a worker was likely to have one minor accident about once every .... weeks.'

17 This graph shows the cost of building the bridge, in £1000s per year against time. Copy the graph and calibrate the vertical axis. Explain your method.

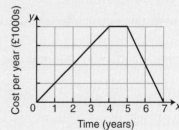

18 Copy and complete this table to show the accumulated cost of building the bridge.

Year	1	2	3	4	5	6	7
Cumulative cost (£1000s)							1600

Draw a cumulative frequency graph from the data and work out an estimate of the time, after the start of construction, when £1 million had been spent.

19 On the main tubes, what was the average number of rivets per square metre?

20 Work out an estimate of the average hourly wage. Use your answer to investigate

   a a likely weekly wage

   b the possible cost of building the bridge at today's prices

Investigation 1

Improving a skill

The time to complete a maze, to the nearest second, was recorded for thirty pupils. The pupils then repeated this exercise on the same maze, and their second attempts were also timed to the same degree of accuracy. The results are as shown. Each pupil's times correspond to the same position in the data tables.

First trial

47	54	59	69	68	67	65	78	77	79
74	73	79	71	88	89	84	89	87	83
88	86	82	91	93	97	94	99	105	109

Second trial

44	51	64	67	65	62	61	67	69	74
77	73	75	78	77	71	75	79	70	79
78	80	85	86	88	85	89	90	99	98

1 Group the data for the first and second trials as frequency distributions in classes:
40–50, 50–60, 60–70, ..., 100–110 seconds

2 Use the frequency distributions of both time trials to

  a estimate the mean times

  b draw two histograms

  c draw two cumulative frequency graphs in order to find the median and interquartile ranges

  d draw two box and whisker diagrams

3 Do the pupils appear to have improved in the skill of completing this maze?
Use statistical evidence to back up your conclusions.

4 **Investigate** the hypothesis that a skill improves with practice.

  ♦ Your teacher will provide each pupil in the class with two consecutive number charts each from 1, 2, 3, 4, 5, ..., 57, 58, 59, 60. Working in pairs, time how long it takes each person to draw the route from 1 to 2 to 3 to 4... to 60. Repeat this process once so that each person has two time trials on the same number chart.

  ♦ Gather the data to draw conclusions based on statistical evidence.

Summary 1

Number

Inverse proportion

It takes 2 hours to cut a school playing field with 3 mowers

In 1 hour it would take 6 mowers (÷ LHS by 2 and × RHS by 2)

In 1.5 hours it would take 4 mowers (× LHS by 1.5 and ÷ RHS by 1.5)

To change a recurring decimal to a fraction

$$x = 0.616161\ldots$$ (Multiply both sides by 100)

$$100 \times x = 61.616161\ldots$$ (Subtract the top from the bottom)

$$99 \times x = 61$$ (Divide both sides by 99)

$$x = \frac{61}{99}$$

Algebra

Proportion

- If r is directly proportional to s, then $r \propto s$ or $r = ks$, where k is a constant.
  So when $r = 6$ and $s = 15$, $k = 0.4$ and the equation is $r = 0.4\,s$.

- If a varies directly with the square of b, then $a \propto b^2$ or $a = kb^2$.
  So when $a = 100$ and $b = 5$, $k = 4$ and the equation is $a = 4b^2$.

- If x is inversely proportional to the square root of y, then

  $$x \propto \frac{1}{\sqrt{y}} \qquad \text{or} \qquad x = k\frac{1}{\sqrt{y}} = \frac{k}{\sqrt{y}}$$

  So when $x = 3.2$ and $y = 49$, $k = 16$ and the equation is $x = \dfrac{16}{\sqrt{y}}$.

Perpendicular lines

Two lines have the equations

$y = m_1 x + c_1$ and $y = m_2 x + c_2$.

◆ If $m_1 = m_2$ then the lines are parallel.

◆ If $m_1 \times m_2 = -1$ then the two lines are
perpendicular to each other.

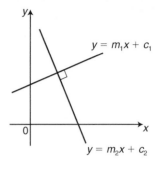

Exponential functions

These are of the form $y = a^x$ where a is any positive number.
The graphs will look like the one shown.

For example, if an investment is bought for £P and its
value doubles every year, after t years, the value is
given by the exponential function $P \times 2^t$.

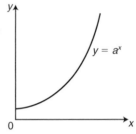

Shape and space

Congruence

For triangles to be congruent (the same size and shape), the corresponding sides and
angles must be: **SSS**, **SAS**, **AAS** or **ASA** (in that order) or **RHS** (right angle, hypotenuse,
side).

Use congruent triangles
to prove that $AD = BC$.

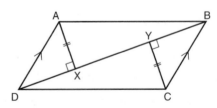

- State the triangles.

- State the three conditions for congruency and give reasons in brackets.

- Write the conclusion.

In triangles BYC and DXA

1 AX = CY   (Given)
2 ∠DBC = ∠BDA   (Alternate angles)
3 ∠BYC = ∠DXA   (Given)

∴ △BYC ≡ △DXA (SAA)
∴   AD = BC

Angles in the alternate segment

To prove $\angle CTB = \angle TDC$.

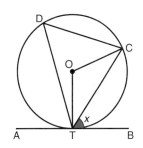

$$\angle OTC = (90° - x) \quad \text{(AB is tangent)}$$
$$\angle OCT = (90° - x) \quad \text{(△OCT is isosceles)}$$
$$\angle TOC + 2(90° - x) = 180° \quad \text{(Angle sum of △)}$$
$$\therefore \qquad \angle TOC = 2x$$
$$\therefore \qquad \angle TDC = x \qquad \text{(Angle at centre twice angle at circumference)}$$

Similarly $\angle CTB = \angle TDC$.

Handling data

Sampling

A sample is taken from a population when it is too time-consuming, or too expensive, or even impossible, to 'test' every 'member' of the population.

A **representative sample** has the same characteristics as the population it is taken from. It is **unbiased** and will

- not stretch the truth and result in false conclusions
- not give a false impression resulting in bad decisions

In a **random sample**, each member of the population has an equal chance of being selected, and such sampling must eliminate any form of human preference or selection.

A **stratified sample** reflects the strata in the same proportions as the population.

Examination practice 1

Paper 1A (Non-calculator)

1 The average fuel consumption of a Boeing 757 is 0.4 mpg (miles per gallon) and in flying from London to Nice it uses 2400 gallons.

  a On the same route another plane uses 800 gallons. Find its fuel consumption.

  b The fuel consumption of another plane is 0.5 mpg. How much fuel would it use on the same route?

2 **a** Match these equations to the graphs.

$$2y = x + 4 \qquad y = x$$
$$y + 2x = -2 \qquad y + 2x = 4$$

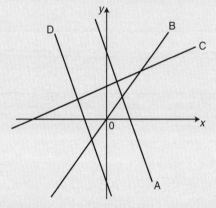

  b Explain why A and D are parallel to each other.

  c Explain why A and D are perpendicular to C.

3 Change these recurring decimals to fractions.

  a $0.5\dot{8}$ **b** $0.\dot{5}6\dot{7}$

4 Which of these fractions produce terminating decimals?

$$\frac{9}{40} \qquad \frac{7}{15} \qquad \frac{7}{8} \qquad \frac{11}{12} \qquad \frac{7}{128}$$

5 DEFGH is a regular pentagon. Prove that, if N is the mid-point of GH, then EN is the perpendicular from E to GH.

6 The graph of $y = -2x + 4$ is drawn.

  a Find the equation of the line that is perpendicular to $y = -2x + 4$ and passes through $(-2, -3)$.

  b Find the coordinates of the point of intersection of the lines.

7 TPK is a tangent to the circle. TSQ is a straight line.
PQ = QR
∠QPK = 50°
∠STP = 26°

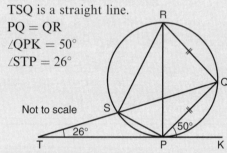

Not to scale

Calculate the size of

  a angle PQR

  b angle QRS

NEAB

8 Prove that $\angle PCB = \angle PBC$

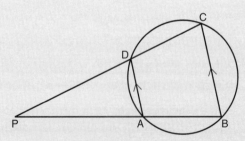

9 Prove that FG + EH = EF + GH.
(Let AF = a,
ED = b,
CH = c
and BG = d.)

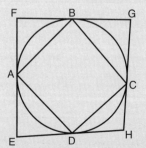

72

Paper 1B (Calculator)

Give all answers correct to 3 significant figures, where appropriate.

1 A machine produces coins, of a fixed thickness, from a given volume of metal. The number of coins, N, produced is inversely proportional to the square of the diameter, d.

   a 4000 coins are made of diameter 1.5 cm. Find the value of the constant of proportionality, k.

   b Find the formula for N in terms of d.

   c Find the number of coins that can be produced of diameter 2 cm.

   d If 1000 coins are produced, find their diameter.

2 x varies directly as the cube root of y. When $y = 27$, $x = 12$.

   a Find a formula connecting x and y.

   b Find the value of y when $x = 32$.

3 Solve these equations.

   a $5^x = 625$ **b** $2^x = 1024$

4 A radioactive substance loses 10% of its activity every day. A laboratory buys some of the substance with an activity of 1000 units. Draw the graph of activity against time (days) for the next 10 days. How long does it take for the activity to halve? (The time is known as the 'half-life' of the substance.)

5 Find the gradient of the lines parallel and perpendicular to AB when A is the point $(4, -4)$ and B is the point $(-2, -2)$.

6

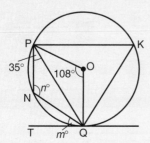

This diagram is NOT drawn accurately.

O is the centre of the circle. P, K, Q, N are points on the circumference.

QT is the tangent to the circle at Q.
Angle POQ = 108°
Angle NPQ = 35°

   a Calculate the values of m and n.

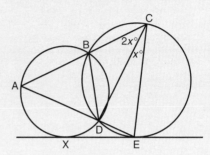

ABC and ADE are straight lines. CE is a diameter.

Angle DCE = $x°$ and angle BCD = $2x°$.

   b Find, in terms of x, the size of the angle

     (i) ABD   (ii) DBE   (iii) BAD

   c Explain why BE × AC = AE × CD

LONDON

7 You have been asked to do a survey of the eating habits of the students in a Sixth Form College. The grid below shows the number of students.

	Year 12	Year 13
Boys	253	198
Girls	201	222

You want your results to give a reliable representation of the students in the college. Explain how you will choose your sample, giving reasons.

NEAB

8 A(2, 4), B(5, 5), C(6, 2), D(2, −1) are four vertices of a quadrilateral.

   a Write down the coordinate of M, the mid-point of AC.

   b Prove that ABCD is a kite.

Number 2

Negative and fractional indices

Single negative and fractional indices

Example 1

Without using a calculator, evaluate these and, where appropriate, leave the answer as a fraction.

a $4^{-3} = \frac{1}{4^3} = \frac{1}{64}$

b $125^{\frac{1}{3}} = \sqrt[3]{125} = 5$

c $3^{-3} \times 3^2 = 3^{(-3+2)} = 3^{-1} = \frac{1}{3}$

d $6^{-4} \div 6^{-2} = 6^{(-4--2)} = 6^{-2} = \frac{1}{6^2} = \frac{1}{36}$

e $(3^{-1})^2 = 3^{(-1 \times 2)} = 3^{-2} = \frac{1}{3^2} = \frac{1}{9}$

Example 2

Use a calculator to work out these, correct to 3 significant figures.

a $4^{-3} = 0.015625 = 0.0156$ 4 3

b $60^{\frac{1}{5}} = 2.27$ 60   1 5

c $(5^{-2})^{-2} = 5^{(-2 \times -2)} = 5^4 = 625$ 5 4

Example 3

Simplify these.

a $a^{\frac{1}{2}} \times a^{\frac{1}{2}} \times a = a^{\left(\frac{1}{2} + \frac{1}{2} + 1\right)} = a^2$

b $3a^2 \times 2a^{-3} = 6 \times a^{2 + (-3)} = 6a^{-1} = \dfrac{6}{a}$

c $(6a^{-2}) \div (2a^2) = 3a^{(-2-2)} = 3a^{-4} = \dfrac{3}{a^4}$

Alternatively: $\dfrac{6}{a^2} \div 2a^2 = \dfrac{6}{a^2} \times \dfrac{1}{2a^2} = \dfrac{3}{a^4}$

Exercise 18

Without using a calculator, evaluate these and, where appropriate, leave the answer as a fraction.

1 3^{-2}	**2** 4^{-2}	**3** $81^{\frac{1}{2}}$	**4** $64^{\frac{1}{2}}$	**5** 4^{-3}
6 3^{-3}	**7** $27^{\frac{1}{3}}$	**8** $8^{\frac{1}{3}}$	**9** $2^2 \times 2^{-1}$	**10** $2^3 \times 2^{-1}$
11 $2^{-1} \div 2^3$	**12** $2^{-2} \div 2^3$	**13** $(3^{-1})^2$	**14** $(2^2)^{-2}$	**15** $2^{-2} \times 2^{-2}$
16 $3^{-1} \times 3^{-2}$	**17** $2^{-2} \div 2^{-1}$	**18** $3^{-3} \div 3^{-2}$	**19** $(2^{-2})^{-2}$	**20** $(3^{-3})^{-2}$

Use your calculator to work out these, correct to 3 significant figures.

21 5^4	**22** 4^3	**23** $23^{\frac{1}{3}}$	**24** $24^{\frac{1}{2}}$
25 $6^2 \times 6^{-3}$	**26** $7^2 \times 7^{-4}$	**27** $3^{-1} \times 3^{-3}$	**28** $4^{-2} \times 4^{-1}$
29 $6^2 \div 6^{-4}$	**30** $5^2 \div 5^{-3}$	**31** $3^{-1} \div 3^2$	**32** $2^{-2} \div 2^3$
33 $(3^2)^{-1}$	**34** $(4^{-1})^3$	**35** $(8^{-2})^{-1}$	**36** $(9^{-2})^{-2}$

Simplify these.

37 $a^2 \times a^{-1}$	**38** $b^4 \times b^{-2}$	**39** $c^{-1} \div c^2$	**40** $d^3 \div d^{-2}$
41 $e^2 \times e^3 \times e^{-4}$	**42** $f^3 \times f^2 \times f^{-4}$	**43** $(a^2)^{-1}$	**44** $(g^{-1})^2$
45 $b^{-2} \div b^3$	**46** $h^{-1} \div h^4$	**47** $(c^{-1})^{-2}$	**48** $(d^{-1})^3$

Exercise 18★

Without using a calculator, evaluate these and, where appropriate, leave the answer as a fraction.

1 2^{-6}	**2** 3^{-4}	**3** $125^{\frac{1}{3}}$	**4** $81^{\frac{1}{4}}$	**5** 6^0
6 3.8^0	**7** $2^{10} \times 2^3 \times 2^{-4}$	**8** $3^4 \times 3^{-3} \div 3^2$	**9** $200 \times (4^2)^{-1}$	**10** $900 \times (3^{-1})^2$

11 $\dfrac{4^{-2}}{4^{-3}}$ **12** $\dfrac{6^{-2}}{6^{-4}}$ **13** 0.1×0.1^{-2} **14** 0.2×0.2^{-3} **15** $\left(\dfrac{1}{2}\right)^{-3}$

16 $\left(\dfrac{2}{3}\right)^{-2}$ **17** $\left(\dfrac{1}{4}\right)^{\frac{1}{2}}$ **18** $\left(2\dfrac{1}{4}\right)^{\frac{1}{2}}$ **19** $(-6)^{-2}$ **20** $\left(-\dfrac{1}{3}\right)^{-3}$

Use your calculator to work out these, correct to 3 significant figures.

21 1.4^{-3} **22** 1.02^{-6} **23** $362^{\frac{1}{9}}$

24 $14.6^{\frac{1}{4}}$ **25** $3^{-3} \times 3^{-2} \times 3^{-1}$ **26** $4^{-5} \times 4^{-4} \div 4^{-5}$

Simplify these.

27 $a^{-2} \times a^{2} \div a^{-2}$ **28** $b^{4} \times b^{-3} \div b^{-2}$ **29** $2(c^{2})^{-2}$

30 $(2c^{-1})^{2}$ **31** $a^{-2} + a^{-2} + a^{-2}$ **32** $b^{-3} + 3b^{-3} - 2b^{-3}$

33 $3a^{-2} \times 4a$ **34** $4b^{2} \times 2b^{-3}$ **35** $a^{\frac{1}{2}} \times a^{\frac{1}{2}}$

36 $b^{\frac{1}{4}} \div b^{\frac{1}{4}}$ **37** $(c^{-2})^{\frac{1}{2}}$ **38** $(d^{\frac{1}{3}})^{-3}$

Solve these for x.

39 $9^{\frac{1}{x}} = 3$ **40** $8^{\frac{1}{x}} = 2$ **41** $81^{\frac{1}{2}} = 3^{x}$

42 $8^{\frac{1}{3}} = 2^{x}$ **43** $2^{x} = \dfrac{1}{8}$ **44** $3^{x} = \dfrac{1}{9}$

45 Find k if $x^{k} = \sqrt[3]{x} \div \dfrac{1}{x^{2}}$ **46** Find k if $x^{k-1} = \dfrac{(x^{2})^{-2}}{x^{3}}$

Simplify these.

47 $1 \div a^{3}$ **48** $1 \div a^{-2}$ **49** $b^{-2} \div \dfrac{1}{b^{3}}$

50 $c \div \dfrac{1}{c^{-3}}$ **51** $a^{-2} + \dfrac{1}{a^{2}}$ **52** $4a^{-2} - \dfrac{4}{a^{2}}$

53 $\dfrac{3}{a^{2}} + 2a^{-2}$ **54** $(2m)^{-2} \times 2m^{2}$ **55** $(3a)^{-2} \div \dfrac{1}{3a^{2}}$

56 $8b^{4} \times 2b \times (2b)^{-2}$ **57** $(-3a)^{3} \div (3a^{-3})$ **58** $(8d^{-3}) \div (2d^{-1})$

59 $\left(\dfrac{a}{b}\right)^{-1}$

60 Find a and b if $2^{2a} = 64$ and $10^{b} = 0.001$

Combined negative and fractional indices

$16^{\frac{3}{4}}$ can be written as $\left(16^{\frac{1}{4}}\right)^{3} = \left(\sqrt[4]{16}\right)^{3} = 2^{3} = 8$

This shows that $16^{-\frac{3}{4}} = \dfrac{1}{16^{\frac{3}{4}}} = \dfrac{1}{2^{3}} = \dfrac{1}{8}$

Exercise 19

Without using a calculator, evaluate these and, where appropriate, leave the answer as a fraction.

1 $25^{-\frac{1}{2}}$ **2** $81^{-\frac{1}{2}}$ **3** $125^{-\frac{1}{3}}$ **4** $64^{-\frac{1}{3}}$

5 $4^{\frac{3}{2}}$ **6** $9^{\frac{3}{2}}$ **7** $4^{-\frac{3}{2}}$ **8** $9^{-\frac{3}{2}}$

Use your calculator to work out these, correct to 3 significant figures.

9 $6^{-\frac{1}{2}}$ **10** $20^{-\frac{1}{2}}$ **11** $100^{-\frac{1}{4}}$ **12** $50^{-\frac{1}{4}}$

13 $5^{\frac{3}{2}}$ **14** $11^{\frac{3}{2}}$ **15** $3^{-\frac{3}{2}}$ **16** $7^{-\frac{3}{2}}$

Simplify these.

17 $a^{2\frac{1}{2}} \times a^{-\frac{1}{2}}$ **18** $b^{-\frac{1}{3}} \times b^{-\frac{1}{3}} \times b^{-\frac{1}{3}}$ **19** $c^{2\frac{1}{2}} \div c^{-\frac{1}{2}}$

20 $d^{\frac{2}{3}} \div d^{-\frac{1}{3}}$ **21** $(e^{\frac{2}{3}})^3$ **22** $(f^2)^{-\frac{1}{2}}$

Exercise 19★

Without using a calculator, evaluate these and, where appropriate, leave the answer as a fraction.

1 $36^{-\frac{1}{2}}$ **2** $144^{-\frac{1}{2}}$ **3** $1 \div 216^{-\frac{1}{3}}$ **4** $1 \div 1000^{-\frac{1}{3}}$

5 $8^{\frac{4}{3}}$ **6** $1^{\frac{3}{2}}$ **7** $8^{-\frac{4}{3}}$ **8** $1^{-\frac{3}{2}}$

Use your calculator to work out these, correct to 3 significant figures.

9 $0.6^{-\frac{1}{2}}$ **10** $0.3^{-\frac{1}{2}}$ **11** $1.4^{-\frac{1}{3}}$ **12** $3.7^{-\frac{1}{3}}$

13 $2.01^{\frac{3}{2}}$ **14** $0.909^{\frac{3}{2}}$ **15** $2.01^{-\frac{3}{2}}$ **16** $0.909^{-\frac{3}{2}}$

Simplify these.

17 $a^{\frac{1}{2}} \times a^{-2\frac{1}{2}}$ **18** $b^{-\frac{1}{2}} \times b^{-2\frac{1}{2}}$ **19** $c^{-2\frac{1}{3}} \div c^{-\frac{1}{3}}$ **20** $d^{1\frac{1}{5}} \div d^{-\frac{4}{5}}$

21 $(e^{-\frac{1}{2}})^{-2}$ **22** $(f^{-\frac{1}{3}})^{-6}$ **23** $(27^2)^{\frac{1}{3}}$ **24** $(16^3)^{\frac{1}{4}}$

25 $216^{-\frac{2}{3}}$ **26** $1000^{-\frac{2}{3}}$

Use your calculator to work out these, correct to 3 significant figures.

27 $1 \div \dfrac{1}{1.02^{-2.5}}$ **28** $\left(1 \div \dfrac{1}{1.02^{-2.5}}\right)^{-2.5}$

Find the values of x and y in these equations.

29 $(a^x b^y)^{\frac{1}{6}} = a^{\frac{1}{2}} \times b^{-\frac{1}{3}}$ **30** $\sqrt[5]{a^4 b^{-3}} = a^x b^y$

Surds

Simplifying surds

The side length of a square of area $2\,\text{m}^2$ is $\sqrt{2}\,\text{m} = 1.414\,213\,562\ldots\text{m}$. Such a number that cannot be written as an exact ratio of two integers is called a **surd**. Surds also appear in trigonometry, for example

$$\tan 60° = \sqrt{3}, \qquad \cos 30° = \frac{\sqrt{3}}{2}$$

Example 4

a Express $\sqrt{18}$ in the form $a\sqrt{b}$

$\begin{aligned} \sqrt{18} &= \sqrt{9 \times 2} \qquad \text{(Write 18 in factor form)} \\ &= \sqrt{9} \times \sqrt{2} \\ &= 3\sqrt{2} \end{aligned}$

b Express $5\sqrt{6}$ in the form $\sqrt{n}$

$\begin{aligned} 5\sqrt{6} &= \sqrt{25} \times \sqrt{6} \qquad \text{(Write 5 as } \sqrt{25}) \\ &= \sqrt{25 \times 6} \\ &= \sqrt{150} \end{aligned}$

Example 5

a Simplify $2\sqrt{3} \times 3\sqrt{3}$

$2\sqrt{3} \times 3\sqrt{3} = 6(\sqrt{3})^2 = 18$

b Simplify $2\sqrt{3} + 3\sqrt{3}$

$2\sqrt{3} + 3\sqrt{3} = \sqrt{3}(2 + 3) = 5\sqrt{3}$

c Simplify $\sqrt{18} - \sqrt{8}$

$\begin{aligned} \sqrt{18} - \sqrt{8} &= 3\sqrt{2} - 2\sqrt{2} \qquad \text{(Write the surds in the form } a\sqrt{b}) \\ &= \sqrt{2} \end{aligned}$

Exercise 20

Square these.

1 $\sqrt{3}$ **2** $\sqrt{5}$ **3** $3\sqrt{3}$ **4** $2\sqrt{3}$ **5** $\sqrt{\frac{2}{3}}$ **6** $\frac{\sqrt{3}}{\sqrt{4}}$

Express these in the form $a\sqrt{b}$.

7 $\sqrt{8}$ **8** $\sqrt{12}$ **9** $\sqrt{45}$ **10** $\sqrt{20}$ **11** $\sqrt{28}$ **12** $\sqrt{63}$

Express these in the form $\sqrt{n}$.

13 $5\sqrt{2}$ **14** $3\sqrt{3}$ **15** $2\sqrt{6}$ **16** $5\sqrt{3}$ **17** $2\sqrt{7}$ **18** $3\sqrt{6}$

Simplify these.

19 $3\sqrt{3} + 4\sqrt{3}$ **20** $5\sqrt{2} - 4\sqrt{2}$ **21** $3\sqrt{2} \times 2\sqrt{2}$

22 $3\sqrt{3} \times 4\sqrt{3}$ **23** $\dfrac{3\sqrt{5}}{3\sqrt{2}}$ **24** $\dfrac{2\sqrt{5}}{3\sqrt{5}}$

Rationalising denominators

When writing fractions, it is not usual to write surds in the denominator (the bottom of the fraction). The process of clearing a surd in a denominator is called **rationalising** the denominator. To do this, multiply the top and bottom of the fraction by the same amount; this is equivalent to multiplying the whole fraction by 1, and so does not change its value.

Example 6

a Rationalise the denominator in $\dfrac{2}{\sqrt{3}}$

$\dfrac{2}{\sqrt{3}} = \dfrac{2}{\sqrt{3}} \times \dfrac{\sqrt{3}}{\sqrt{3}}$ (Multiply top and bottom by $\sqrt{3}$)

$\quad\ = \dfrac{2\sqrt{3}}{3}$

b Rationalise the denominator in $\dfrac{1}{\sqrt{2} - 1}$

$\dfrac{1}{\sqrt{2} - 1} = \dfrac{1}{\sqrt{2} - 1} \times \dfrac{\sqrt{2} + 1}{\sqrt{2} + 1}$ (Multiply the top and bottom by the denominator with the sign changed)

$\qquad\quad = \dfrac{\sqrt{2} + 1}{2 - 1}$

$\qquad\quad = \sqrt{2} + 1$

Note: $(\sqrt{2} - 1)(\sqrt{2} + 1) = 2 - \sqrt{2} + \sqrt{2} - 1 = 2 - 1$

Exercise 20★

Express these in the form $a\sqrt{b}$.

1 $\sqrt{44}$ **2** $\sqrt{99}$ **3** $\sqrt{1000}$ **4** $\sqrt{216}$

Express these in the form $\sqrt{n}$.

5 $5\sqrt{5}$ **6** $10\sqrt{3}$ **7** $\dfrac{\sqrt{2}}{2}$ **8** $\dfrac{\sqrt{5}}{3}$

Express these in terms of the simplest possible surds.

9 $3\sqrt{2} + 5\sqrt{2}$　　　　　　　　　　**10** $3\sqrt{3} - 5\sqrt{3}$

11 $3\sqrt{5} \times 4\sqrt{5}$　　　　　　　　　　**12** $3\sqrt{7} \times 2\sqrt{7}$

13 $\sqrt{3} \div (2\sqrt{3})$　　　　　　　　　**14** $\sqrt{2} \div (3\sqrt{2})$

15 $\sqrt{18} + \sqrt{32}$　　　　　　　　　　**16** $\sqrt{75} - \sqrt{12}$

17 $3\sqrt{10} + 2\sqrt{10} - 5\sqrt{10}$　　　　**18** $2\sqrt{28} - \sqrt{63}$

19 $2(\sqrt{3} + 1) + 3(1 - \sqrt{3})$　　　　　**20** $\sqrt{2} - (2\sqrt{2} - 1)$

21 $(\sqrt{5} + 2)^2$　　　　　　　　　　　**22** $(2 - \sqrt{3})^2$

Express these with rational denominators.

23 $\dfrac{1}{\sqrt{2}}$　　　　**24** $\dfrac{5}{\sqrt{5}}$　　　　**25** $\dfrac{4}{\sqrt{2}}$　　　　**26** $\dfrac{6}{\sqrt{3}}$

27 $\dfrac{6}{\sqrt{2}}$　　　　**28** $\dfrac{3}{\sqrt{2}}$　　　　**29** $\dfrac{2}{\sqrt{12}}$　　　　**30** $\dfrac{2}{\sqrt{18}}$

31 $\dfrac{1}{\sqrt{2} + 1}$　　　**32** $\dfrac{1}{\sqrt{3} - 2}$　　　**33** $\dfrac{1}{7 - 4\sqrt{3}}$　　　**34** $\dfrac{\sqrt{2} + 1}{\sqrt{2} - 1}$

Irrational numbers

Before the sixth century BC, mathematicians thought that all numbers could be expressed as a fraction, i.e. the ratio of two integers; hence the word **rational**. Then the Pythagoreans, an ancient Greek philosophical school and religious brotherhood, calculated the length of the diagonal of a unit square as $\sqrt{2}$. They found that this number could *not* be written as a fraction and, as a result, they called it 'an anomaly of the square'. However, they soon found other numbers, such as $\sqrt{3}$ and $\sqrt{5}$, that could not be written as the ratio of two integers; hence the word **irrational**. The first person to *prove* that these numbers were irrational was the Greek, Theodorus, who taught mathematics to Plato.

Apart from the square root of all prime numbers, called **surds**, another common irrational number is π. When written as decimals, irrational numbers have no recurring digits, and the digits seem to appear almost at random, as can be seen from the first 115 digits of π:

> π = 3.141 592 653 589 793 238 462 643 383 279 502 884 197 169 399 375 105 820 974 944
> 　　592 307 816 404 286 208 998 628 034 825 342 117 067 982 148 086 513 282 . . .

Together, the rational and irrational numbers form a set of real numbers from minus infinity to plus infinity, called a **continuum**; in other words, *every* number can be placed on this number line.

Example 7

Which of these numbers are rational and which are irrational?

0.789 $0.6\dot{7}$ $\sqrt{2} \times \sqrt{2}$ $\sqrt{2} + \sqrt{2}$

Explain your answers.

$0.789 = \frac{789}{1000}$ ∴ rational $\sqrt{2} \times \sqrt{2} = 2$ ∴ rational

$0.6\dot{7} = \frac{67}{99}$ ∴ rational $\sqrt{2} + \sqrt{2} = 2\sqrt{2}$ ∴ irrational

Example 8

a Write down an irrational number between 4 and 5.

$4^2 = 16$ and $5^2 = 25$

∴ any square root between $\sqrt{17}$ and $\sqrt{24}$ inclusive is irrational.

b Write down a rational number between $\sqrt{24}$ and $\sqrt{26}$.

$\sqrt{24} = 4.8989795\ldots$ and $\sqrt{26} = 5.0990195\ldots$

∴ any terminating decimal between 4.899 and 5.099

5, for example, is rational.

Remember

The most common irrational numbers are the square roots of prime numbers and π.

Exercise 21

For Questions 1–12, state which of the numbers are rational and which are irrational, and then express each of the rational numbers in the form $\frac{a}{b}$ where a and b are integers.

1 5.7 **2** $0.4\dot{7}$ **3** $\sqrt{4}$

4 π **5** $\sqrt{2}$ **6** $\sqrt{2} + 3$

7 $\sqrt{7} \times \sqrt{7}$ **8** $\sqrt{7} + \sqrt{7}$ **9** $7\sqrt{7} - \sqrt{7}$

10 $\sqrt{7} \div \sqrt{7}$ **11** $3.5 \times \pi$ **12** $4\pi \div \pi$

13 Write down a rational number between $\sqrt{3}$ and $\sqrt{5}$.

14 Write down a rational number between $\sqrt{48}$ and $\sqrt{50}$.

15 Write down an irrational number between 7 and 8.

16 Write down an irrational number between 3 and 4.

Exercise 21★

For Questions 1–12, state which of the numbers are rational and which are irrational, and then express each of the rational numbers in the form $\dfrac{a}{b}$ where a and b are integers.

1 $\pi + 2$ **2** $\sqrt{2} + \sqrt{2}$ **3** $\sqrt{20}$

4 $\sqrt{2\frac{1}{4}}$ **5** $\sqrt{\frac{4}{25}}$ **6** $\sqrt{3.6}$

7 $\sqrt{0.81}$ **8** $\sqrt{3} - \sqrt{5}$ **9** $(\sqrt{7} + \sqrt{5})(\sqrt{7} - \sqrt{5})$

10 $(\sqrt{3} + \sqrt{5})(\sqrt{3} + \sqrt{5})$ **11** $\dfrac{\sqrt{20} + \sqrt{28}}{\sqrt{5} + \sqrt{7}}$ **12** $\dfrac{\sqrt{27} + 3}{\sqrt{3} + 1}$

13 Write down two irrational numbers whose product is rational.

14 Write down an irrational number y such that y^3 is rational.

15 Write down an irrational number between 2 and 3.

16 Write down an irrational number less than 1.

17 Right angled triangles can have sides with lengths which are a rational or irrational number of units. Give an example of a right angled triangle to fit each description below. Draw a separate triangle for each part.

  a All sides are rational.

  b The hypotenuse is rational and the other two sides are irrational.

  c The hypotenuse is irrational and the other two sides are rational.

  d The hypotenuse and one of the other sides are rational and the remaining side is irrational.

LONDON

Exercise 22 (Revision)

Work out these and, where appropriate, leave the answer as a fraction.

1 2^{-4} **2** $100^{\frac{1}{2}}$ **3** $64^{\frac{1}{3}}$ **4** $3^3 \times 3^{-1}$

5 $3^{-1} \div 3^3$ **6** $(3^{-3})^{-1}$ **7** $36^{-\frac{1}{2}}$ **8** $9^{\frac{3}{2}}$

Simplify these.

9 $a^3 \times a^{-1}$ **10** $a^3 \div a^{-1}$ **11** $(d^{-1})^2$

12 $b^{\frac{1}{2}} \times b^{-2}$ **13** $b^{\frac{1}{2}} \div b^{-2}$ **14** $\left(c^{-\frac{1}{2}}\right)^{-2}$

15 Write $\sqrt{75}$ in the form $a\sqrt{b}$.   **16** Write $2\sqrt{5}$ in the form $\sqrt{n}$.

Simplify these.

17 $5\sqrt{3} + 2\sqrt{3}$ **18** $2\sqrt{2} - 5\sqrt{2}$ **19** $4\sqrt{2} \times 3\sqrt{2}$ **20** $\dfrac{3\sqrt{3}}{2\sqrt{3}}$

Exercise 22★ (Revision)

Work out these and, where appropriate, leave the answer as a fraction.

1 2^{-5}

2 $216^{\frac{1}{3}}$

3 9.7^0

4 $27 \times (3^{-1})^2$

5 $2^8 \times 2^{-2} \times 2^{-4}$

6 $49^{-\frac{1}{2}}$

7 $\left(\frac{1}{2}\right)^{-3} \div 2^{-3}$

8 $16^{\frac{3}{4}}$

9 $\left(\frac{1}{27}\right)^{\frac{2}{3}}$

10 $(125)^{-\frac{4}{3}}$

11 $(0.125)^{-\frac{2}{3}}$

12 $(4^{\frac{1}{3}})^{-1\frac{1}{2}}$

Simplify these.

13 $3c^3 \times c^{-2}$

14 $b^{-2} + 4b^{-2}$

15 $a^3 \times a^{-2} \div a^{-1}$

16 $3 \times (c^{-1})^2$

17 $2\left(a^{\frac{1}{3}}\right)^{-3}$

18 $d^{\frac{1}{2}} \times d^{\frac{2}{3}}$

19 $(-3a)^3 \div (3a^{-3})$

20 $(2b^2)^{-1} \div (-2b)^{-2}$

21 Write $\sqrt{98}$ in the form $a\sqrt{b}$.

22 Write $\dfrac{\sqrt{3}}{2}$ in the form $\sqrt{n}$.

Express these in terms of the simplest possible surds.

23 $4\sqrt{3} + 6\sqrt{3}$

24 $\sqrt{45} - \sqrt{20}$

25 $\sqrt{27} \times 2\sqrt{3}$

26 $(4\sqrt{3}) \div (6\sqrt{3})$

27 $(2\sqrt{2} + 1)^2$

28 $2\sqrt{3}(\sqrt{27} + \sqrt{3})$

Express these with rational denominators.

29 $\dfrac{3}{\sqrt{75}}$

30 $-\dfrac{1}{\sqrt{2}}$

31 $\dfrac{1}{\sqrt{3} - 1}$

32 $\dfrac{4}{\sqrt{11} - \sqrt{7}}$

Algebra 2

Using formulae

Activity 14

How to discover someone's age

- ◆ Ask someone to
  - ▸ write down their age
  - ▸ double it
  - ▸ add 5
  - ▸ multiply the result by 50
  - ▸ add any number they chose between 1 and 100
  - ▸ subtract 365.
- ◆ When they give you the result, you add 115. Their age will be revealed and also the number they chose between 1 and 100.
- ◆ Show that this works, and investigate why it works. Let their age be x and the number they chose between 1 and 100 be y.

Area and perimeter of quarter and half circles

Example 1

Find the area, A cm^2, of the shaded region

a correct to 3 significant figures, when $x = 4$ cm

b in terms of x and π.

a $A = \frac{1}{4} \times \pi \times 4^2 = 12.6$

b $A = \frac{1}{4} \times \pi \times x^2 = \dfrac{\pi x^2}{4}$

Example 2

Find the area, A cm^2, of the shaded region

a correct to 3 significant figures, when $x = 4$ cm

b in terms of x and π and factorise your answer.

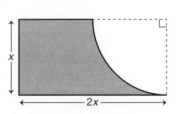

a $A = (8 \times 4) - \frac{1}{4} \times \pi \times 4^2 = 32 - 12.6 = 19.4$

b $A = (2x \times x) - \frac{1}{4} \times \pi \times x^2 = 2x^2 - \dfrac{\pi x^2}{4} = x^2\left(2 - \dfrac{\pi}{4}\right)$

Exercise 23

1 Find the area of the shaded region

   a correct to 3 significant figures, when $x = 3\,\text{cm}$

   b in terms of x and π.

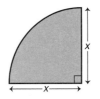

2 Find the area of the shaded region

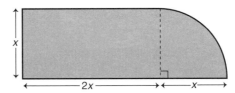

   a correct to 3 significant figures, when $x = 5\,\text{cm}$

   b in terms of x and π, and factorise your answer.

3 Find the area of the shaded region

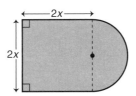

   a correct to 3 significant figures, when $x = 1.5\,\text{cm}$

   b in terms of x and π, and factorise your answer.

4 Find the area of the shaded region

   a correct to 3 significant figures, when $x = 1.5\,\text{cm}$

   b in terms of x and π, and factorise your answer.

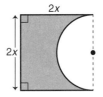

5 Find the perimeter of the shape

   a correct to 3 significant figures, when $x = 5\,\text{cm}$

   b in terms of x and π, and factorise your answer.

6 Find the perimeter of the shape

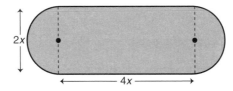

   a correct to 3 significant figures, when $x = 5\,\text{cm}$

   b in terms of x and π, and factorise your answer.

7 Find the area of the shaded region

    a when $x = 2\,\text{cm}$

    b in terms of x.

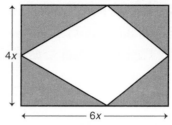

8 Find the area of the shaded region

    a when $x = 2\,\text{cm}$

    b in terms of x.

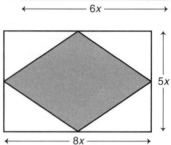

Exercise 23★

1 Find the area of the shaded region

    a correct to 3 significant figures, when $x = 3\,\text{cm}$

    b in terms of x and π, and factorise your answer.

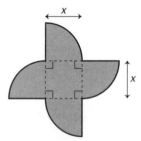

2 Find the area of the shaded region

    a correct to 3 significant figures, when $x = 5\,\text{cm}$

    b in terms of x and π, and factorise your answer.

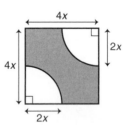

3 Find the perimeter of the shaded region

    a correct to 3 significant figures, when $x = 1.5\,\text{cm}$

    b in terms of x and π.

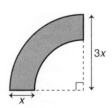

4 Find the perimeter of the shaded region

    a correct to 3 significant figures, when $x = 1.5\,\text{cm}$

    b in terms of x and π.

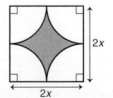

5 Find the area of the shaded region

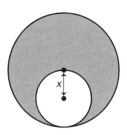

    a correct to 3 significant figures, when $x = 5\,cm$

    b in terms of x and π.

6 Find the area of the shaded region

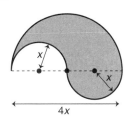

    a correct to 3 significant figures, when $x = 3\,cm$

    b in terms of x and π.

For Questions 7–11, find the shaded area in terms of x and π, and factorise your answers.

7 a

b

c
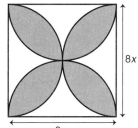

8
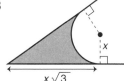

9
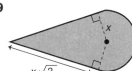

10
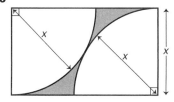

11
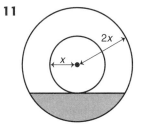

Area of a triangle

Activity 15

A formula to give the area of any triangle is

$$\text{area} = \tfrac{1}{2} \times a \times b \sin C$$

(Notice that this is the product of the lengths of **two sides** and the sine of the **included angle**.)

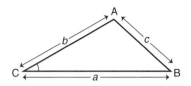

◆ Copy the triangle and draw the perpendicular from A onto BC. Use this to prove the formula.
◆ Find the area of triangle ABC when
  ▸ angle $C = 40°$, $a = 4\,\text{cm}$ and $b = 6\,\text{cm}$
  ▸ angle $C = 140°$, $a = 4\,\text{cm}$ and $b = 6\,\text{cm}$.

Comment on your two answers.

Arcs, sectors and segments

An **arc** is the length of part of the circumference of a circle:

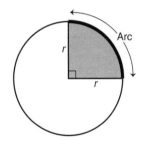

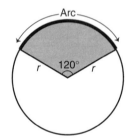

arc length $= \tfrac{1}{4}$ of the circumference

$$= \tfrac{1}{4} \times 2\pi r$$

$$= \frac{\pi r}{2}$$

arc length $= \frac{120°}{360°}$ of the circumference

$$= \tfrac{1}{3} \times 2\pi r$$

$$= \frac{2\pi r}{3}$$

Key Point

$$\text{Arc length} = \frac{x}{360°} \times 2\pi r$$

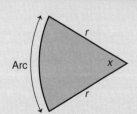

Example 3

Find the length of the arc XY correct to 3 significant figures.

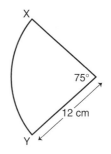

Arc length $= \frac{75°}{360°} \times 2\pi \times 12\,\text{cm}$

$\quad\quad\quad = 15.7\,\text{cm}$

Example 4

Find the angle x correct to 3 significant figures.

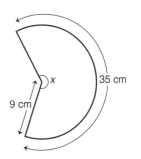

$$35 = \frac{x}{360°} \times 2\pi \times 9 \quad \text{(Rearrange this equation)}$$

$$\frac{35 \times 360}{2\pi \times 9} = x$$

$$x = 223°$$

A **sector** of a circle is a region whose boundary is an arc and two radii:

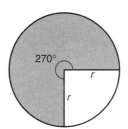

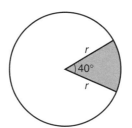

sector area $= \frac{3}{4}$ of the area of circle

$\quad\quad\quad = \frac{3}{4}\pi r^2$

sector area $= \frac{40°}{360°}\pi r^2$

$\quad\quad\quad = \frac{1}{9}\pi r^2$

Key Point

Sector area $= \dfrac{x}{360°} \times \pi r^2$

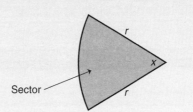

Sector

Example 5

Find the area of the sector $A\,\text{cm}^2$, correct to 3 significant figures.

$$A = \frac{65°}{360°} \times \pi \times 7.6^2$$

$$= 32.8$$

So, sector area is $32.8\,\text{cm}^2$.

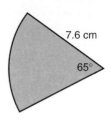

7.6 cm

65°

Example 6

Find the angle x correct to 3 significant figures.

$$13.4 = \frac{x}{360°} \times \pi \times 5.5^2$$

$$\frac{13.4 \times 360°}{\pi \times 5.5^2} = x$$

$$x = 50.8°$$

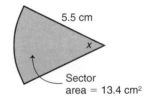

5.5 cm

x

Sector
area = 13.4 cm²

Example 7

Find the radius of the sector correct to 3 significant figures.

$$87 = \frac{210°}{360°} \times \pi r^2$$

$$\sqrt{\frac{87 \times 360}{210\pi}} = r$$

$$r = 6.89$$

So the radius is $6.89\,\text{cm}$.

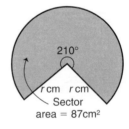

210°

r cm   r cm
Sector
area = 87cm²

A **segment** of a circle is the region whose boundary is an arc and a chord.
(A chord is a line joining two points of the circumference of a circle.)

Key Point

♦ The area of a triangle ABC is $\frac{1}{2}ab\sin C$.

♦ Segment area = area of sector OXY − area of triangle OXY

$$= \frac{x}{360°} \times \pi r^2 - \frac{1}{2}r^2 \sin x$$

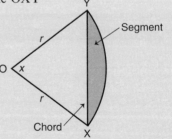

Y

Segment

r

O x

r

Chord

X

Example 8

Find the shaded area $A\,\text{cm}^2$, correct to 3 significant figures.

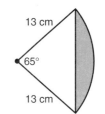

$$A = \frac{65}{360} \times \pi \times 13^2 - \frac{1}{2} \times 13^2 \sin 65°$$

$$= 95.86 - 76.58$$

$$= 19.3$$

The shaded area is $19.3\,\text{cm}^2$.

Exercise 24

Give all answers correct to 3 significant figures.

1 Find the arc lengths.

a
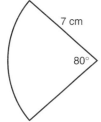

b
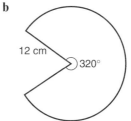

2 Find the arc lengths.

a
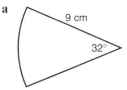

b
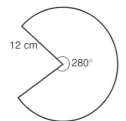

3 Find the sector areas.

a
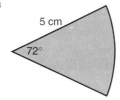

b
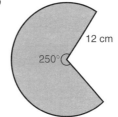

4 Find the sector areas.

a

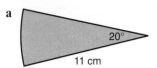

b

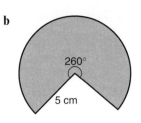

5 Find the area of the shaded segments.

a

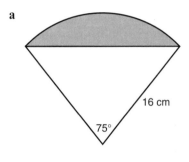

b

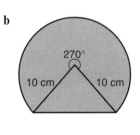

6 Find the area of the shaded segments.

a

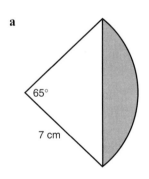

b

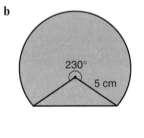

Exercise 24★

Give all answers correct to 3 significant figures.

1 Calculate the radius r.

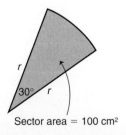

Sector area = 100 cm²

2 Calculate the angle x.

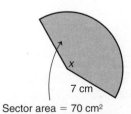

Sector area = 70 cm²

3 Calculate the radius r.

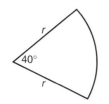

Sector perimeter = 36 cm

4 Calculate the radius r.

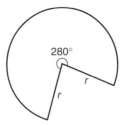

280°

Sector perimeter = 45cm

5 Calculate the radius r.

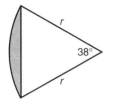

38°

Segment area = 26 cm²

6 Calculate the radius r.

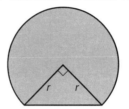

Segment area = 43 cm²

7 A girl is positioned 15 m from the edge of a circular pond of radius 5 m. She walks around the pond and returns to her original position. What is the shortest distance she walks?

8 The minute hand of a clock is 10 cm long.
Calculate how far the tip of the hand moves in 25 minutes.

9 An 'S shape' is drawn by joining two arcs, each of radius 5 cm and subtending an angle of 210° at the centre. If the 'S shape' were to be straightened, find its length.

10 A door, with a curved top, is shown below. Find its area.

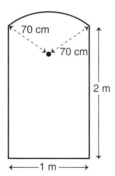

70 cm

70 cm

2 m

1 m

11 Calculate the shaded area ABC.

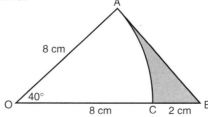

A

8 cm

40°

O

8 cm   C   2 cm   B

12 Find

    a the perimeter of HKLM

    b the area of HKLM

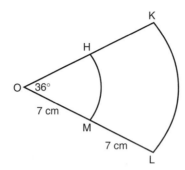

13 The triangle ABC has pulleys of radius 2 cm centred at each corner as shown.
Find the length of an elastic band that is stretched around the pulleys.

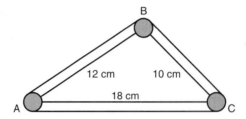

14 A builder is constructing a stone archway with dimensions as shown.
Calculate the radius of curvature *r*.

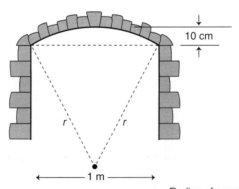

r = Radius of curvature

15 Calculate the angle *x*, given that the shaded segment area is $40\,\text{cm}^2$.

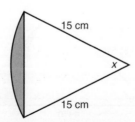

16 A 50p coin has rotational symmetry of order 7.
   Each side is an arc of radius 27 mm.
   Calculate the area of the coin.

Sector of circle radius 27 mm

Investigate

One of the greatest engineers of ancient times was a Greek called Heron, who lived in the first century AD in Alexandria. He pioneered the science of applied mathematics and engineering. Two of his formulae, for the area of quadrilaterals, are shown below, where in each p is half the perimeter and the side lengths are a, b, c and d.

◆ The area of a **cyclic quadrilateral** is

$$\sqrt{(p-a)(p-b)(p-c)(p-d)}$$

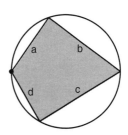

◆ The area of **any quadrilateral** is

$$\sqrt{(p-a)(p-b)(p-c)(p-d) - abcd(\cos q)^2}$$

where q is half the sum of two opposite angles.

Investigate these formulae by considering some simple cases.

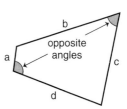

Surface areas and volumes of solids

Remember

◆ Any solid with parallel sides that has a constant cross-section is called a **prism**.

◆ Volume of a prism = cross-sectional area × height

◆ A cylinder is a prism with a circular cross-section.

◆ Volume of a cylinder = $\pi r^2 \times h$

◆ Curved surface area of a cylinder = $2\pi rh$

◆ Length of AB around curved surface = $\sqrt{h^2 + (2\pi r)^2}$

◆ Volume of a pyramid = $\frac{1}{3} \times$ base area × vertical height

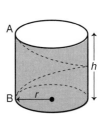

Cone

A cone is a pyramid on a circular base. It can be constructed from a sector of a circular piece of paper, as shown, when OA is joined to OB. The result is also shown.

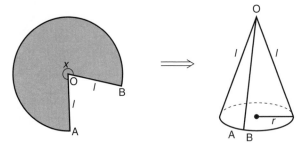

To find the curved surface area of the cone, in terms of π, r and l:

From the left-hand diagram

$$\text{arc length} = \frac{x}{360} 2\pi l \qquad \textcircled{1}$$

From the right-hand diagram

$$\text{circumference of the base} = 2\pi r \qquad \textcircled{2}$$

But the arc length is the same as the base circumference, $\textcircled{1} = \textcircled{2}$, and so

$$\frac{x}{360} \times 2\pi l = 2\pi r$$

$$\therefore \qquad \frac{x}{360} = \frac{r}{l} \qquad \textcircled{3}$$

From the first left-hand diagram

$$\text{sector area} = \frac{x}{360} \times \pi l^2 \qquad \textcircled{4}$$

Substituting $\textcircled{3}$ in $\textcircled{4}$:

◆ Curved surface area of a cone $= \pi r l$

Sphere

◆ Volume of sphere $= \frac{4}{3} \pi r^3$

◆ Surface area of a sphere $= 4\pi r^2$

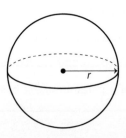

Example 9

A sphere has volume $100\,\text{cm}^3$. Find its radius r cm, correct to 3 significant figures.

$$100 = \tfrac{4}{3}\pi r^3$$

$$\sqrt[3]{\frac{3 \times 100}{4\pi}} = r$$

$$r = 2.88$$

The radius of the sphere is $2.88\,\text{cm}$.

Exercise 25

Give all answers correct to 3 significant figures.

1 The figure shows a hemispherical water tank. Calculate

    a the volume   **b** the curved surface area

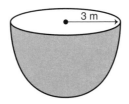

2 The figure shows a cylindrical farmyard slurry tank. Calculate

    a the volume   **b** the curved surface area

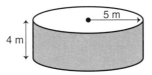

3 A witch's hat is made from a sector cut from a large circular piece of card. If the circumference of the base is $40\,\text{cm}$, calculate

    a the base radius   **b** the height, h **c** the volume

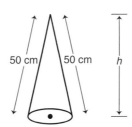

4 The diagram shows part of a farm grain hopper which is in the shape of an inverted cone. If the circumference of the top is 6 m, calculate

   a the radius of the top

   b the depth (d)

   c the volume

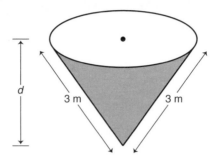

5 Find the height of a cone of base 300 cm^2 and slant height of 20 cm.

6 Find the radius of a cylinder of height 20 cm and volume 1500 cm^3.

7 Find the radius of a sphere of volume 500 cm^3.

8 Find the radius of a hemisphere of volume 500 cm^3.

Exercise 25★

Give all answers correct to 3 significant figures.

  1 Calculate the height of a cylinder of diameter 10 cm and volume 1000 cm^3.

  2 Calculate the height of a cylinder of diameter 10 cm and curved surface area 1000 cm^2.

  3 Calculate the radius of a hemisphere of volume 500 cm^3.

  4 Calculate the radius of a sphere of volume 500 cm^3.

  5 A sphere of radius 8 cm has the same volume as a cone of base radius 16 cm. Find the height of the cone.

  6 A solid metal sphere of radius 5 cm is melted down and cast into a cuboid. Calculate the surface area of the cube.

  7 A sphere of radius r cm has the same volume as a cone of base radius $2r$ cm. Find the height of the cone h in terms of r.

  8 A circular cylinder of height a cm and volume V cm^3, open at both ends, is made out of a rectangular piece of card measuring a cm by b cm. Find a formula for V in terms of a, b and π. (The overlap of the join is to be neglected.)

  9 A solid cone has a volume of 1000 cm^3 and a height of 10 cm. Calculate the total surface area.

10 A solid cone has a base area of 100 cm^2 and a height of 10 cm. Calculate the total surface area.

11 The diagram shows a lead sphere of volume 40 cm³, covered with water, at the bottom of a cylinder. Calculate the decrease in water level when the sphere is removed.

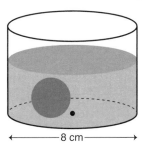

← 8 cm →

12 All the rain that falls on the roof of a rectangular house, of length 15 m and width 8 m, is collected in a large cylindrical rain-butt of diameter 1.4 m. If 2 cm of rain falls, by how much does the water level in the rain-butt rise? (Assume that the butt does not overflow.)

13 The diagram shows a solid inverted cone.
If the circumference of the top is 20 cm, calculate

  a the volume

  b the total surface area

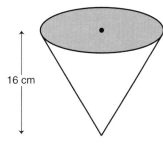

16 cm

14 The diagram shows a solid inverted cone.
If the area of the top is 20 cm², calculate

  a the volume

  b the total surface area

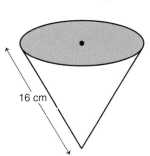

16 cm

15 The diagram shows a solid cylinder of height 10 cm. If the shortest route from A to B, around the curved surface, is 40 cm, calculate

  a the radius

  b the total surface area of the cylinder

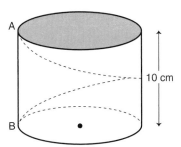

10 cm

16 The diagram shows a solid cylinder of cross-sectional area $130\,cm^2$. If the shortest route from A to B, around the curved surface, is $50\,cm$, calculate

a the radius

b the height h

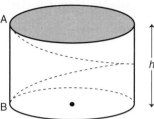

17 An inverted cone represents a glass of depth $6\,cm$ when full. Find the percentage drop in depth when the glass is half full.

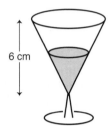

6 cm

Similar solids and shapes

This section explores the relationship between the area of shapes and the volume of solids that are mathematically **similar**.

This diagram shows the connection between scale factor of enlargement and similar triangles.

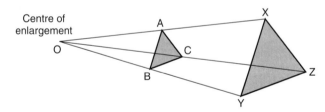

Centre of enlargement

The scale factor of enlargement when triangle ABC is mapped onto triangle XYZ is:

$$\frac{OX}{OA} = \frac{OY}{OB} = \frac{OZ}{OC} \quad \text{or} \quad \frac{XY}{AB} = \frac{XZ}{AC} = \frac{YZ}{BC}$$

Activity 16

Draw x and y axes from 0 to 8. Plot the points (0, 0), (2, 0), (2, 1) and (0, 1) and join up to form a rectangle. Label the rectangle A.

◆ On your axes, apply an enlargement, centre (0, 0), of
  ▶ scale factor 2, and label the result B
  ▶ scale factor 3, and label the result C
  ▶ scale factor 4, and label the result D.

♦ Copy the table and use your answers to part **a** to help you to complete it.

Rectangle	Area in square units	Scale factor of enlargement	Area multiplied by
B	8	2	$2^2 = 4$
C			$\ldots = 9$
D			$\ldots = \ldots$
*	*	n	n^2

If the area of rectangle A is $10 \, \text{cm}^2$, the area of rectangle B is $10 \times 2^2 = 40 \, \text{cm}^2$.
A similar reasoning can be applied to 3D shapes.

Key Points

When applying a scale factor of enlargement of $n > 1$

♦ to an area, the larger area = smaller area × (scale factor)^2

$$A = an^2$$

♦ to a volume, the larger volume = smaller volume × (scale factor)^3

$$V = vn^3$$

Example 10

These two picture frames have similar shapes. Find the area of the larger frame.

| Area = 800 cm² | 20 cm | Area = ? | 30 cm |

The scale factor of enlargement $= \frac{30}{20} = 1.5$

Using the area formula:

larger area = smaller area × (scale factor)^2

$= 800 \, \text{cm}^2 \times 1.5^2$

$= 1800 \, \text{cm}^2$

Example 11

The two cones have similar shapes and the volume of cone X is $32\,\text{cm}^3$.

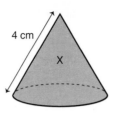 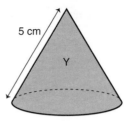

Find the volume of cone Y.

The scale factor of enlargement $= \frac{5}{4} = 1.25$

Using the volume formula:

larger volume = smaller volume $\times$ (scale factor)^3

volume of Y $= 32 \times 1.25^3$

$= 62.5$

The volume of the cone Y is $62.5\,\text{cm}^3$.

Example 12

In these two similar triangles, find the value of x.

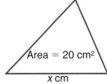

The scale factor of enlargement $= \dfrac{x}{3}$

Using the area formula:

larger area = smaller area $\times$ (scale factor)^2

$$20 = 11.25 \times \left(\frac{x}{3}\right)^2$$

$$3 \times \sqrt{\frac{20}{11.25}} = x$$

$$x = 4$$

Example 13

These glasses are similar in shape. Find

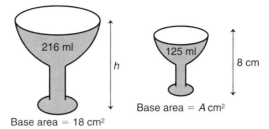

Base area = 18 cm²   Base area = A cm²

a the height h cm of the larger glass
b the base area A cm² of the smaller glass

a The scale factor of enlargement $= \dfrac{h}{8}$

Using the volume formula:

larger volume = smaller volume × (scale factor)³

$$216 = 125 \times \left(\frac{h}{8}\right)^3$$

$$\sqrt[3]{\frac{216}{125}} \times 8 = h$$

$$h = 9.6$$

The height of the larger glass is 9.6 cm.

b Using the area formula:

larger area = smaller area × (scale factor)²

$$18 = A \times \left(\frac{9.6}{8}\right)^2$$

$$18 \div \left(\frac{9.6}{8}\right)^2 = A$$

$$A = 12.5$$

The base area of the smaller glass is 12.5 cm².

Exercise 26

1 X and Y are similar shapes. The area of X is 32 cm². Find the area of Y.

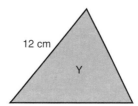

2 X and Y are similar shapes. The area of Y is 50 cm². Find the area of X.

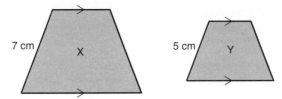

3 X and Y are similar shapes. The volume of X is 40 cm³. Find the volume of Y.

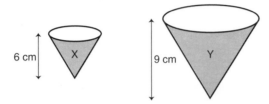

4 X and Y are similar shapes. The volume of Y is 50 cm³. Find the volume of X.

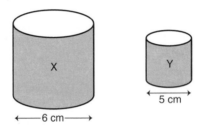

5 Two rectangular rugs of the same type and quality have diagonals of 1.5 m and 2 m.
The smaller rug cost £90. Find the cost of the larger one.

6 Two similar buckets have depths of 30 cm and 20 cm.
The smaller bucket holds 8 litres of water. Find the capacity of the larger bucket.

7 Two wedding cakes are made from the same mixture and have similar shapes.
The larger cake costs £135 and is 30 cm in diameter.
Find the cost of the smaller cake, which has a diameter of 20 cm.

8 A garage has a floor area of 15 m² and is drawn to a scale of 1:50.
Find the area on the plans in cm².

Exercise 26★

1 X and Y are similar shapes. The volume of Y is 128 cm³. Find the volume of X.

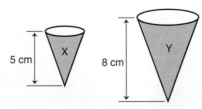

2 X and Y are similar shapes.
The volume of X is 108 cm³.
Find the volume of Y.

3 Two solid statues are similar in shape and made of the same material.
One is 1m high and weighs 64 kg. The other weighs 1kg.

  a What is the height of the smaller statue?

  b If 3 g of gold is required to cover the smaller statue, how much is needed for the larger one?

4 A solid sphere weighs 10 g.

  a What will be the weight of another sphere made from the same material but having three times the diameter?

  b The surface area of the 10 g sphere is 20 cm². What is the surface area of the larger sphere?

5 X and Y are similar shapes. The area of X is 81 cm²; the area of Y is 49 cm². Find x.

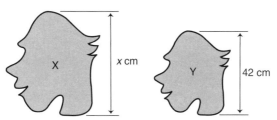

6 X and Y are similar shapes. The area of X is 72 m²; the area of Y is 50 m². Find the length of x.

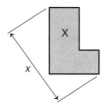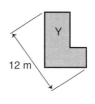

7 The inverted cones represent a full glass of depth 6 cm. Glass A is full and glass B is half full by volume. Find h.

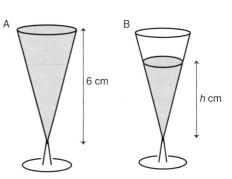

8 A glass is in the shape of a circular cone. The diameter of the top is 6 cm and when filled to the brim it can hold 80 ml. If the glass contains 10 ml of wine, what is the diameter of the surface of the wine?

9 Calculate the shaded area A.

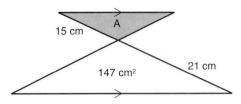

10 Calculate the shaded area B.

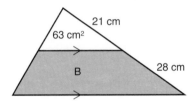

11 Two solid cylinders, A and B, have their length in the ratio 4:3 and their diameters in the ratio 2:3 respectively. They are made of materials whose densities are in the ratio 5:3. Find which is the heavier cylinder, A or B.

12 In the figure DC′B is a quarter circle, centre A. ABCD and AB′C′D′ are squares. Find the value of

$$\frac{\text{area ABCD}}{\text{area AB}'\text{C}'\text{D}'}$$

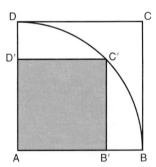

13 Suppose that a grown-up hedgehog is an exact enlargement of a baby hedgehog on a scale of 3:2, and that the baby hedgehog has 2000 quills with a total length of 15 m and a skin area of 360 cm².

a How many quills would the grown-up hedgehog have?

b What would be their total length?

c What would be the grown-up hedgehog's skin area?

d If the grown-up hedgehog weighed 810 g, what would the baby hedgehog weigh?

Activity 17

The most renowned theorem of all time – that of Pythagoras – is believed to have been known to the Babylonians as far back as 2000 BC but it was 1500 years later when the Greek mathematician Pythagoras (about 580–500 BC) actually proved it. There are many ways to prove Pythagoras' theorem, but the 'classical proof' explored below was devised by Euclid around 300 BC.

◆ XYZ is a right-angled triangle. I, II and III are the squares drawn on each side of the triangle, and XG is parallel to AY.
Euclid used congruent triangles to prove that

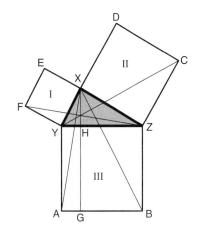

area of I + area of II = area of III

Show full working for the first two parts to this method:

▸ Prove that triangles XYA and FYZ are congruent.

▸ Explain why △XYA is half the area of AGHY, and △FYZ is half the area of EXYF.

Therefore,   area AGHY = area EXYF

Similarly,   area CDXZ = area HGBZ

and therefore   area I + area II = area III

◆ Later, simpler ways were found. In about AD 1150, the Indian mathematician Bhaskara used this diagram, showing two squares, to prove that $c^2 = a^2 + b^2$. How?

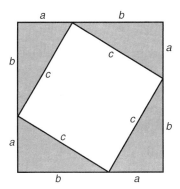

Exercise 27 (Revision)

Where appropriate, give answers to 3 significant figures.

1 Find the area of the shaded region

   a when $x = 4\,cm$

   b in terms of x and π

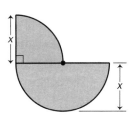

2 A school has an epidemic of mumps. The number of pupils off sick on the nth day of February is N, where $N = 10 + 2(n - 3)$.

   a How many pupils were off sick on the fifth day of February?

   b Find the day on which there were 44 pupils off sick.

3 Use the formula $A = \frac{1}{2}ab \sin C$ to find the area of this triangle.

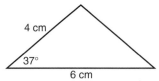

4 cm   37°   6 cm

4 The diagram shows a sector AOB of radius 6 cm. Calculate

   a the arc length AB

   b the sector area

   c the shaded segment area.

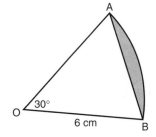

5 A metal hemisphere of radius 8 cm is melted down to make a cuboid.

   a The surface area of a sphere $= 4\pi r^2$. Use this formula to find the curved surface area of the hemisphere.

   b The volume of a sphere $= \frac{4}{3}\pi r^3$. Use this formula to find the volume of the hemisphere.

   c Find the side length of the cuboid.

6 The sphere and cone shown have the same volume. Calculate the height of the cone. (The volume of a cone is a third of the base area times the height.)

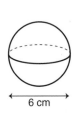

6 cm

h

6 cm

7 A formula for finding the area, A, of any triangle is

$$A = \sqrt{p(p-a)(p-b)(p-c)}$$

where a, b and c are the side lengths and

$$p = \frac{a+b+c}{2}$$

Calculate the area of a triangle with sides of 5 cm, 6 cm and 7 cm.

Exercise 27★ (Revision)

Where appropriate, give answers to 3 significant figures.

1 Find the perimeter of the shaded region

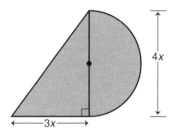

   a when $x = 6$ cm

   b in terms of x and π, and factorise your answer.

2 The formula $R = 3.85 - 0.0075N$ gives a good estimate of the men's world record in the 1500 metres, where R is in minutes and N is the number of years after 1930.

   a What do you think the world record was in 1930?

   b Estimate the world record set by Seb Coe in 1985.

   c Estimate the year in which the world record is likely to be 3 minutes 20 seconds.

The world record in 1975 was 3 minutes 32.2 seconds.

   d Work out the world record using the formula.

   e Use your answer to part **d** to calculate, to 1 significant figure, the percentage error.

3 The area of the sector is 25 cm². Calculate

   a the sector radius   **b** the shaded segment area.

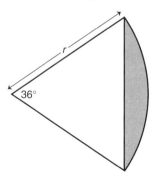

4 The sector shown is made into a cone of slant height 5 cm. Calculate

   a the base radius

   b the volume of the cone.

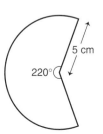

5 The two shapes X and Y are similar and their areas are $55\,\text{cm}^2$ and $140.8\,\text{cm}^2$. Find x.

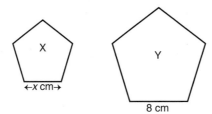

6 X, Y and Z are three similar cylinders. The height of Y is 1.5 times the height of X. The volume of Z is 8 times the volume of X. Z is $4\,\text{cm}$ high and the area of its cross-section is $16\,\text{cm}^2$. Find

a the height of X   **b** the area of cross-section of X   **c** the volume of Y.

Graphs 2

Equation of a circle

A circle is the locus of all points in a plane that are the same distance from a fixed point, called the centre.

Activity 18

♦ Using a pair of compasses, draw on graph paper a circle, with centre at the origin and a radius of 5 cm.

♦ Mark any five points, A, B, C, D and E, on the circumference of the circle. Space your points out all round the circle.

♦ For these five points read off the x and y coordinates, and copy and complete this table.

Point	A	B	C	D	E
x					
x^2					
y					
y^2					
$x^2 + y^2$					

♦ Do you think the same relationship will hold for *all* points on the circle?

Pythagoras' theorem can be used to prove the relationship found in Activity 18.

Example 1

Find the equation of the circle, centre the origin, with radius 5 units.

Any point P with coordinates (x, y) lies on the circle if OP is 5 units long.

$$OP = 5 \qquad OQ = x \qquad PQ = y$$

Using Pythagoras' theorem

$$x^2 + y^2 = 5^2$$

So the equation of the circle is

$$x^2 + y^2 = 25$$

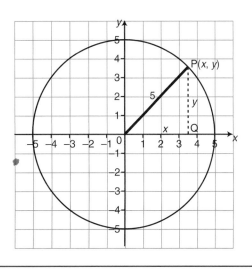

Key Point

$x^2 + y^2 = r^2$ is the equation of a circle with radius r and centre at the origin.

Activity 19

◆ The equation $x^2 + y^2 = 25$ can be rearranged as $y = \pm\sqrt{(25 - x^2)}$.
Copy and complete this table of values.

x		-5	-4	-3	-2	-1	0	1	2	3	4	5
x^2				9								
$25 - x^2$									21			
$y = +\sqrt{25 - x^2}$										4		
$y = -\sqrt{(25 - x^2)}$										-4		

◆ Plot these pairs of values for x and y on a graph. Make sure you use equal scales for the axes. What would happen if you did not use equal scales?

◆ What happens if you try to use x values larger than 5 or smaller than -5?

Exercise 28

1 Find the equation of a circle, centre the origin, with radius 4.

2 Find the equation of a circle, centre the origin, with radius 6.

3 Find the equation of a circle, centre the origin, with radius 0.5.

4 Find the equation of a circle, centre the origin, with radius 0.2.

5 State the centre and radius of the circle $x^2 + y^2 = 81$.

6 State the centre and radius of the circle $x^2 + y^2 = 64$.

7 Find the equation of the circle, centre the origin, passing through $(0, 3)$.

8 Find the equation of the circle, centre the origin, passing through $(2, 0)$.

9 Find the equation of the circle, centre the origin, passing through $(4, 6)$.

10 Find the equation of the circle, centre the origin, passing through $(2, 4)$.

11 Find the equation of the circle, centre the origin, passing through $(-2, 5)$.

12 Find the equation of the circle, centre the origin, passing through $(3, -1)$.

Example 2 shows how to find the equation when the origin is *not* the centre of the circle.

Example 2

Find the equation of the circle with centre $(5, 4)$ and radius 3 units.

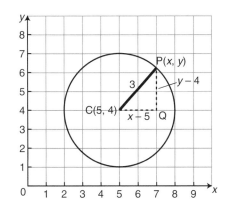

Any point P with coordinates (x, y) lies on the circle if CP is 3 units long.

$$CP = 3 \qquad CQ = x - 5 \qquad QP = y - 4$$

Using Pythagoras' theorem: $(x - 5)^2 + (y - 4)^2 = 3^2$

The brackets could be multiplied out and the expression simplified, but the equation is usually left in this form because it is then easy to see the centre $(5, 4)$ and radius $\sqrt{9}$.

So the required equation is $(x - 5)^2 + (y - 4)^2 = 9$.

Key Point

$(x - a)^2 + (y - b)^2 = r^2$ is the equation of a circle with radius r and centre (a, b).

Example 3

Find the centre and radius of the circle $(x + 7)^2 + (y - 2)^2 = 64$.

Write the equation as $(x - -7)^2 + (y - 2)^2 = 8^2$.

Then it can be seen that the centre is $(-7, 2)$ and the radius is 8.

Exercise 28★

1 Find the equation of the circle with radius 8 and centre $(-2, 6)$.

2 Find the equation of the circle with radius 1 and centre $(1, -5)$.

3 Find the equation of the circle with radius 7 and centre $(3, -9)$.

4 Find the equation of the circle with radius 9 and centre $(-3, 3)$.

5 State the centre and radius of the circle $(x + 4)^2 + (y - 7)^2 = 100$.

6 State the centre and radius of the circle $(x - 5)^2 + (y + 1)^2 = 121$.

7 Find the equation of the circle with centre $(1, 0)$ passing through $(5, 0)$.

8 Find the equation of the circle with centre $(0, 4)$ passing through $(0, 7)$.

9 Find the equation of the circle with centre $(1, 2)$ passing through $(4, -2)$.

10 The origin and $(12, 16)$ are the ends of a diameter of a circle.
Find the coordinates of the centre, the radius and the equation of the circle.

11 Find the equations of the circles with radius 4 that have the x and y axes as tangents.

12 Find the equation of the circles passing through $(8, 0)$ and $(18, 0)$ that have the y-axis as a tangent.

13 A tangent to a circle is perpendicular to the radius. Use this to find the equation of the tangent to the circle $(x - 1)^2 + (y - 2)^2 = 25$ at the point $(4, 6)$.

14 Find the equation of the perpendicular bisector of A$(0, 2)$ and B$(2, 0)$, and of B$(2, 0)$ and C$(14, 0)$. Hence find the equation of the circle that passes through A, B and C.

15 By writing $x^2 + 4x + y^2 - 8y + 11 = 0$ in the form $(x + a)^2 + (y + b)^2 = r^2$ where a, b and r are numbers to be found, show that it is a circle and state the radius and the coordinates of its centre.

16 Find the equation of the circles with radius 13 that pass through the points $(2, 0)$ and $(12, 0)$.

Investigate

The graph of $x^2 - y^2 = 4$ is not a circle. What shape is it?

Using graphs to solve equations

Using the graph of $y = x^2$ to solve quadratic equations

An accurately drawn graph can be used to solve equations that may prove difficult to solve exactly by other methods.

The graph of $y = x^2$ is easy to draw and can be used to solve quadratic equations.

Example 4

Draw the graph of $y = x^2$. Use this graph to solve these three equations:

$$x^2 - x - 3 = 0 \qquad x^2 + 2x - 2 = 0 \qquad 2x^2 + x - 8 = 0$$

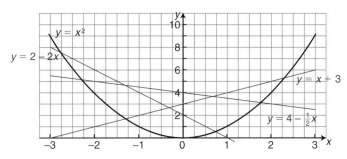

$$x^2 - x - 3 = 0 \qquad \text{(Rearrange)}$$
$$x^2 = x + 3$$

This can be solved by finding the x coordinates of the intersection points of the graphs $y = x^2$ and $y = x + 3$.
From the graph, the solutions are approximately $x = -1.3$ or $x = 2.3$.

$$x^2 + 2x - 2 = 0 \qquad \text{(Rearrange)}$$
$$x^2 = 2 - 2x$$

This can be solved by finding the x coordinates of the intersection points of the graphs $y = x^2$ and $y = 2 - 2x$.
From the graph, the solutions are approximately $x = -2.7$ or $x = 0.7$.

$$2x^2 + x - 8 = 0 \qquad \text{(Rearrange)}$$
$$x^2 = 4 - \frac{1}{2}x$$

This can be solved by finding the x coordinates of the intersection points of the graphs $y = x^2$ and $y = 4 - \frac{1}{2}x$.
From the graph the solutions are approximately $x = -2.3$ or $x = 1.8$.

Exercise 29

Draw an accurate graph of $y = x^2$ for $-4 \leqslant x \leqslant 4$. Use this graph to solve these equations.

1 $x^2 - 5 = 0$

2 $x^2 - 3 = 0$

3 $x^2 - x - 2 = 0$

4 $x^2 + x - 3 = 0$

5 $x^2 + 2x - 7 = 0$

6 $x^2 - 2x - 6 = 0$

7 $x^2 - 4x + 2 = 0$

8 $x^2 + 4x + 1 = 0$

9 $2x^2 - x - 20 = 0$

10 $2x^2 + x - 16 = 0$

11 $x^2 - x + 1 = 0$

12 $x^2 + x + 2 = 0$

Exercise 29★

Draw an accurate graph of $y = x^2$ for $-4 \leqslant x \leqslant 4$. Use this graph to solve these equations.

1 $x^2 - x - 3 = 0$

2 $x^2 + x - 4 = 0$

3 $x^2 + 3x + 1 = 0$

4 $x^2 - 2x - 2 = 0$

5 $x^2 - 4x + 4 = 0$

6 $x^2 + 2x + 1 = 0$

7 $2x^2 + x - 12 = 0$

8 $2x^2 - x - 10 = 0$

9 $3x^2 - x - 27 = 0$

10 $3x^2 + x - 21 = 0$

11 $3x^2 - 3x + 6 = 0$

12 $4x^2 + 6x + 3 = 0$

Using other graphs to solve quadratic equations

Example 5

Draw the graph of $y = x^2 - 5x + 5$ for $0 \leqslant x \leqslant 5$. Use this graph to solve these three equations:

$$0 = x^2 - 5x + 5 \qquad 0 = x^2 - 5x + 3 \qquad 0 = x^2 - 4x + 4$$

To solve: $0 = x^2 - 5x + 5$

Find where the graph of $y = x^2 - 5x + 5$ cuts the line $y = 0$ (the x-axis).

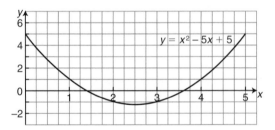

The graph cuts the x-axis at approximately $x = 1.4$ and $x = 3.6$.

So the approximate solutions to $0 = x^2 - 5x + 5$ are $x = 1.4$ or $x = 3.6$.

To solve: $0 = x^2 - 5x + 3$

$$0 = x^2 - 5x + 3 \qquad \text{(Add 2 to both sides)}$$
$$2 = x^2 - 5x + 5$$

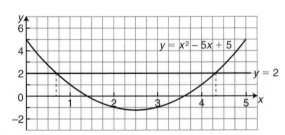

The graph of $y - x^2 - 5x + 5$ cuts the line $y = 2$, at $x = 0.7$ and $x = 4.3$ approximately.

So the approximate solutions to $0 = x^2 - 5x + 3$ are $x = 0.7$ or $x = 4.3$.

To solve: $0 = x^2 - 4x + 4$

$$0 = x^2 - 4x + 4 \qquad \text{(Add } 1 - x \text{ to both sides)}$$

$$1 - x = x^2 - 5x + 5$$

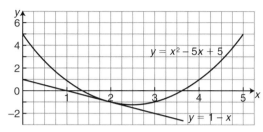

The graph of $y = x^2 - 5x + 5$ cuts the line $y = 1 - x$ at $x = 2$ approximately.

So the approximate solution to $0 = x^2 - 4x + 4$ is $x = 2$.

In this case, it looks as if this is an *exact* solution, but this would have to be checked by substitution.

Note: If the line had not cut the graph, there would be *no* real solutions.

Example 6

If the graph of $y = 6 + 2x - x^2$ has been drawn, find the equation of the line that should be drawn to solve

a $0 = 2 + 2x - x^2$ \qquad\qquad\qquad **b** $0 = 7 + x - x^2$

a $0 = 2 + 2x - x^2$ must be rearranged so that $6 + 2x - x^2$ is on the right-hand side. Adding 4 to both sides gives $4 = 6 + 2x - x^2$, so the line to be drawn is $y = 4$.

b $0 = 7 + x - x^2$ must be rearranged so that $6 + 2x - x^2$ is on the right-hand side. Adding $x - 1$ to both sides gives $x - 1 = 6 + 2x - x^2$, so the line to be drawn is $y = x - 1$.

The graphs are shown.

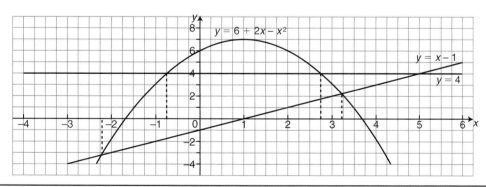

Exercise 30

1 Draw the graph of $y = x^2 - 3x$ for $-1 \leqslant x \leqslant 5$. Use your graph to solve these equations.

  a $x^2 - 3x = 0$ **b** $x^2 - 3x = 2$ **c** $x^2 - 3x = -1$

  d $x^2 - 3x = x + 1$ **e** $x^2 - 3x - 3 = 0$ **f** $x^2 - 5x + 1 = 0$

2 Draw the graph of $y = x^2 - 2x$ for $-2 \leqslant x \leqslant 4$. Use your graph to solve these equations.

  a $x^2 - 2x = 0$ **b** $x^2 - 2x = 5$ **c** $x^2 - 2x = -\frac{1}{2}$

  d $x^2 - 2x = 1 - x$ **e** $x^2 - 2x - 2 = 0$ **f** $x^2 - 4x + 2 = 0$

3 Draw the graph of $y = x^2 - 4x + 3$ for $-1 \leqslant x \leqslant 5$. Use your graph to solve these equations.

  a $x^2 - 4x + 3 = 0$ **b** $x^2 - 4x - 3 = 0$ **c** $x^2 - 5x + 3 = 0$ **d** $x^2 - 3x - 2 = 0$

4 Draw the graph of $y = x^2 - 3x - 4$ for $-2 \leqslant x \leqslant 5$. Use your graph to solve these equations.

  a $x^2 - 3x - 4 = 0$ **b** $x^2 - 3x + 1 = 0$ **c** $x^2 - 2x - 4 = 0$ **d** $x^2 - 4x + 2 = 0$

5 Find the equations solved by the intersection of these pairs of graphs.

  a $y = 2x^2 - x + 2, y = 3 - 3x$ **b** $y = 4 - 3x - x^2, y = 2x - 1$

6 Find the equations solved by the intersection of these pairs of graphs.

  a $y = 3x^2 + x - 5, y = 2x + 1$ **b** $y = 2x + 3 - x^2, y = 1 - 2x$

7 If the graph of $y = 3x^2 + 4x - 2$ has been drawn, find the equations of the lines that should be drawn to solve these equations.

  a $3x^2 + 2x - 4 = 0$ **b** $3x^2 + 3x - 2 = 0$ **c** $3x^2 + 7x + 1 = 0$

8 If the graph of $y = 3x^2 - 3x + 5$ has been drawn, find the equations of the lines that should be drawn to solve these equations.

  a $3x^2 - 4x - 1 = 0$ **b** $3x^2 - 2x - 2 = 0$ **c** $3x^2 + x - 3 = 0$

9 Romeo is throwing a rose up to Juliet's balcony. The balcony is 2 m away from him and 3.5 m above him. The equation of the path of the rose is $y = 4x - x^2$, where the origin is at Romeo's feet. Find by a graphical method where the rose lands.
The balcony has a 1m high railing. Does the rose pass over the railing?

10 A cat is sitting on a 2 m high fence when it spots a mouse 1.5 m away from the foot of the fence. The cat leaps along the path $y = -0.6x - x^2$, where the origin is where the cat was sitting and x is measured in metres. Find, by a graphical method, whether the cat lands on the mouse.

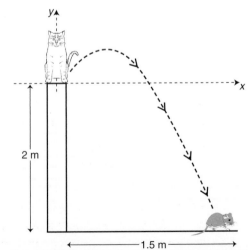

Exercise 30★

1 Draw the graph of $y = 5x - x^2$ for $-1 \leqslant x \leqslant 6$. Use your graph to solve these equations.

  a $5x - x^2 = 0$ **b** $5x - x^2 = 3$ **c** $5x - x^2 = x + 1$ **d** $x^2 - 6x + 4 = 0$

2 Draw the graph of $y = x - 2x^2$ for $-2 \leqslant x \leqslant 3$. Use your graph to solve these equations.

  a $x - 2x^2 = 0$ **b** $x - 2x^2 = -4$ **c** $x - 2x^2 = -x - 3$ **d** $2x^2 - 2x - 2 = 0$

3 Draw the graph of $y = 2x^2 + 3x - 1$ for $-3 \leqslant x \leqslant 2$. Use your graph to solve these equations.

  a $2x^2 + 3x - 1 = 0$ **b** $2x^2 + 3x - 4 = 0$ **c** $2x^2 + 5x + 1 = 0$

4 Draw the graph of $y = 3x^2 - x - 2$ for $-2 \leqslant x \leqslant 3$. Use your graph to solve these equations.

  a $3x^2 - x - 2 = 0$ **b** $3x^2 - x - 4 = 0$ **c** $3x^2 - 3x - 1 = 0$

5 Find the equations solved by the intersection of these pairs of graphs.

  a $y = 6x^2 - 4x + 3$, $y = 3x + 5$ **b** $y = 7 + 2x - 5x^2$, $y = 3 - 5x$

6 Find the equations solved by the intersection of these pairs of graphs.

  a $y = 4x^2 - 5x + 2$, $y = 2x + 7$ **b** $y = 3x + 1 - 3x^2$, $y = 3 - 4x$

7 If the graph of $y = 5x^2 - 9x - 6$ has been drawn, find the equations of the lines that should be drawn to solve these equations.

  a $5x^2 - 10x - 8 = 0$ **b** $5x^2 - 7x - 5 = 0$

8 If the graph of $y = 4x^2 + 7x - 8$ has been drawn, find the equations of the lines that should be drawn to solve these equations.

  a $4x^2 + 8x - 5 = 0$ **b** $4x^2 + 4x - 3 = 0$

9 Jason is serving at tennis. He hits the ball from a height of 2.5 m and the path of the ball is given by $y = -0.05x - 0.005x^2$, where the origin is the point where he hits the ball.

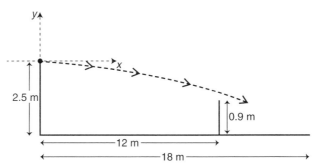

  a The net is 0.9 m high and is 12 m away. Does the ball pass over the net?

  b For the serve to be legal it must land between the net and the service line, which is 18 m away. Is the serve legal?

10 A young girl is playing a game, which consists of throwing marbles up a flight of stairs. Each step is 20 cm high and 25 cm wide. The path of the marble is given by $y = \frac{5}{2}x - \frac{2}{3}x^2$, where x and y are both measured in metres. Where should the girl stand to throw the marble up the most number of steps, and how many steps is this?

Using graphs to solve cubic and other equations

Example 7

Draw the graph of $y = x^3$.

Use this graph to solve these two equations:

$$x^3 + 2x - 4 = 0 \qquad x^3 - 3x + 1 = 0$$

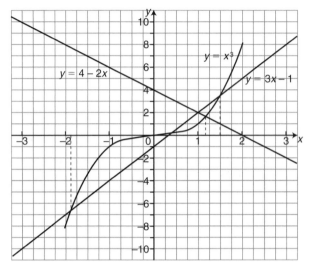

To solve: $x^3 + 2x - 4 = 0$

$$x^3 + 2x - 4 = 0 \qquad \text{(Rearrange)}$$
$$x^3 = 4 - 2x$$

This can be solved by finding the x coordinates of the intersection points of the graphs $y = x^3$ and $y = 4 - 2x$.

From the graph the solution is approximately $x = 1.2$.
The graph shows there is only one solution.

To solve: $x^3 - 3x + 1 = 0$

$$x^3 - 3x + 1 = 0 \qquad \text{(Rearrange)}$$
$$x^3 = 3x - 1$$

This can be solved by finding the x coordinates of the intersection points of the graphs $y = x^3$ and $y = 3x - 1$.

From the graph, the solutions are approximately $x = -1.9$, $x = 0.4$ or $x = 1.5$.

Exercise 31

1 Draw an accurate graph of $y = x^3$ for $-3 \leqslant x \leqslant 3$.
Use your graph to solve these equations.

   a $x^3 - 3x = 0$ **b** $x^3 - 3x - 1 = 0$ **c** $x^3 - 2x + 1 = 0$

2 Draw an accurate graph of $y = x^4$ for $-2 \leqslant x \leqslant 2$.
Use your graph to solve these equations.

   a $x^4 - 4x = 0$ **b** $x^4 - 2x - 3 = 0$ **c** $x^4 + x - 3 = 0$

3 Draw an accurate graph of $y = 3x^2 - x^3 - 1$ for $-2 \leqslant x \leqslant 3$.
Use your graph to solve these equations.

   a $3x^2 - x^3 - 1 = 0$ **b** $3x^2 - x^3 - 4 = 0$ **c** $3x^2 - x^3 - 4 + x = 0$

4 Draw an accurate graph of $y = x^3 - 5x + 1$ for $-3 \leqslant x \leqslant 3$.
Use your graph to solve these equations.

   a $x^3 - 5x + 1 = 0$ **b** $x^3 - 5x - 2 = 0$ **c** $x^3 - 7x - 1 = 0$

5 Use a graphical method to solve $x - 2 = \dfrac{3}{x}$.

6 Use a graphical method to solve $4 - x^2 = \dfrac{1}{x}$.

Exercise 31 ★

1 Draw an accurate graph of $y = \dfrac{12}{x^2}$ for $-4 \leqslant x \leqslant 4$. Use your graph to solve these equations.

   a $\dfrac{12}{x^2} - x - 2 = 0$ **b** $\dfrac{12}{x^2} = 12 - x^2$ **c** $3x^3 + 10x^2 - 12 = 0$

2 Draw an accurate graph of $y = x^4 - 4x^2 + 2$ for $-3 \leqslant x \leqslant 3$. Use your graph to solve these equations.

   a $x^4 - 4x^2 + 2 = 0$ **b** $x^4 - 4x^2 - 2x + 3 = 0$ **c** $2x^4 - 8x^2 + x + 2 = 0$

3 If the graph of $y = x^2 + \dfrac{16}{x}$ has been drawn, what graph must be drawn to solve
$x^3 - 3x^2 - 8x + 16 = 0$?

4 If the graph of $y = x - 4 + \dfrac{3}{x}$ has been drawn, what graph must be drawn to solve
$x^3 - x^2 + 5x - 3 = 0$?

5 Use a graphical method to solve $x^3 - x = x^2 + x - 1$.

6 Use a graphical method to solve $2^x = 4x^2 - x^3$.

Investigate

For what values of k does the equation $x^3 - 12x + k = 0$ have

   a one solution?   **b** two solutions?   **c** three solutions?

Using graphs to solve nonlinear simultaneous equations

Activity 20

Mary is watering her garden with a hose. Her little brother, Peter, is annoying her so she tries to squirt him with water.

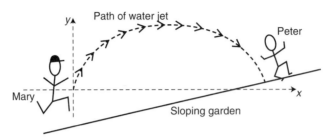

The path of the water jet is given by $y = 2x - \frac{1}{4}x^2$.

The slope of the garden is given by $y = \frac{1}{4}x - 1$.

Peter is standing at $(8, 1)$.

The origin is the point where the water leaves the hose, and units are in metres.

◆ Copy and complete these tables.

x	0	2	4	6	8	10
$2x$			8			
$-\frac{1}{4}x^2$				-9		
$y = 2x - \frac{1}{4}x^2$		3				

x	0	2	4	6	8	10
$\frac{1}{4}x$					2	
$y = \frac{1}{4}x - 1$				0.5		

◆ On one set of axes, draw the two graphs representing the path of the water and the slope of the garden.

◆ Is Mary successful in making Peter wet?

◆ Mary alters the angle of the hose so that the path of the water is given by $y = x - 0.1x^2$. Draw in the new path. Is Peter made wet this time?

◆ When Mary alters the angle of the hose, the path of the water changes. The path is given by

$$y = ax - \frac{(1 + a^2)x^2}{20}$$

for different positive values of a. If Mary does not move, where is the closest Peter can stand to be safe?

In Activity 20, the simultaneous equations $y = 2x - \frac{1}{4}x^2$ and $y = \frac{1}{4}x - 1$ were solved graphically by drawing both graphs on the same axes and finding the x coordinates of the points of intersection.

Example 8

Draw on one set of axes the graphs of $y = x^2 - 5$ and $y = x + 1$. Use these graphs to solve the simultaneous equations $y = x^2 - 5$ and $y = x + 1$.

First make a table of values.

x	-3	-2	-1	0	1	2	3
$x^2 - 5$	4	-1	-4	-5	-4	-1	4
$x + 1$	-2	-1	0	1	2	3	4

Then draw the graphs.

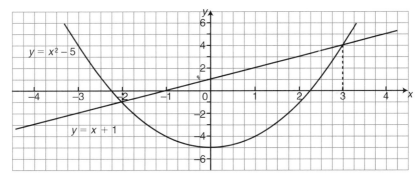

The coordinates of the intersection points are $(-2, -1)$ and $(3, 4)$, so the solutions are $x = -2, y = -1$ or $x = 3, y = 4$.

Key Point

To solve simultaneous equations graphically, draw *both* graphs on *one* set of axes. The coordinates of the intersection points are the solutions of the simultaneous equations.

Exercise 32

For Questions 1–14, solve the simultaneous equations graphically, drawing graphs for $-4 \leqslant x \leqslant 4$.

1 $y = x^2 + 2, \ y = 5$

2 $y = x^2 - 1, \ y = 4$

3 $y = 4 - x^2, \ y = 1 + 2x$

4 $y = 1 - x^2, \ y = x - 1$

5 $y = x^2 + 2x - 1, \ y = 1 + 3x$

6 $y = x^2 + 4x - 3, \ y = x + 1$

7 $y = x^2 - 4x + 6, \ y = 2x - 2$

8 $y = x^2 - 2x + 4, \ y = 1 + 2x$

9 $x^2 + y^2 = 4$, $y = 1 - \dfrac{x}{4}$

10 $x^2 + y^2 = 9$, $y = 2x + 1$

11 $y = \dfrac{4}{x}$, $y = x - 1$

12 $y = 1 - \dfrac{6}{x}$, $y = 2 - x$

13 $y = x^3 + 2x^2$, $y = \frac{1}{2}x + 1$

14 $y = x - x^3$, $y = \frac{1}{2} - x$

15 Tracy is designing a paper weight, which is part of a sphere 8 cm in diameter. The paper weight is 7 cm high. The diagram shows a cross-section of the paper weight, with the origin taken at the centre of the sphere.

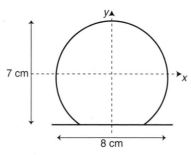

a Write down the equation of the circle.

b Write down the equation of the base.

c Solve these simultaneous equations graphically to find the diameter of the base.

16 The handle on a kitchen cabinet door is an arc of a circle of radius 14 cm. The handle sticks out by 2 cm.

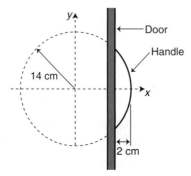

a Write down the equation of the circle.

b Write down the equation of the surface of the door.

c Solve these simultaneous equations graphically to find the height of the handle.

17 During a match, Matthew kicks a football on to the roof of the stand. The path of the football is given by

$$y = 2.5x - \frac{x^2}{15}$$

The equation of the roof of the stand is given by

$$y = \frac{x}{2} + 10 \text{ for } 20 \leqslant x \leqslant 35$$

All units are in metres. Find by a graphical method where the football lands on the roof.

18 A volcano shaped like a cone ejects a rock from the summit.

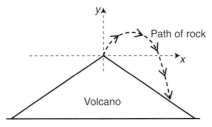

The path of the rock is given by

$$y = 2x - x^2$$

and the side of the volcano is given by

$$y = -\frac{2x}{3}$$

where the units are in kilometres and the origin is at the summit. Find by a graphical method where the rock lands.

Exercise 32★

For Questions 1–14, solve the simultaneous equations graphically. (For Questions 1–8, draw graphs for $-4 \leqslant x \leqslant 4$.)

1 $y = x^2 + x + 1$, $y = 3$

2 $y = x^2 - 2x - 1$, $y = 2$

3 $y = x^2 - x - 5$, $y = 1 - 2x$

4 $y = x^2 + 4x - 5$, $y = 2x + 3$

5 $y = 2x^2 - 2x - 4$, $y = 6 - x$

6 $y = 2x^2 - 5x - 6$, $y = 3 - 2x$

7 $y = 10x^2 + 3x - 4$, $y = 2x - 2$

8 $y = 8x^2 + 3x - 4$, $y = 5 - 3x$

9 $(x + 1)^2 + (y - 2)^2 = 9$, $y = 2x + 3$

10 $(x - 3)^2 + (y + 4)^2 = 4$, $y = 1 - 2x$

11 $y = x^3 - 4x^2 + 5$, $y = 3 - 2x$, $-1 \leqslant x \leqslant 4$

12 $y = x^3 + 3x^2 - 7$, $y = 2x - 1$, $-4 \leqslant x \leqslant 2$

13 $y = \dfrac{10}{x} + 4$, $y = 5x + 2$, $-2 \leqslant x \leqslant 3$

14 $y = \dfrac{12}{x} - x$, $y = 2x - 3$, $-3 \leqslant x \leqslant 4$

15 A stage director is planning lighting for a play. An actor walks across the stage along the line

$$y = \frac{x}{4} + 1$$

where x and y are measured in metres. A spot light casts a circular pool of light with radius 2 m and centre $(4, 3)$.

a Write down the equation of the circle giving the outline of the pool of light.

b Find graphically the points where the actor moves into and out of the light.

c If the actor moves at 1 m/s, for how long is he lit up?

16 The detector of an intruder alarm has a range of 10 m and is situated at the point (20, 15). An intruder is walking along the path

$$y = \frac{x}{5} + 2$$

where x and y are measured in metres.

a Write down the equation of the circle giving the range of the detector.

b Find, by a graphical method, the coordinates of the points where the detector is triggered and released.

c If the difference in times between the detector being triggered and released is less than $\frac{1}{2}$ s, then the alarm does not sound.
Can the intruder run fast enough to avoid setting off the alarm?

17 In a ski jump, the path of the jumper is given by

$$y = 0.6x - \frac{x^2}{40}$$

while the landing slope is given by

$$y = -\frac{x}{2}$$

The origin is at the point of take-off of the jumper, and all units are in metres.

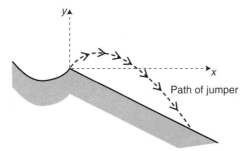

Solve the simultaneous equations by a graphical method and find how long the jump is.

18 A car travelling too fast along a road comes to a hump-back bridge and takes off.

Taking the origin as the point where the car takes off, the path of the car is given by

$$y = 0.5x - \frac{x^2}{50}$$

while the shape of the bridge is given by

$$(x - 14)^2 + (y + 48)^2 = 50^2$$

Solve the simultaneous equations by a graphical method to find where the car lands.

Exercise 33 (Revision)

1   Find the equation of a circle with radius 3 and centre $(0, 0)$.

2   Find the equation of a circle with radius 4 and centre $(1, -3)$.

3   A distress rocket is fired out to sea from the top of a 50 m high cliff.
    Taking the origin at the top of the cliff, the path of the rocket is given by $y = x - 0.01x^2$.
    Use a graphical method to find where the rocket lands in the sea.

4   Draw the graph of $y = x^2 - 2x - 1$ for $-2 \leqslant x \leqslant 4$.
    Use your graph to solve these equations.

    a $x^2 - 2x - 1 = 0$ **b** $x^2 - 2x - 4 = 0$ **c** $x^2 - x - 3 = 0$

5   The area of a rectangle is 30 cm; the perimeter is 24 cm. If x is the length of the rectangle and y is the width, form two equations for x and y and solve them graphically.

Exercise 33★ (Revision)

1   Find the equation of a circle with radius 7 and centre $(-3, 2)$.

2   Find the equation of the circle passing through $(0, 1)$ and $(0, 9)$ that has the x-axis as a tangent.

3   Lauren is marketing a handbag. The shape of the handbag is a circle 24 cm in diameter and the handle is a parabola with equation

$$y = 22 - \frac{x^2}{4}$$

where the origin is at the centre of the circle. Lauren needs to tell a subcontractor where to attach the fasteners for the handle to the bag. Write down the equation of the circle and solve the equations by a graphical method to find the position of the fasteners.

4   Draw the graph of $y = 3x + 5 - 2x^2$ for $-2 \leqslant x \leqslant 4$.
    Use your graph to solve these equations.

    a $3x + 2 - 2x^2 = 0$ **b** $x + 7 - 2x^2 = 0$ **c** $2x + 2 - x^2 = 0$

5   The hypotenuse of a right-angled triangle is 4 cm long; the sum of the lengths of the other two sides is 5 cm. If the lengths of the other two sides are x and y, form two equations for x and y and solve them graphically.

Shape and space 2

Trigonometric ratios for all angles

This section extends the $\sin x$, $\cos x$ and $\tan x$ ratios beyond acute angle where $0° \leqslant x \leqslant 90°$ to consider angles less than $0°$ (i.e. negative angles) and angles greater than $90°$ (obtuse and reflex angles).

> **Remember**
> ♦ To work out sine of $-80°$, press
>
>
>
> $\sin(-80°) = -0.985$ (to 3 s.f.)
> ♦ To work out x in $\sin x = -0.9°$, press
>
>   0.9 ▣
>
> $x = -64.2°$ (to 3 s.f.)

Activity 21

Sine ratio

This is the graph of $y = \sin x$, drawn for $-180° \leqslant x \leqslant 360°$.

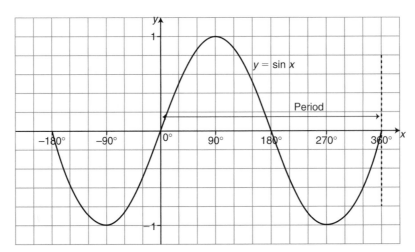

♦ Copy this table, and use the graph and your calculator to complete it.

x	140°	200°	300°	$-20°$	$-140°$
$\sin x$ (graph)					
$\sin x$ (calc. to 2 s.f.)					

◆ Copy and complete this table.

sin x	0	1.0	0.2	0.6	−0.6
x (graph)					
x (calc. to 2 s.f.)					

◆ Use your calculator and the graph to solve these equations, correct to 3 significant figures.
  ▶ sin x = 0.8 (2 possible answers)
  ▶ sin x = −0.8 (4 possible answers)

Cosine ratio
This is the graph of $y = \cos x$, drawn for $-180° \leqslant x \leqslant 360°$.

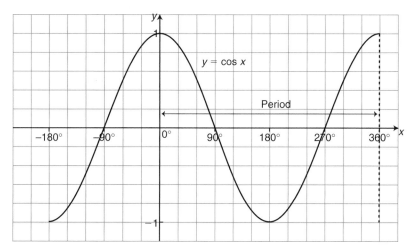

◆ Copy this table, and use the graph and your calculator to complete it.

x	150°	200°	310°	−20°	−150°
cos x (graph)					
cos x (calc. to 2 s.f.)					

◆ Copy and complete this table.

cos x	0	0.2	0.8	−0.2	−0.6
x (graph)					
x (calc. to 2 s.f.)					

◆ Use your calculator and the graph to solve these equations, correct to 3 significant figures.
  ▶ cos x = 0.7 (3 possible answers)
  ▶ cos x = −0.7 (3 possible answers)

Tangent ratio

This is the graph of $y = \tan x$, drawn for $-180° \leqslant x \leqslant 360°$.

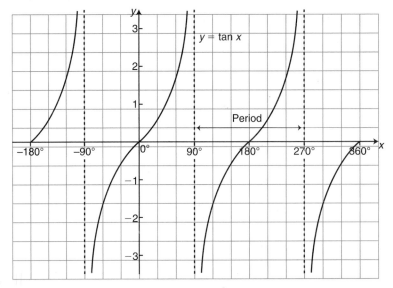

◆ From the graph, show that the value of $\tan 75°$ is the same as $\tan 255°$ and $\tan(-105°)$.

◆ From the graph, find two other angles that have the same tangent as

  ▸ $\tan 65°$
  ▸ $\tan(-65°)$

◆ Solve the equation $\tan x = 0.6$ correct to 3 significant figures (3 possible answers).

◆ Solve the equation $\tan x = -0.6$ correct to 3 significant figures (3 possible answers).

Exercise 34

Use the accurately drawn graphs given in Activity 21 to help you in this Exercise.

For Questions 1–10, find another angle x, for $0° \leqslant x \leqslant 360°$, that has the same trigonometric ratio as these.

1 $\sin 10°$	**2** $\sin 80°$	**3** $\cos 20°$	**4** $\cos 80°$
5 $\tan 40°$	**6** $\tan 30°$	**7** $\sin 210°$	**8** $\cos 190°$
9 $\tan 160°$	**10** $\tan 315°$		

For Questions 11–22, calculate all possible values of x, for $0° \leqslant x \leqslant 360°$, to 3 significant figures.

11 $\sin x = 0.3$	**12** $\sin x = 0.7$	**13** $\cos x = 0.3$	**14** $\cos x = 0.6$
15 $\tan x = 3$	**16** $\tan x = 2$	**17** $\cos x = -0.3$	**18** $\cos x = -0.6$
19 $\sin x = -0.3$	**20** $\sin x = -0.7$	**21** $\tan x = -3$	**22** $\tan x = -2$

Exercise 34★

Use the accurately drawn graphs given in Activity 21 to help you in this Exercise.

For Questions 1–12, find other angles x, for $-180° \leqslant x \leqslant 360°$, that have the same trigonometric ratio as these.

1 $\sin 26°$ **2** $\sin 154°$ **3** $\sin 220°$ **4** $\sin(-20°)$

5 $\cos 45°$ **6** $\cos 290°$ **7** $\cos(-95°)$ **8** $\cos(-145°)$

9 $\tan 47°$ **10** $\tan 138°$ **11** $\tan(-50°)$ **12** $\tan(-132°)$

For Questions 13–24, solve the equation for $-180° \leqslant x \leqslant 360°$, correct to 3 significant figures.

13 $\sin x = 0.4567$ **14** $\sin x = 0.6543$ **15** $\sin x = -0.4567$

16 $\sin x = -0.6543$ **17** $\cos x = 0.2468$ **18** $\cos x = 0.6428$

19 $\cos x = -0.3789$ **20** $\cos x = -0.8416$ **21** $\tan x = 2.458$

22 $\tan x = 0.6789$ **23** $\tan x = -1.453$ **24** $\tan x = -0.7342$

Activity 22

♦ Look carefully at these two diagrams.

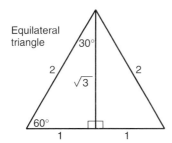

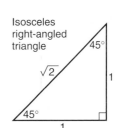

♦ Copy this table and use the diagrams to help you to complete it.
You should only use the numbers shown on the diagrams, or 0 or ∞ (infinity).

x	0°	30°	45°	60°	90°	120°	135°
$\sin x$				$\dfrac{\sqrt{3}}{2}$			
$\cos x$					0		
$\tan x$			1				

Using trigonometry graphs to solve equations

Example 1

Draw the graph of $y = 3\cos x$, for $-180° \leqslant x \leqslant 180°$ and use it to find approximate solutions to these two equations

$$3\cos x = 1.5 \qquad 3\cos x = \frac{x}{90°}$$

First, create a table of values.

x	$-180°$	$-135°$	$-90°$	$-45°$	$0°$	$45°$	$90°$	$135°$	$180°$
$\cos x$	-1	-0.707	0	0.707	1	0.707	0	-0.707	-1
$3\cos x$	-3	-2.12	0	2.12	3	2.12	0	-2.12	-3

Then draw the graph of $y = 3\cos x$.

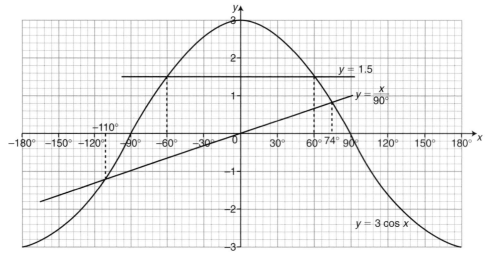

To solve: $3\cos x = 1.5$

Draw the line $y = 1.5$.

The points of intersection give the solution $x = 60°$ and $x = -60°$.

Checking algebraically:

$$3\cos x = 1.5 \qquad \text{(Divide both sides by 3)}$$
$$\cos x = 0.5$$
$$x = 60° \quad \text{or} \quad x = -60°$$

To solve: $3\cos x = \dfrac{x}{90°}$

Draw the line $y = \dfrac{x}{90°}$.

The points of intersection are at $x = 74°$ and $x = -110°$ (to the nearest whole number).

Example 2

A giant Ferris wheel has a diameter of 100 m. Seat S starts at A ($x = 0°$) and moves clockwise towards B ($x = 180°$) and then on to A again ($x = 360°$).

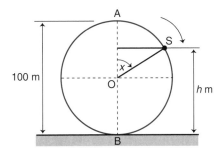

a Show that the height h, in metres, of seat S above the ground is given by

$$h = 50(1 + \cos x)$$

b Draw the graph of h against x for $0° \leqslant x \leqslant 180°$, and use your graph to find: the height of the seat above the ground when $x = 75°$, and the angle x when the seat is 30 m from the ground.

a $h = OB + 50 \cos x$
$h = 50 + 50 \cos x$
$\quad = 50(1 + \cos x)$

b A table of values is completed, and then the graph of $h = 50(1 + \cos x)$ can be drawn.

x	$0°$	$30°$	$60°$	$90°$	$120°$	$150°$	$180°$
h(m)	100	93.3	75	50	25	6.70	0

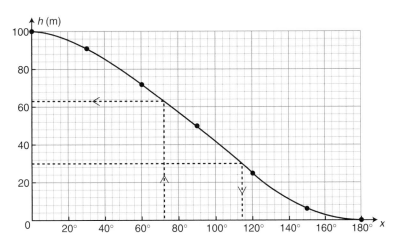

From the graph, when $x = 75°$, the seat will be 63 m above the ground.
From the graph, when the seat is 30 m from the ground, $x = 114°$.

Exercise 35

Give your answers correct to the nearest whole number.

	Draw the graph of ...	with domain ...	to solve the equation ...
1	$y = \sin 2x$	$0° \leqslant x \leqslant 90°$	$\sin 2x = 0.5$
2	$y = \sin 3x$	$0° \leqslant x \leqslant 90°$	$\sin 3x = 0.4$
3	$y = 2 \cos x$	$0° \leqslant x \leqslant 90°$	$2 \cos x = 1.5$
4	$y = 3 \cos x$	$0° \leqslant x \leqslant 90°$	$3 \cos x = 2$
5	$y = \tan 2x$	$0° \leqslant x \leqslant 45°$	$\tan 2x = 3$
6	$y = \tan 2x$	$0° \leqslant x \leqslant 45°$	$\tan 2x = 2$

Exercise 35★

Give your answers correct to 2 significant figures.

1 **a** Draw the graph of $y = \sin 2x$, for $0° \leqslant x \leqslant 360°$, and hence solve the equation $\sin 2x = 0.6$.

   b Compare the shape of your graph to that of $y = \sin x$.

   c What is the period of your graph?

2 **a** Draw the graph of $y = \cos 2x$, for $0° \leqslant x \leqslant 360°$, and hence solve the equation $\cos 2x = 0.3$.

   b Compare the shape of your graph to that of $y = \cos x$.

   c What is the period of your graph?

3 By drawing sketch graphs, investigate the difference between these four graphs.

   $y = \sin x$ \qquad $y = 2 \sin x$ \qquad $y = 3 \sin x$ \qquad $y = 4 \sin x$

4 By drawing sketch graphs, investigate the difference between these four graphs.

   $y = \cos x$ \qquad $y = \frac{1}{2} \cos x$ \qquad $y = \frac{1}{3} \cos x$ \qquad $y = \frac{1}{4} \cos x$

5 Draw the graph of $y = \cos x + \sin x$, for $0° \leqslant x \leqslant 360°$.

   a Find the *smallest* value of y and the value of x at which this occurs.
   Substitute these two values into the equation. Comment on your answers.

   b Use your graph to solve the equation $0.6 = \cos x + \sin x$.

   c Comment on the shape and position of your graph.

6 Draw the graph of $y = \cos x - \sin x$, for $0° \leqslant x \leqslant 360°$.

   a Use your graph to solve the equation $0 = \cos x - \sin x$. Comment on your answers.

   b Comment on the shape and position of your graph.

7 The depth of water, d metres, at the entrance of a harbour, t hours after midnight, is modelled by $d = 5 - 3\sin 30t$.

a Draw a graph of d against t for $0 \leqslant t \leqslant 24$.

b Use your graph to find the times of high tide and low tide at the harbour entrance.

c A boat requires 4-metre depth of water. Between what times may it enter the harbour?

Sine rule

The **sine rule** is a method to calculate sides and angles for scalene triangles, i.e. triangles that do not have a right angle. It is useful for finding the length of one side when all angles and one other side are known, or finding an angle when two sides and the included angle are known.

Key Points

The sine rule

In triangle ABC, notice that side a is opposite angle A, side b is opposite angle B, etc.

♦ To find a side, use the sine rule written as

$$\frac{a}{\sin A} = \frac{b}{\sin B} = \frac{c}{\sin C}$$

♦ To find an angle, use the sine rule written as

$$\frac{\sin A}{a} = \frac{\sin B}{b} = \frac{\sin C}{c}$$

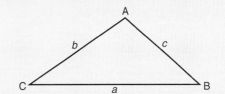

Example 3

In triangle ABC, find the length of side a, correct to 3 significant figures.

$$\frac{a}{\sin 48°} = \frac{7.4\,\text{cm}}{\sin 50°}$$

$$a = \frac{7.4\,\text{cm}}{\sin 50°} \times \sin 48°$$

$$a = 7.179\,\text{cm} \quad \text{(to 4 s.f.)}$$

$$a = 7.18\,\text{cm} \quad \text{(to 3 s.f.)}$$

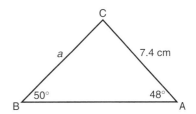

Example 4

In triangle XYZ, find angle Y correct to 3 significant figures.

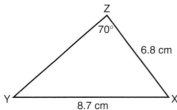

$$\frac{\sin Y}{6.8} = \frac{\sin 70°}{8.7} \qquad \text{(Multiply both sides by 6.8)}$$

$$\sin Y = \frac{\sin 70°}{8.7} \times 6.8$$

$$\sin Y = 0.734\,47 \text{ (to 5 s.f.)}$$

$$Y = 47.26° \quad \text{(to 4 s.f.)}$$

$$Y = 47.3° \quad \text{(to 3 s.f.)}$$

Remember

◆ Bearings are measured clockwise from North.

◆ When drawing bearings, start by drawing an arrow to indicate North.

◆ When calculating angles on a bearings diagram, look for 'alternate angles'.

Example 5

A yacht crosses the start line of a race at C, on a bearing of 026°. After 2.6 km, it rounds a buoy B and sails on a bearing of 335°. When it is due North of its start, at A, how far has it sailed altogether?

◆ Draw a diagram and include all the facts.

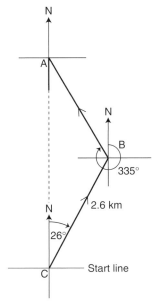

◆ Work out any necessary angles and redraw the triangle and include only the relevant facts.

$\angle CBA = 335° - 26° - 180° = 129°$

$\therefore \quad \angle BAC = 25°$

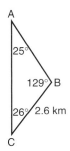

◆ Use the sine rule: in triangle ABC, the length AB has to be calculated.

$$\frac{AB}{\sin 26°} = \frac{2.6\,\text{km}}{\sin 25°} \qquad \text{(Multiply both sides by } \sin 26°\text{)}$$

$$AB = \frac{2.6\,\text{km}}{\sin 25°} \times \sin 26°$$

$$AB = 2.697\,\text{km} \quad \text{(to 4 s.f.)}$$

$\therefore \quad$ total distance travelled $= CB + BA$

$$= 2.6\,\text{km} + 2.697\,\text{km} = 5.30\,\text{km} \quad \text{(to 3 s.f.)}$$

Exercise 36

Write your answers correct to 3 significant figures.

1 Find x.

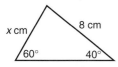

2 Find y.

3 Find MN.

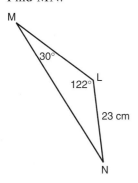

4 Find RT.

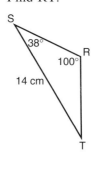

5 In triangle ABC, BC = 34 cm, ∠BAC = 37°, ∠ABC = 42°. Find AC.

6 In triangle XYZ, XZ = 19 cm, ∠XYZ = 34°, ∠YXZ = 104°. Find YZ.

7 Find x.

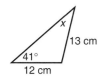

8 Find y.

9 Find ∠ABC.

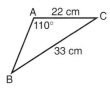

10 Find ∠XYZ.

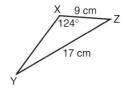

11 In triangle ABC, BC = 19 cm, AC = 24 cm, ∠BAC = 48°. Find ∠ACB.

12 In triangle EDC, CE = 27 cm, CD = 33 cm, ∠CED = 36°. Find ∠ECD.

13 A yacht crosses the start line of a race on a bearing of 031°. After 4.3 km, it rounds a buoy and sails on a bearing of 346°. When it is due North of its start, how far has it sailed altogether?

14 A yacht crosses the start line of a race on a bearing of 340°. After 700 m, it rounds a buoy and sails on a bearing of 038°. When it is due North of its start, how far has it sailed altogether?

Activity 23

The ambiguous case

◆ Use a pair of compasses to construct triangle ABC, with AB = 7 cm, BC = 6 cm and ∠BAC = 50°.

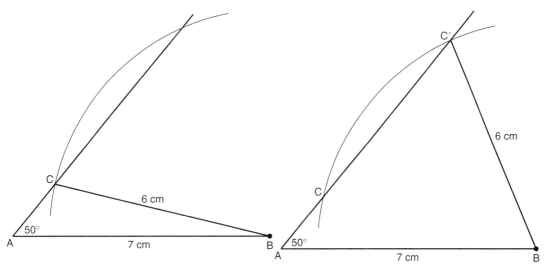

◆ Note that two triangles can be constructed: ABC and ABC′. The arc centred at B cuts the line from A at C *and* C′. This is an example of the 'ambiguous' case where two triangles can be constructed from the same facts.

◆ Show by calculation that AC ≈ 1.8 cm and AC′ ≈ 7.2 cm.

Exercise 36★

Write your answers correct to 3 significant figures.

1 Find x.

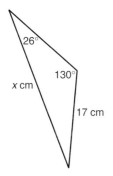

2 Find y.

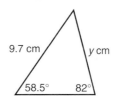

3 Find ∠LMN.

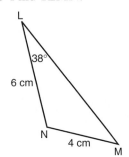

4 Find ∠RST.

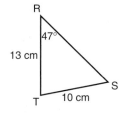

5 In triangle DEF, DF = 7.8 cm, DE = 8.5 cm, ∠DFE = 53.5°.
Find EF, ∠DEF and ∠FDE.

6 In triangle LMN, LM = 8.9 cm, LN = 10.3 cm, ∠LMN = 62°.
Find MN, ∠MLN and ∠LNM.

7 The bearing of B from A is 065°. The bearing of C from B is 150°, and the bearing of A from C is 305°. If AC = 300 m, find BC.

8 The bearing of Y from X is 205°. The bearing of Z from Y is 315°, and the bearing of X from Z is 085°. If XZ = 4 km, find the distance XY.

9 P and Q are points 80 m apart on the bank of a straight river. R is a point on the opposite bank where ∠QPR = 76° and ∠PQR = 65°. Calculate PR and the width of the river.

10 From two points X and Y, the angles of elevation of the top T of a church TZ are 14° and 19°, respectively. If XYZ is a horizontal straight line and XY = 120 m, find YT and the height of the tower.

11 When the angle of elevation of the Sun is 62°, the shadow of a vertical post on a hillside is of length 1.5 m and is down the line of greatest slope.
If the slope of the hillside is 18°, calculate the height of the post.

12 Draw triangle ABC and include BX, the perpendicular from B on to AC. Use your diagram to prove that

$$\frac{BC}{\sin A} = \frac{AB}{\sin C}$$

Cosine rule

The **cosine rule** is another method to calculate sides and angles of scalene triangles. It is used either to find the third side when two sides and the included angle are given, or to find an angle when all three sides are given.

Key Point

The cosine rule

In triangle ABC:

$$a^2 = b^2 + c^2 - (2bc \cos A)$$

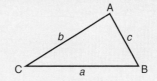

Activity 24

♦ Refer to the diagram and the cosine rule formula, and copy and complete these equations.
  - ▶ $b^2 = a^2 + \ldots^2 - (\ldots\ldots\ldots\ldots \cos B)$
  - ▶ $c^2 = \ldots^2 + \ldots^2 - (\ldots\ldots\ldots\ldots \cos C)$

♦ Rearrange these to make X the subject.

▶ $x = y - X$	▶ $x = y - 2X$	▶ $x = y - 2yX$
▶ $x = y - 2yzX$	▶ $x = y + z - 2yzX$	▶ $x^2 = y^2 + z^2 - 2yzX$

♦ Rearrange these to make $\cos X$ the subject.

▶ $x = y - \cos X$	▶ $x = y - 2 \cos X$	▶ $x = y - 2y \cos X$
▶ $x = y - 2yz \cos X$	▶ $x = y + z - 2yz \cos X$	▶ $x^2 = y^2 + z^2 - 2yz \cos X$

Key Points

In triangle ABC

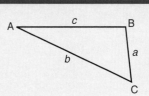

♦ To find side c, use the cosine rule written as

$$c^2 = a^2 + b^2 - (2ab \cos C)$$

♦ To find angle C, use the cosine rule written as

$$\cos C = \frac{a^2 + b^2 - c^2}{2ab}$$

Example 6

In triangle $\mathbf{XYZ}$ find x correct to 3 significant figures.

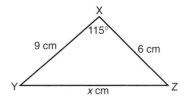

$$x^2 = y^2 + z^2 - 2yz \cos X$$

$$= 6^2 + 9^2 - 2 \times 6 \times 9 \times \cos 115°$$

$$= 36 + 81 - 108 \times (-0.4226)$$

$$= 36 + 81 + 45.64$$

$$x = \sqrt{162.6}$$

$$= 12.75 \quad \text{(to 4 s.f.)}$$

$$= 12.8 \quad \text{(to 3 s.f.)}$$

If you use the calculator efficiently, no intermediate working is necessary.

$$x^2 = y^2 + z^2 - 2yz \cos X$$

$$x = \sqrt{y^2 + z^2 - 2yz \cos X}$$

Substituting values for y, z and X

$$x = \sqrt{6^2 + 9^2 - (2 \times 6 \times 9 \times \cos 115°)}$$

Example 7

In triangle $\mathbf{XYZ}$, find angle X correct to 3 significant figures.

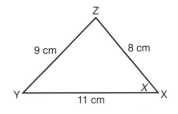

$$\cos X = \frac{y^2 + z^2 - x^2}{2yz}$$

$$= \frac{8^2 + 11^2 - 9^2}{2 \times 8 \times 11}$$

$$= \frac{104}{176}$$

$$X = 53.78° \quad \text{(to 4 s.f.)}$$

$$X = 53.8° \quad \text{(to 3 s.f.)}$$

Using the calculator:

Exercise 37

Write your answers correct to 3 significant figures.

1 Find *x*.

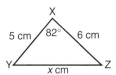

2 Find *y*.

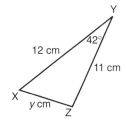

3 Find AB.

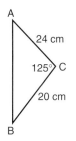

4 Find XY.

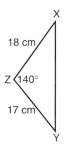

5 In triangle RST, RS = 32 cm, ST = 42 cm, ∠RST = 35°. Find RT.

6 In triangle LMN, LM = 15 cm, LN = 19 cm, ∠MLN = 18°. Find MN.

7 Find *X*.

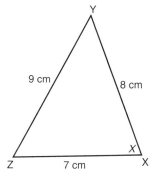

8 Find *Y*.

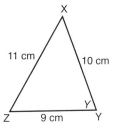

9 Find ∠ABC.

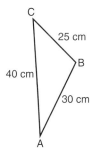

10 Find ∠XYZ.

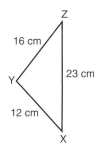

11 In triangle ABC, AB = 14 cm, AC = 10 cm, BC = 16 cm. Find ∠BAC.

12 In triangle RST, RS = 8 cm, RT = 7 cm, ST = 13 cm. Find ∠RST.

13 From S, a yacht sails on a bearing of 040°. After 3 km, at buoy A, it sails on a bearing of 140°. After another 4 km, at buoy B, it heads back to the start S. Draw a diagram and include all the facts. Calculate the total length of the course.

14 Copy and label this diagram using the facts: VW = 50 km, WU = 45 km, VU = 30 km.

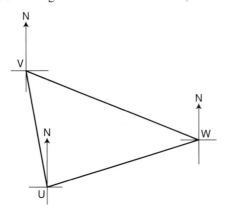

   a Find ∠VWU.

   b If the bearing of V from W is 300°, find the bearing of U from W.

Exercise 37★

Write your answers correct to 3 significant figures.

1 Find x.

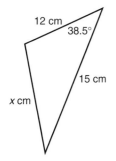

2 Find y.

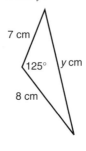

3 Find ∠XYZ.

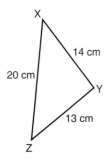

4 Find ∠ABC.

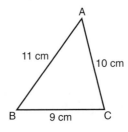

5 In triangle PQR, PQ = 3.8 cm, PR = 2.7 cm, ∠RPQ = 78°. Find QR, ∠PQR and ∠QRP.

6 In triangle LMN, LN = 6.1 cm, MN = 7.3 cm, ∠LNM = 117°. Find LM, ∠NLM and ∠LMN.

For Questions 7–14, use either the cosine rule or the sine rule.

7 The diagonals of a parallelogram have lengths 12 cm and 8 cm, and the angle between them is 120°. Find the side lengths of the parallelogram.

8 Two circles, centres X and Y, have radii 10 cm and 8 cm and intersect at A and B. XY = 13 cm. Find ∠BXA.

9 From a point A, the bearings of B and C are 040° and 160°, respectively. AB = 12 km and AC = 15 km. Find BC and the bearing of C from B.

10 SBC is a triangular orienteering course, with details as in this table.

	Bearing	Distance
Start S to B	195°	2.8 km
B to C	305°	1.2 km

Find the distance CS, and the bearing of S from C.

11 In the figure, find

    a ∠XZY   **b** WX

12 In the figure, find

    a BD   **b** ∠BCD

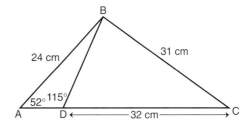

13 In triangle XYZ, YZ = 8 cm, XZ = 5 cm and angle $X = 60°$.
If XY = x, use the cosine rule to show that $x^2 - 5x - 39 = 0$. Find x.

14 In triangle ABC, AB = 7.2 cm, BC = 9.4 cm, ∠ABC = 104.2°. Find ∠ACB.

15 Use this diagram to prove that
$a^2 = b^2 + c^2 - 2bc \cos A$.

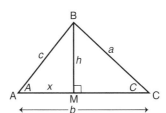

16 a Write down two equations involving x and y and show that $x^4 - 26x^2 + 100 = 0$.

    b Use the equation to find the length of each diagonal correct to 2 significant figures.

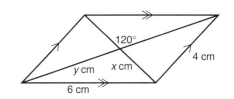

3D trigonometry

Place one end of a pencil B on a flat surface and put your ruler against the other end T as shown. The angle TBA is the angle between the straight line TB and the plane WXYZ.

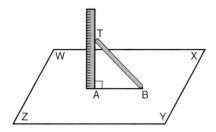

Activity 25

This activity will help you to visualise angles in three dimensions.

◆ Copy the net onto a piece of card. Cut it out and fold it, along the broken lines, to make the model of a roof. (Keep the net, to use in Exercises 38 and 38★.)

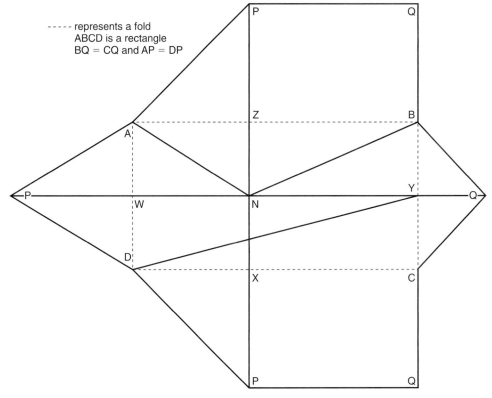

- - - - - represents a fold
ABCD is a rectangle
BQ = CQ and AP = DP

◆ Copy and complete this table. (The word 'angle' refers to the angle between the given line and the plane ABCD. For example, the angle between PZ and ABCD is PZN.)

Line	PZ	QC	PX			PW	PA		PB	QA
Angle	PZN			QBY	PDN			QDY		

◆ Name the length equal to   BN   AQ   DY   PA   AN   QY
◆ Name the angle equal to   ∠NAP   ∠CQB   ∠QDY   ∠PBN   ∠DPQ   ∠APW

Remember

When calculating in three dimensions:

♦ draw a large 3D cuboid and then superimpose onto the cuboid the appropriate diagram in pen – in this case the roof made from the net in Activity 25.

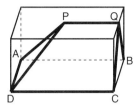

♦ Include all the facts on your 3D diagram.
♦ Redraw the appropriate triangle, with the facts, before doing any calculation.

The net in Activity 25 is used in Example 8 and the first few questions in Exercises 38 and 38★.

Example 8

This 3D diagram represents a roof. PQ = 5 cm, BC = 8 cm, CD = 10 cm and BQ = 10 cm. Find QY and the angle PW makes with ABCD.

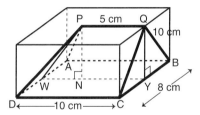

To find QY, the triangle CQB is drawn.

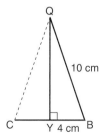

By Pythagoras' theorem

$QY^2 = 10^2 - 4^2$

$QY = \sqrt{84}$

$QY = 9.165 \text{ cm}$ (to 4 s.f.)

$\quad\quad = 9.17 \text{ cm}$ (to 3 s.f.)

To find ∠PWN, triangle PWN is drawn.

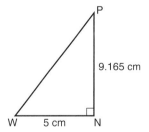

PN = QY = 9.165 cm, so

$\tan \angle PWN = \dfrac{9.165}{5}$

$\quad\quad\quad\quad = 1.833$ (to 4 s.f.)

$\angle PWN = 61.4°$ (to 3 s.f.)

Exercise 38

Give all answers correct to 3 significant figures.

Use this diagram to answer Questions 1–8. It shows a 3D figure of the net used in Activity 25.

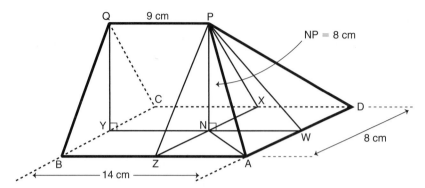

1 Find NW and the angle between PW and ABCD.

2 Find NZ and the angle between PZ and ABCD.

3 Find NA and the angle between PA and ABCD.

4 Find NB and the angle between PB and ABCD.

5 Find the angle between PZ and PX.

6 Find the angle between PQ and PW.

7 Find the angle between QX and ABCD.

8 Find the angle between QD and ABCD.

Use this diagram to answer Questions 9 and 10. It represents a ski slope, where BCEF and ADEF are rectangles.

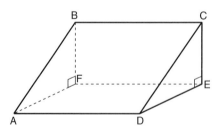

9 Copy this diagram of the ski slope and include these facts:
   DE = 300 m, AD = 400 m, CE = 100 m. Find

   a the angle that CD makes with ADEF

   b AE

   c the angle that CA makes with ADEF

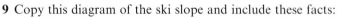

10 Copy this diagram of the ski slope and include these facts:
AD = 300 m, AB = 200 m, CE = 50 m. Find

   a DE

   b AE

   c the angle that CA makes with ADEF

Use this diagram to answer Questions 11 and 12. It shows a pyramid on a square base, where V
is vertically above the centre of RSTU.

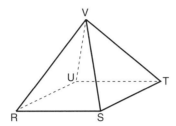

11 Copy the diagram and include these facts:
RS = 6 m, vertical height of V above RSTU = 8 m. Find

   a RT

   b the angle that VT makes with RSTU

   c VT

12 Copy the diagram and include these facts:
RS = 4 m, VT = 5 m. Find

   a US

   b the angle that VU makes with RSTU

   c the height of V above RSTU

Exercise 38★

Give all answers correct to 3 significant figures.

For Questions 1–6, use your net from Activity 25. Draw separate diagrams for each question.

1 AD = 5 cm, PA = 7 cm, WN = 4 cm. Find NA and the perpendicular height of P above
ABCD.

2 ∠PZN = 28°, AD = 8.6 cm, DX = 4.8 cm. Find the perpendicular height of P above ABCD,
and PW.

3 PA = 9.5 cm, ZN = 3.5 cm, WN = 5.5 cm. Find AN and the angle that PA makes with
ABCD.

4 YC = 6 cm, DC = 15 cm, YQ = 5 cm. Find DY and the angle that QD makes with ABCD.

5 ∠APD = 36°, AD = 9.2 cm, WN = 7.4 cm. Find the angle that PW makes with ABCD.

6 PN = 6.2 cm, PQ = 9.5 cm, AD = 8.4 cm. Find the angle that QZ makes with ABCD.

Use this diagram to answer Questions 7 and 8. It represents a ski slope, where BCEF and ADEF are rectangles.

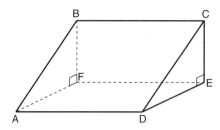

7 Copy the diagram and draw the line CA to represent a beginner's ski slope of 15° to ADEF. CD = 300 m, ∠CDE = 25°. Find

    a the height of C above E   **b** the length CA   **c** the distance AD.

8 Copy the diagram and draw the line CA to represent a ski slope of 40° to the slope CD. CE = 75 m, CD = 350 m. Find

    a AC   **b** AE   **c** the angle that CA makes with ADEF.

Use this diagram to answer Questions 9 and 10. It shows a pyramid on a square base, where V is vertically above the centre of RSTU.

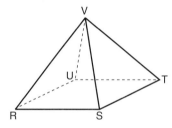

9 Copy the diagram and include these facts: VT = 12 m, ST = 8 m. Find the angle that VT makes with RSTU.

10 Copy the diagram and include these facts: VT = 12 m, the angle that VT makes with RSTU = 55°. Find ST.

11 Calculate the angle between a diagonal of a cube and

    a an edge   **b** a face   **c** another diagonal

12 A cube of side 8 cm stands on a horizontal table. A hollow cone of height 20 cm is placed over the cube so that it rests on the table and touches the top four corners of the cube. Find the vertical angle of the cone.

13 A hemispherical bowl of radius 18 cm is suspended from a point by three chains of length 30 cm attached to points equally spaced on the rim of the bowl. Find

    a the inclination of each chain to the horizontal

    b the angle between two chains

14 The base of a tetrahedron is an equilateral triangle of side 10 cm and each sloping face is an isosceles right-angled triangle. Find the angle between an edge and the base.

15 The angle of elevation to the top of a church tower is measured from A and from B.

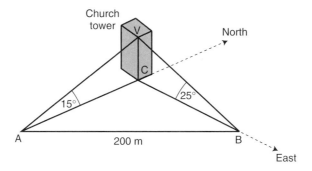

From A, due South of the church tower VC, the angle of elevation ∠VAC = 15°.
From B, due East of the church, the angle of elevation ∠VBC = 25°. AB = 200 m.
Find the height of the tower.

16 An aircraft is flying at a constant height of 2000 m. It is flying due East at a constant speed.
At T, the plane's angle of elevation from O is 25°, and on a bearing from O of 310°. One
minute later, it is at R and due North of O.

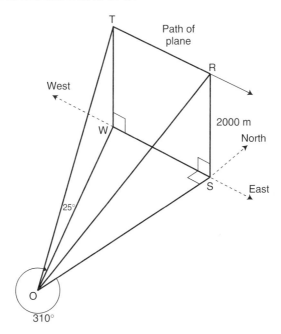

RSWT is a rectangle and the points O, W and S are on horizontal ground.

Find

a the lengths OW and OS

b the angle of elevation of the aircraft ∠ROS

c the speed of the aircraft in km/h.

3D coordinates

To identify a point on x and y axes, *two* coordinates are needed. In three dimensions, *three* axes are used and, to identify a point, *three* coordinates are needed.

Activity 26

In the diagram, O is the origin. The coordinates of point A are written $(4, 2, 2)$, in the order (x, y, z).

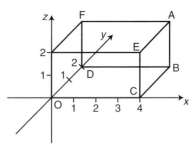

♦ Write down the coordinates of the points B, C, D, E and F.

♦ Copy the figure and mark the points $G(-3, 0, 2)$, $H(0, -3, 0)$ and $I(-3, -3, -2)$.

♦ Use Pythagoras' theorem to calculate the length OB, giving your answer in 'units'.

♦ Use trigonometry to find the angle between the line AO and the plane OCBD.

Exercise 39

Give your answers correct to 3 significant figures.

Copy this diagram and use it to answer Questions 1–6.

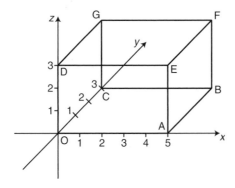

For Questions 1–4, write down the 3D coordinates.

	Points …	Mid-point of …	Centre of face …
1	O and E	AE	OABC
2	C and A	OB	DEFG
3	B and G	CB	BCGF
4	D and F	AF	OCGD

5 a Work out OB in units.   **b** Work out the angle between FO and the plane OABC.

6 a Work out AC in units.   **b** Work out the angle between GA and the plane OABC.

Use this diagram to answer Questions 7–10.

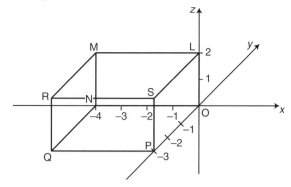

	Write down the coordinates of . . .	Find the length in units of . . .	Find the angle between . . .
7	P, Q and S	OS	OS and OPQN
8	N, M and R	OM	OM and OPQN
9	the mid-point of SL	OQ	RO and OPQN
10	the mid-point of ML	NP	SN and OPQN

Exercise 39★

Give your answers correct to 3 significant figures.

Use this diagram to answer Questions 1–6.

X is the point in the centre of the square ONQP.

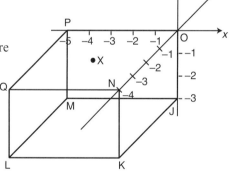

	Write down the coordinates of . . .	Find the length in units of . . .	Find the angle between . . .
1	P and Q	LP	OL and LMPQ
2	K and L	OK	PK and ONKJ
3	the mid-point of PQ	OX	PX and OPMJ
4	the mid-point of LK	PX	PX and LMPQ
5	X	JX	JX and JKLM
6	the mid-point of ONKJ	LX	LX and LMPQ

7 Find the distance between

   a $(0, -2, 6)$ and $(-3, 0, 6)$

   b $(0, -2, 6)$ and $(-3, 0, 0)$.

8 Find the distance between

   a $(-5, 0, 4)$ and $(-5, -3, 0)$

   b $(-5, 0, 4)$ and $(0, -3, 0)$.

9 Five vertices of a cuboid are: $O(0, 0, 0)$, $A(-5, 0, -4)$, $B(-5, 6, -4)$, $C(-5, 6, 0)$ and $E(0, 6, -4)$.

   a By drawing a suitable diagram, write down the coordinates of the other three vertices.

   b Imagine the cuboid is made of wood and the pyramid ACEB is cut off. Find the area of the triangle ACE.

Exercise 40★

For this exercise, use the sine and cosine rules, and give all answers correct to 3 significant figures.

ABCDEFGH is a cuboid. For each of questions 1–4, copy this diagram and include all the given facts.

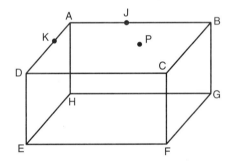

1 EJ = 17 cm, GJ = 14 cm, EF = 16 cm, FG = 12 cm. Calculate EG and ∠JEG.

2 GA = 17 cm, DE = 12 cm, EH = 5 cm, EG = 20 cm. Calculate EA and ∠EAG.

3 EF = 16 m, FG = 6 m, GP = 7 m, ∠PGE = 50°. Calculate EG and EP.

4 EF = 30 m, FG = 12 m, FP = 10 m, ∠PFH = 35° Calculate FH and HP.

ABCDV is a pyramid on a square base. For each of Questions 5 and 6, copy this diagram and include all the given facts.

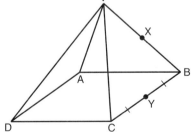

5 AB = $\sqrt{50}$ cm, BX = 12 cm, ∠XDB = 40°. Calculate BD and ∠DXB.

6 AB = 30 cm, ∠XAY = 65°, and ∠XYA = 70°. Calculate AY and XY.

7 On a pair of axes, plot D (30, 20, 0), E (0, 0, 0) and G (10, 20, 10), and calculate ∠GED.

8 On a pair of axes, plot A (0, 0, 0), B (15, 20, 10) and C (30, 20, 0), and calculate ∠BAC.

9 ABCDEFGH is a cuboid. Calculate BK.

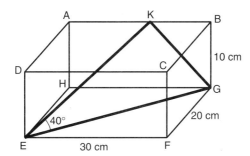

Exercise 41 (Revision)

Where appropriate give answers correct to 3 significant figures.

For Questions 1–6, use the sine, cosine and tangent graphs in Activity 21 (page 128).

Find another angle x, where $0° \leqslant x \leqslant 360°$, that has the same trigonometric ratio as these.

1 $\sin 40°$ **2** $\cos 50°$ **3** $\tan 70°$

Solve these equations for x, where $0° \leqslant x \leqslant 360°$.

4 $\sin x = 0.4$ **5** $\cos x = 0.2$ **6** $\tan x = 0.6$

7   **a**   Copy and complete this table of values for the equation $y = \sin 3x$, correct to 2 significant figures and on squared paper, draw the graph of $y = \sin 3x$.

x	0°	25°	30°	35°	45°	60°	85°	90°	95°	120°
$\sin 3x$					0.71			−1.0		

    b   Draw the graph of $y = 0.6$ to solve the equation $\sin 3x = 0.6$.

8   **a**   Write down the coordinates of A and F.

    b   Write down the coordinates of the centre of the face ABCD.

    c   Find the length OF.

    d   Find the angle between AF and the plane OEFG.

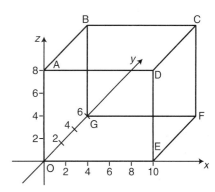

9 Copy this diagram. It shows a pyramid on a square base, where V is vertically above the centre of ABCD.

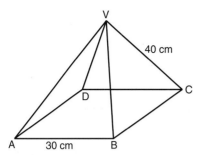

Calculate

a the length AC

b the height of the pyramid

c the angle that VC makes with BC

d the angle that VC makes with ABCD

10 The bearing of B from A is 150°, the bearing of C from B is 280°, the bearing of A from C is 030°.

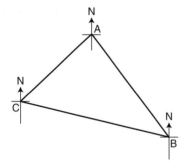

a Find the angles of △ABC.

b The distance AC is 4 km. Use the sine rule to find the distance AB.

11 In △ABC, AB = 6 cm, BC = 5 cm and AC = 10 cm. Use the cosine rule to find the ∠A.

Exercise 41★ (Revision)

Where appropriate give answers correct to 3 significant figures.

Find another angle, between −180° and 180°, that has the same trigonometric ratio as these.

1 $\sin(-35°)$ **2** $\cos 135°$ **3** $\tan(-75°)$ **4** $\tan(-165°)$

Solve these equations for x, between $-180°$ and $180°$.

5 $\sin x = -0.069\,76$ **6** $\cos x = -0.8973$ **7** $\tan x = -4$

8 $4\sin x = 1$ **9** $3\cos x = 1$ **10** $5\tan x = 7$

11 Draw separate triangles to show why

    a $\sin 45° = \dfrac{1}{\sqrt{2}}$ **b** $\cos 30° = \dfrac{\sqrt{3}}{2}$ **c** $\tan 60° = \sqrt{3}$

12 Draw the graph of $y = 4\sin 2x$ for values of x between $-180°$ and $180°$.

    a What is the period of the graph?

    b Write down the maximum and minimum values of y and the values of x at which these occur.

13 A yacht at point A is due West of a headland H. It sails on a bearing of $125°$, for $800\,\text{m}$, to a point B. If the bearing of H from B is $335°$, find the distance BH.

14 The sides of a parallelogram are $4.6\,\text{cm}$ and $6.8\,\text{cm}$, with an included angle of $116°$. Find the length of each diagonal.

15 A cuboid is a metres long, b metres wide and c metres high. Show that the length of the longest diagonal is given by $\sqrt{a^2 + b^2 + c^2}$.

16 A doll's house has a horizontal square base ABCD and V is vertically above the centre of the base.

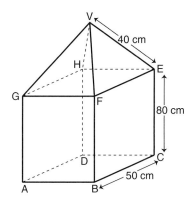

Calculate

    a the length AC

    b the height of V above ABCD

    c the angle VE makes with the horizontal

    d the total volume.

Handling data 2

Histograms

Histograms look similar to bar charts, but . . .

- A bar chart measures *frequency* on the vertical axis.

- A histogram measures *frequency density* on the vertical axis.

- Frequency is proportional to the *height* of the bar.

- Frequency is proportional to the *area* of the bar.

When data are divided into groups of *different* sizes, a histogram, rather than a bar chart should be used to display the distribution.

> ## Key Point
>
> $$\text{Frequency density} = \frac{\text{frequency}}{\text{width of group}}$$
>
> $\therefore$ (frequency density) × (width of group) = frequency

Example 1

A horticulturist recorded the heights of a sample of 100 plants that he had grown from a new seed.
The results are shown in this table.

Height, h (cm)	Frequency, f
$16 \leqslant h < 24$	6
$24 \leqslant h < 28$	16
$28 \leqslant h < 30$	14
$30 \leqslant h < 32$	15
$32 \leqslant h < 36$	26
$36 \leqslant h < 40$	15
$40 \leqslant h < 50$	8

Represent the results on a bar chart and on a histogram..

The frequency densities are worked out in a calculation table. Four columns are needed.

Group	Frequency, f	Width	Frequency density
$16 \leqslant h < 24$	6	8	$6 \div 8 = 0.75$
$24 \leqslant h < 28$	16	4	$16 \div 4 = 4.00$
$28 \leqslant h < 30$	14	2	$14 \div 2 = 7.00$
$30 \leqslant h < 32$	15	2	$15 \div 2 = 7.50$
$32 \leqslant h < 36$	26	4	$26 \div 4 = 6.50$
$36 \leqslant h < 40$	15	4	$15 \div 4 = 3.75$
$40 \leqslant h < 50$	8	10	$8 \div 10 = 0.80$
	$\sum = 100 = n$		

The bar chart displays the frequencies.

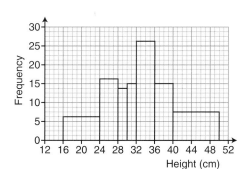

The histogram displays the frequency densities.

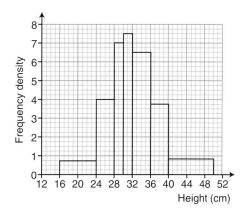

◆ The bar chart gives a misleading impression of the data because the groups are of different widths.
A bar chart is *only* suitable when the data are divided into groups of the *same* size.

◆ In a histogram, the area of each 'bar' is:
length × breadth = f.d. × (width of group)
= frequency

'Twice as wide' ⟶ 'Half as high'

Example 2

Use the horticulturist's data from Example 1.

a Calculate the mean height of the 100 plants.

b Estimate the percentage of plants which are longer than 38 cm.

a Extend the calculation table to include the mid-point (x cm) of each group and fx for each group.

Group	Freq., f	Width	Freq. density	Mid-point, x	fx
$16 \leqslant h < 24$	6	8	$6 \div 8 = 0.75$	20	120
$24 \leqslant h < 28$	16	4	$16 \div 4 = 4.00$	26	416
$28 \leqslant h < 30$	14	2	$14 \div 2 = 7.00$	29	406
$30 \leqslant h < 32$	15	2	$15 \div 2 = 7.50$	31	465
$32 \leqslant h < 36$	26	4	$26 \div 4 = 6.50$	34	884
$36 \leqslant h < 40$	15	4	$15 \div 4 = 3.75$	38	570
$40 \leqslant h < 50$	8	10	$8 \div 10 = 0.80$	45	360
	$n = 100$				$\Sigma fx = 3221$

$$\text{Mean} = \frac{\Sigma fx}{n} = \frac{3221}{100} = 32.21 \text{ cm}$$

So, the mean height is 32.21 cm.

b From the histogram in Example 1:

$$\text{area of 'number over 38'} = (2 \times 3.75) + (10 \times 0.8)$$
$$= 7.5 + 8.0$$
$$= 15.5$$

Of the 100 plants in the sample, 15.5 are longer than 38 cm.
So 15.5% of the plants are longer than 38 cm.

Exercise 42

1 A survey revealed these results for the time spent on homework for a Friday night by a group of 60 school children.

Calculate the frequency densities for each group and construct a histogram to display the results.

Time, t (min)	Number of children, f
$0 \leqslant t < 30$	6
$30 \leqslant t < 60$	12
$60 \leqslant t < 80$	18
$80 \leqslant t < 100$	12
$100 \leqslant t < 120$	9
$120 \leqslant t < 180$	3

Use these scales: horizontal axis, 1 cm = 10 min; vertical axis, 1 cm = 0.1.

2 The ages (in completed years) of the teaching staff at a school are given in this table.

Calculate the frequency densities for each group and construct a histogram to display the results.

Age, (years) x	Number of teachers, f
$22 \leqslant x < 25$	12
$25 \leqslant x < 30$	10
$30 \leqslant x < 35$	14
$35 \leqslant x < 40$	15
$40 \leqslant x < 45$	13
$45 \leqslant x < 50$	9
$50 \leqslant x < 60$	17

Use these scales: horizontal axis, 2 cm = 5 years; vertical axis, 1 cm = 0.5.

3 A turkey farmer produced 89 turkeys for the Christmas market. Their weights are given in this table.

a Calculate the frequency densities for each group and construct a histogram to display the results.

b What is the modal group for the weight of the turkeys?

c Estimate the percentage of turkeys weighing between 10 lb and 15 lb.

Weight (lb)	Frequency, f
4–8	7
8–10	7
10–12	10
12–13	12
13–14	19
14–16	16
16–20	18

Use these scales: horizontal axes, 1 cm = 2 lb; vertical axis, 1 cm = 0.5.

4 A fruit farmer checks the weights of 100 apples for quality control. The results are given in this table.

a Calculate the frequency densities for each group and construct a histogram to display the results.

b What is the modal group for the weight of the apples?

c Estimate the percentage of apples weighing between 75 g and 100 g.

Weight (g)	Frequency, f
50–80	24
80–90	12
90–100	17
100–105	14
105–110	11
110–120	13
120–140	9

Use these scales: horizontal axis, 1 cm = 10 g; vertical axis, 1 cm = 0.2.

5 The ages (in completed years) of women giving birth in a local hospital during January 2000 are given in this table.

a Calculate the frequency densities for each group in the table.

b Draw a histogram to illustrate the results.

c Calculate an estimate of the mean age of the mothers.

Age (years)	Frequency
14–16	7
16–20	38
20–25	60
25–30	68
30–35	52
35–45	25

Use these scales: horizontal axis, 1 cm = 2 years; vertical axis, 1 cm = 1.

6 The race times of cross-country runners are shown in this table.

a Calculate the frequency densities for each group in the table.

b Draw a histogram to illustrate the results.

c Calculate an estimate of the mean time, correct to the nearest second.

Time, t (min)	Frequency, f
11–12	3
12–14	9
14–16	22
16–18	25
18–21	15
21–24	6

Use these scales: horizontal axis, 1 cm = 1 min; vertical axis, 1 cm = 1.

Exercise 42★

1 Fifty responses were received from a survey of French camp sites close to the Atlantic Coast. The 'size' of a camp site was defined by the number of mobile homes on it, and the results are shown in this table.

a Draw a histogram of the data.

b Estimate the percentage of sites with between 250 and 500 mobile homes.

c Calculate an estimate of the mean number of mobile homes per site.

Size of camp site	Number of sites
0–100	4
100–200	7
200–350	13
350–500	17
500–750	6
750–1000	3

2 This frequency table shows the distribution of ages for a cinema audience.

a Draw a histogram of the data.

b Estimate the percentage of the audience aged between 35 and 55.

c Calculate an estimate of the mean age of the audience.

Age (years)	Frequency
18–20	24
20–25	42
25–30	24
30–40	16
40–50	30
50–60	30
60–80	34

3 The ages of children attending a summer camp are given in this table.

a Calculate the frequency densities for each group in the table.

b Calculate an estimate of the mean age of the children.

c Given that the height of the first bar of the histogram is 5 cm, calculate the heights of the other bars in the histogram.

Age (years)	Number
3–5	30
6–7	26
8–9	30
10	15
11	13
12–14	21
15–17	21

4 The ages (in completed years) of the members of a health and fitness club are shown in this table.

a Calculate the frequency densities for each group in the table.

b Calculate an estimate of the mean age of the membership.

c Given that the height of the first bar is 5 cm, calculate the heights of the other bars.

Age (years)	Number
18–19	30
20–24	57
25–29	69
30–34	42
35–39	36
40–49	36
50–59	30

5 A snack bar manager has prepared a histogram that displays the trade on a typical Friday. This allows the manager to prepare the right quantity of snacks and to employ enough staff.

Read all parts of this question before preparing a calculation table.

a How many customers does the manager expect on a typical Friday?

b If each customer spends an average of £3, how much money does the manager expect to take?

c Calculate the mean number of customers per hour. Is this a useful statistic?

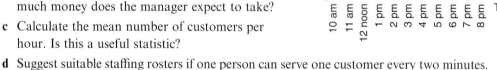

d Suggest suitable staffing rosters if one person can serve one customer every two minutes.

6 Traffic flow is recorded on a trunk road as part of an investigation into a road improvement scheme. The results, for one weekday, are displayed on the histogram.

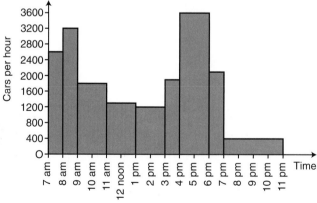

Read all parts of this question before preparing a calculation table.

a How many cars travelled on this road during the survey?

b Calculate the mean flow for the time of this survey.

c How many cars are passing through every five minutes at the busiest time?

d How might rate of traffic flow and total traffic flow affect the decisions of the planners?

7 This table and the unfinished histogram represent the playing times of a sample of video films.

Playing time (min)	Frequency, f
60–80	
80–90	
90–95	13
95–100	18
100–110	17
110–120	6
120–150	3

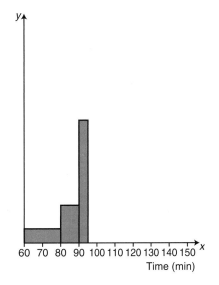

a Use the histogram to find the missing frequencies.

b Copy and complete the histogram, using the same scales and clearly labelling the vertical axis.

c Calculate the mean playing time of the videos.

8 A sample of batteries were tested by being continually used to power a toy train. This table and the unfinished histogram represent the times it took for the train to stop moving.

Time (hours)	Frequency, f
4–5	10
5–5.5	9
5.5–6	16
6–6.5	18
6.5–7	7
7–8	
8–10	

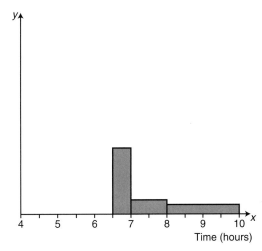

a Use the histogram to find the missing frequencies.

b Copy and complete the histogram, using the same scales and clearly labelling the vertical axis.

c Calculate the mean lifetime of the batteries.

Exercise 43 (Revision)

1 The motorway police conducted a survey on the distance between cars in the fast lane of a motorway. The results are recorded in this frequency table.

a Calculate the frequency densities of each group.

A histogram is drawn of this distribution, and the height of the bar for the '10–25' group is 12 cm. Work out the heights of the bars for

b the group 75–100

c the group 100–150.

Distance (m)	Frequency, f
0–10	28
10–25	120
25–50	358
50–75	516
75–100	150
100–150	78

2 The table shows the time spent travelling to school by Year 10 pupils.

a Calculate the frequency densities for each group in the table.

b Display the distribution in a histogram, and indicate on it the frequency represented by 1 cm^2.

c Calculate the total number of pupils in Year 10 and their mean travelling time.

d Estimate the percentage of pupils who take between 30 and 45 min to travel to school.

Time, t (min)	Number of pupils, f
0–10	12
10–20	23
20–40	32
40–60	18
60–90	9
90–120	6

Use these scales: horizontal axis, 1 cm = 10 min; vertical axis, 1 cm = 2.

Exercise 43★ (Revision)

1 This table summarises Joseph's calls from the monthly itemised telephone bill for August. His father allows him £5 worth of calls but charges him for any extra.

Read all parts of this question before constructing a calculation table.

a Draw a histogram to represent the information.

b Estimate the total time that Joseph spent on the phone.

c Calculate an estimate for the mean length, to the nearest second, of a call.

d Estimate the mean time, to the nearest second, that Joseph spent on the phone each day.

Duration of calls, t (min)	Number of calls, f
$0 \leqslant t < 5$	20
$5 \leqslant t < 15$	5
$15 \leqslant t < 30$	4
$30 \leqslant t < 40$	12
$40 \leqslant t < 50$	15
$50 \leqslant t < 60$	7
$60 \leqslant t < 75$	4
$75 \leqslant t < 90$	2
	$\Sigma f = 69$

e If calls cost 0.8p per minute, estimate how much Joseph owes his father.

2   This frequency table and the histogram show the number of days that a sample of patients had to wait to see a specialist after referral from their GP in one particular Health Authority.

Waiting time, t (days)	f
$0 \leqslant t < 7$	14
$7 \leqslant t < 20$	65
$20 \leqslant t < 30$	
$30 \leqslant t < 60$	
$60 \leqslant t < 90$	342
$90 \leqslant t < 180$	207

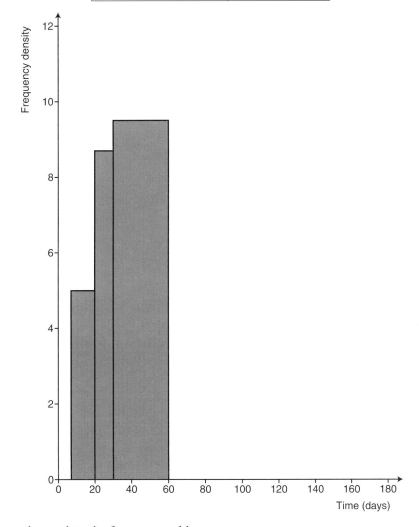

a Copy and complete the frequency table.

b Write down the heights of the missing bars in the histogram.

c Calculate estimates for the mean and median waiting times for referral to a specialist in this Health Authority.

Numeracy practice 2

Skills practice

Number

Work out these.

1 $6.7 \div 100$

2 $81 \div 1000$

3 45.3×0.01

4 99.8×0.01

5 $67.8 - 123$

6 $34.9 - 87.5$

7 $3^5 + 2^4$

8 $2^5 + 3^4$

9 7.54×8

10 5.29×7

11 $(0.6)^2$

12 $(0.2)^3$

13 $125^{\frac{1}{3}}$

14 $216^{\frac{1}{3}}$

15 $585 \div 13$

16 $1394 \div 17$

17 $54 \div 2^{-2}$

18 $64 \div 4^{-2}$

19 $0.39 + 10^{-3}$

20 $0.87 + 10^{-2}$

21 $3 + 5 \times 6$

22 $8 + 6 \times 3$

23 $\sqrt{3600}$

24 $\sqrt{4900}$

Estimate these.

25 767.9×0.0582

26 $79.92 \div 0.386$

27 $\dfrac{\sqrt{7946}}{92.8}$

28 $\dfrac{\sqrt{389.2}}{5.2}$

Algebra

Simplify these.

1 $\dfrac{6a^3b^2}{3a^2b^3}$

2 $\dfrac{8a^3b^3}{2a^2b^2}$

3 $\dfrac{xy^2}{z^2} \times \dfrac{yz}{x}$

4 $\dfrac{x^2y^2}{z^2} \times \dfrac{y^2z}{x^2}$

5 $\dfrac{3x + x^2}{2x}$

6 $\dfrac{2a + a^2}{2a}$

7 $\dfrac{xy^2}{6} \div \dfrac{x^2y}{15}$

8 $\dfrac{x - y}{2} - \dfrac{y - x}{3}$

Factorise these.

9 $x^2 - 5x + 6$

10 $x^2 - x - 6$

11 $6a^3b^2 - 27ab^3$

12 $4x^2 - 9y^4$

Make x the subject of these.

13 $ax + b = c$

14 $c + cx = a$

15 $a(x - b) = c$

16 $d = c(x + d)$

17 $ax = by - cx$

18 $\left(b + \dfrac{a}{x}\right)^2 = c$

Substitute $a = -1$, $b = -2$ to find the value of these.

19 ab^3

20 ba^3

21 $(a - b)^2$

22 $(b - a)^2$

23 $a - b^3$

24 $b - a^3$

25 $(ab)^2$

26 $(ba)^2$

Challenges

1 Copy and complete this cross number. You do not need clues to all the numbers to be able to complete it.

Across

1A Square of 1D
8A Square of 4A
10A $(6D - 1) \times 13$
12A $3 \times 11D$
13A $(1A - 1) \div 2$
14A $2 \times 19D$
16A $2 \times 4A \times 4D$
19A $10A + 16A$
23A $(21A)^4$

Down

1D Digit sum is 6
2D $4A \times 7A$
3D $(4D \times 90) + 1$
6D Digit sum is 5
7D $8A \times 7A$
9D $7A \times 19D$
10D $4A \times 22A$
15D $19A \times 5$
18D Multiple of 3

2 A rock climber climbs a rock face at a uniform rate. At 9 o'clock, he was one-sixth of the way up and, at 11 o'clock, he was three-quarters of the way up.
What fraction of the total rock face had he completed at 10 o'clock?

3 By folding a rectangular piece of paper as shown, you can create angles of $30°$ and $60°$. Investigate why this works and any other properties of triangle ABC.

Fold the paper in half

Fold corner A onto the first fold, and mark the point C

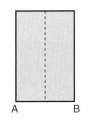 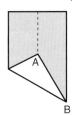 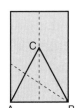

4 This puzzle was invented by the Chinese, but used by the Vikings to lock up their trunks on expeditions abroad.

The object is to remove the handle. The number of moves necessary depends on the number of rings on the puzzle. The diagram shows a six-ring puzzle.

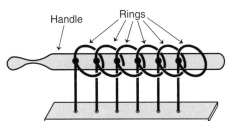

The number of moves necessary to remove the handle, if there are n rings on the puzzle, is given by

$$\frac{2^{n+1} - 2}{3}$$

a Find the number of moves to remove the handle from a 20-ring puzzle.

b Another puzzle takes nearly 100 years to do, at one move per second.
Find the number of rings on the puzzle.

Fact finder: The Channel Tunnel

The building of The Channel Tunnel between Folkestone and Calais is the largest civil engineering project ever undertaken in Europe. The first proposal for such a connection was in **1802**, but was ill-timed due to war resuming between Britain and France. The construction was completed in **1994**.

The tunnel itself is in fact three: **two running tunnels** and **one service tunnel**. The tunnels are **30.7 miles** in length with **23.6 miles** under the English Channel, **25–40 m** below the sea bed, reaching **100 m** below sea level at the deepest point.

The internal diameters of the running and service tunnels are **7.6 m** and **4.8 m** respectively and their maximum gradient is about **1:90**.

Conditions underground during construction were hot, damp, noisy and dangerous. The main engineering challenge was having to drill through fractured chalk saturated with water. This problem was particularly acute on the French side, where tunnellers were expected to progress at half the speed of their English counterparts. Special boring machines were fitted with a seal behind the cutting head to prevent water gushing in as boring progressed; in fact water had to be pumped away at **9 gallons per second**! The British workers advanced at **300 m** per week (**100 m** more than planned) while the French also exceeded their target of **100 m per week**.

The total cost of the construction was about **£8 billion**, and there were **15 000 workers** on site at its busiest.

The crossing by ferry takes **90–100 minutes**, but the train crossing takes **35–40 minutes**. The high-speed trains (HSTs) are designed to travel at **80 mph** in the tunnel and **100 mph** once outside, reducing the travel time between London and Paris from **5 hours and 12 minutes** to just **3 hours**, not much longer than by air! Each train carries an estimated **800 passengers** in 24 specially designed wagons. In **1994**, there were **315 000** passengers, only four years later this rose to **12 799 000**. As more people become accustomed to this service, it is expected that these figures will continue to rise.

Exercise

1 After how many years since its first proposal was the Channel Tunnel completed?

2 What percentage of the tunnel length is actually underneath the English Channel?

3 Calculate the total volume of air in the three tunnels in m³ expressed in standard form to 3 significant figures.
(Assume the tunnels are empty and are perfectly straight cylinders. 1 mile $\simeq$ 1600 m.)

4 All three tunnels were coated with a sealant costing £1.40 per square metre.
Find the cost of this coating.

5 On average, how many people used the tunnel per hour in 1994?

6 Use the photograph to show that the diameter of the drill-head is about 10 m.

7 The whole construction started at the beginning of 1987 and was completed at the end of 1994. Calculate the mean cost of the scheme per second.

8 According to initial estimates, how long after tunnelling began were the British tunnellers expected to meet the French?

9 How many litres of water were pumped away per day by one boring machine?
(Answer in standard form to 3 significant figures using 1 gallon $\simeq$ 4.5 litres.)

10 Calculate the percentage increase in the number of trains required from 1994 to 1998.

11 A particular tunnel crossing takes 35 minutes. For the first third of the journey, the train travels at x mph. The final two-thirds is completed at three times this speed. Find x.

12 If $p \times 10^3$ is the number of passengers using the tunnel, y years after 1994, and assuming that this passenger increase is constant up to 1998, show that $p = ay + b$, where a and b are constants, and find the values of a and b.

Investigation 2

Golf ball motion

Nina plays a round of golf. She *always* hits her shots on line with the hole. The starting speed (U m/s) of the ball and its angle of elevation ($e°$) are constant for each club she uses. These are shown below.
(Assume all shots are stationary on landing!)

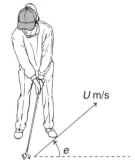

U m/s

1 The horizontal distance (d metres) that Nina hits the ball is given by the formula:

$$d = \frac{U^2 \sin (2e)}{10}$$

Copy and complete this table to show Nina's golfing capabilities with each club.

Club	Driver	No. 3 wood	No. 5 iron	No. 7 iron	Wedge
U (m/s)	63	53	38	33	
$e°$	12°	17°	31°		41°
d (m)				105	62

2 The equation of the flight path of Nina's ball when hit by her driver is

$$y = 0.213x - 0.001\,32x^2$$

where y is the ball's height and x the horizontal distance moved by the ball in metres, as shown on the graph.

a On the 17th hole, Nina takes a short cut: instead of using the fairway which is dog-legged (cornered), she tees off with the driver aiming straight at the hole! An 8 m tree lies on her line of sight to the hole 65 m from the tee. Does she clear the tree?

b On the 18th hole, the situation described in part **a** is repeated. This time her drive from the tee clears a 6.5 m tree by just 10 cm. What is the distance from tee to tree?

c What is the maximum height reached by Nina's drive?

3 The length of the clubs (L cm) in Nina's golf bag are shown in this table.

Club	Driver	No. 3 wood	No. 5 iron	No. 7 iron	Wedge
L (cm)	108	100	95	91	89

The time of flight, t seconds, for a ball struck by each club in Nina's bag is $t = \dfrac{U \sin (e)}{5}$

Investigate, for the clubs in Nina's bag, the relationships between U and L, d and L, d and U, and the time of flight for each club.

Summary 2

Negative and fractional indices

$$a^m \times a^{-n} = a^{m-n} \qquad \text{(Add indices)}$$

$$a^m \div a^{-n} = a^{m--n} \qquad \text{(Subtract indices)}$$
$$= a^{m+n}$$

$$(a^m)^{-n} = a^{-mn} \qquad \text{(Multiply indices)}$$

$$a^{\frac{1}{2}} = \sqrt{a} \qquad\qquad\qquad a^{\frac{1}{3}} = \sqrt[3]{a}$$

$$a^{-n} = \frac{1}{a^n} \qquad\qquad\qquad a^{-\frac{1}{2}} = \frac{1}{a^{\frac{1}{2}}} = \frac{1}{\sqrt{a}}$$

$$a^{\frac{3}{2}} = \sqrt{a^3} \qquad\qquad\qquad a^{-\frac{3}{2}} = \frac{1}{a^{\frac{3}{2}}} = \frac{1}{\sqrt{a^3}}$$

Surds

$$\sqrt{24} = \sqrt{4 \times 6} \qquad\qquad 3\sqrt{5} = \sqrt{9} \times \sqrt{5}$$
$$= \sqrt{4} \times \sqrt{6} \qquad\qquad\quad = \sqrt{9 \times 5}$$
$$= 2\sqrt{6} \qquad\qquad\qquad\quad = \sqrt{45}$$

$$a\sqrt{b} \times \sqrt{b} = ab \qquad\qquad 2\sqrt{a} + 3\sqrt{a} = 5\sqrt{a}$$

To **rationalise** the denominator means to clear the surd from the denominator.

$$\frac{3}{\sqrt{5}} = \frac{3}{\sqrt{5}} \times \frac{\sqrt{5}}{\sqrt{5}} \qquad \text{(Multiply top and bottom by } \sqrt{5}\text{)}$$

$$= \frac{3\sqrt{5}}{5}$$

Note: $\dfrac{\sqrt{5}}{\sqrt{5}} = 1$

Algebra

Area and perimeter of parts of circles and of triangles

♦ In terms of x, the area of the shaded region

$$= 2x^2 - \frac{1}{2}\pi x^2 = x^2\left(2 - \frac{\pi}{2}\right)$$

♦ In terms of x, the perimeter of the shaded region

$$= 4x + \frac{1}{2} \times 2\pi x = x(4 + \pi)$$

♦ For triangle ABC, area $= \frac{1}{2} \times a \times b \times \sin C$

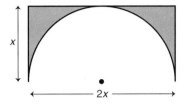

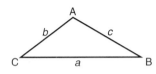

Arcs, sectors and segments

♦ Arc length XY $= \dfrac{a}{360} \times 2\pi r$

♦ Sector area OXY $= \dfrac{a}{360} \times \pi r^2$

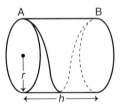

♦ Segment area $=$ area of sector OXY $-$ area of triangle OXY

$$= \frac{a}{360} \times \pi r^2 - \frac{1}{2}r^2 \sin a$$

Surface areas and volumes of solids

♦ Cylinder
Volume $= \pi r^2 \times h$

Curved surface area $= 2\pi rh$
Shortest length of AB around curved surface $= \sqrt{h^2 + (2\pi r)^2}$

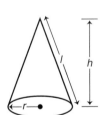

♦ Cone
Volume $\frac{1}{3}\pi r^2 \times h$
Curved surface area $= \pi rl$

♦ Sphere
Volume $\frac{4}{3}\pi r^3$
Surface area $= 4\pi r^2$

Similar solids and shapes

When applying a scale factor of enlargement of more than 1

♦ to an area, the larger area $=$ smaller area $\times$ (scale factor)^2. So $A = an^2$

♦ to a volume, the larger volume $=$ smaller volume $\times$ (scale factor)^3. So $V = vn^3$

Graphs

Graph of $r^2 = x^2 + y^2$

The equation of the circle with radius r and centre at the origin is

$$x^2 + y^2 = r^2$$

The equation of the circle with radius r and centre (a, b) is

$$(x - a)^2 + (y - b)^2 = r^2$$

Solution of equations

◆ To solve simultaneous equations graphically, draw both graphs on one set of axes. The coordinates of the intersection points are the solutions of the simultaneous equations.

To find roots of ...	Draw graphs ...	Roots are intersection points ...
$d = ax^2 + bx + c$	$y = ax^2 + bx + c$ $y = d$	
$x + d = ax^2 + bx + c$	$y = ax^2 + bx + c$ $y = x + d$	
$cx + d = ax^3 + bx^2$	$y = ax^3 + bx^2$ $y = cx + d$	
$r^2 = 2x^2$	$r^2 = x^2 + y^2$ $y = x$	

Shape and space

To solve $\sin x = -0.6$ for $-180° \leqslant x \leqslant 360°$

- ◆ Sketch the sine graph.
- ◆ Draw $y = -0.6$.
- ◆ Calculate x, in $\sin x = -0.6$. To the nearest whole number $x = -37°$.
- ◆ Use the sketch graph to find the other values:
  $x = -(180° - 37°) = -143°$, $x = -37°$, $x = 180° + 37° = 217°$, $x = 360° - 37° = 323°$.

Sketch graph of sin x

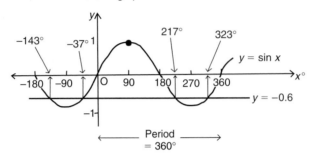

Period = 360°

To solve cosine and tangent equations

Use the same method as shown for $\sin x$, but using the cosine and tangent graphs.

Sine rule

$$\frac{a}{\sin A} = \frac{b}{\sin B} = \frac{c}{\sin C}$$

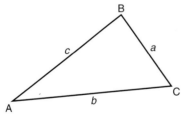

Cosine rule

$$a^2 = b^2 + c^2 - 2bc \cos A$$
$$b^2 = a^2 + c^2 - 2ac \cos B$$
$$c^2 = a^2 + b^2 - 2ab \cos C$$

3D coordinates

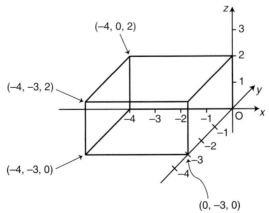

Histograms

The horizontal axis is a continuous number line.

The **area** of each bar represents the frequency.

The **frequency density** is given by

$$\text{frequency density (height of bar)} = \frac{\text{frequency}}{\text{width of group}}$$

Group time (sec)	Frequency	Width	Frequency density (frequency ÷ bar width)
15–20	12	5	$12 \div 5 = 2.4$
20–28	16	8	$16 \div 8 = 2$
28–36	8	8	$8 \div 8 = 1$
36–40	5	4	$5 \div 4 = 1.25$

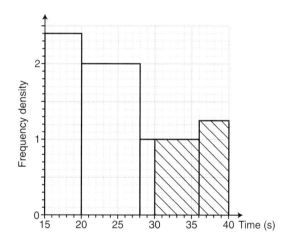

The percentage $> 30 = \dfrac{\left(\frac{3}{4} \times 8\right) + 5}{41} \times 100\% = 27\%$

Examination practice 2

Paper 2A (Non-calculator)

1 Work these out and, where appropriate, leave your answer as a fraction.

   a 3^{-2} **b** $64^{\frac{1}{3}}$

   c $2^{-3} \times 2^2$ **d** $5^{-4} \div 5^{-2}$

   e $(4^{-1})^2$

2 Simplify these.

   a $b^2 \times b^{-1}$ **b** $c^{-1} \div c^2$

   c $(b^2)^{-1}$ **d** $c^{\frac{1}{2}} \times c^{\frac{1}{2}}$

   e $a^{\frac{1}{4}} \div a^{\frac{1}{4}}$

3 The figure shows three semicircles.

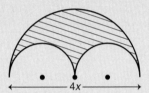

Find, in terms of x, in its simplest form:

   a the shaded area

   b the perimeter of the figure

4 The diagram shows a rubbish skip in the shape of a prism with cross-section ABCD.

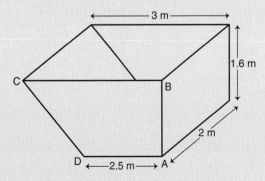

   a Work out its volume.

   b Find the volume of another skip of the same shape but half the width.

5 For each of these, find another angle x, for $0° \leqslant x \leqslant 360°$, that has the same trigonometric ratio.

   a $\sin 185°$

   b $\cos 185°$

   c $\tan 185°$

6 Express $\sqrt{75}$ in the form $a\sqrt{b}$.

7 Simplify these.

   a $3\sqrt{5} + 2\sqrt{5}$

   b $3\sqrt{5} \times 2\sqrt{5}$

   c $\dfrac{\sqrt{45} + \sqrt{18}}{\sqrt{5} + \sqrt{2}}$

8 Rationalise the denominator in $\dfrac{7}{\sqrt{5}}$.

9 *Answer this question on graph paper.*

   a Construct a table of values of y for $-4 \leqslant x \leqslant 2$ where $y = x^3 + x^2$.

   b Plot the graph of $y = x^3 + x^2$.

   c Use your graph to solve the equation $1 = x^3 + x^2$.

   d By drawing a suitable line on your graph solve the equation $2x = x^3 + x^2$.

10 Leon recorded the lengths, in minutes, of the films shown on television in one week. His results are shown in the histogram.

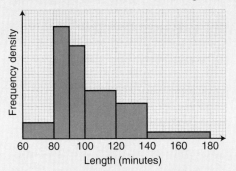

20 films had lengths from 60 minutes, up to, but not including, 80 minutes.

a Use the information in the histogram to complete the table.

Length (minutes)	Frequency
60 up to but not including 80	20
80 up to but not including 90	
90 up to but not including 100	
100 up to but not including 120	
120 up to but not including 140	
140 up to but not including 180	

Leon also recorded the lengths, in minutes, of all the films shown on television in the following week. His results are given in the table below.

Length (minutes)	Frequency	Frequency density
60 up to but not including 90	72	48
90 up to but not including 140	x	
140 up to but not including 180	y	

b Copy and complete the table giving your answers in terms of x and y.

LONDON

11 a Explain why $\cos 60° = 0.5$.

b Use the cosine rule to work out the length YZ.

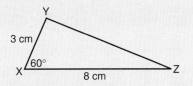

12 Solve these equations.

a $27^{\frac{1}{x}} = 3$

b $64^{\frac{1}{3}} = 2^x$

c $216^x = \dfrac{1}{6}$

13 The table shows the volume $V\,\text{cm}^3$ of pyramids of the same shape for different heights $h\,\text{cm}$.

V	0.8	6.4	21.6	51.2
h	1	2	3	4

a From this data, suggest a possible formula for V as a function of h.

b From your formula, express h as a function of V.

MEG

Paper 2B (Calculator)

Give all your answers correct to 3 significant figures.

1 Calculate the value of these.

   a 1.03^{-5} **b** $16.7^{\frac{1}{5}}$ **c** $2^{-\frac{3}{2}}$

2 Calculate the shaded area of these figures.

   a

   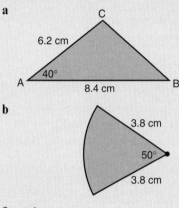

   b

   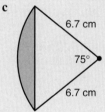

   c

   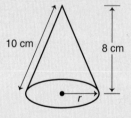

3 The figure shows a solid cone of height 8 cm and slant height 10 cm.

   Calculate

   a the base radius r

   b the volume

   c the total surface area

4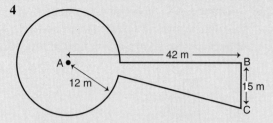

   The diagram shows a plan of a water-hazard on a new golf course. The hazard is bounded by the arc of a circle centre A and part of a right-angled triangle ABC. The radius of the circle is 12 metres, AB = 42 m, BC = 15 m. Calculate the surface area of the water.

   MEI

5 Solve these equations, correct to 3 significant figures, for $-180° \leqslant x \leqslant 360°$.

   a $\sin x = 0.3579$

   b $\cos x = 0.3579$

   c $\tan x = 0.3579$

6 The diagram shows part of the roof of a new out-of-town superstore. The point X is vertically above A, and ABCD is a horizontal rectangle in which CD = 5.6 m, BC = 6.4 m. The line XB is inclined at 70° to the horizontal. Calculate the angle that the ridge XC makes with the horizontal.

   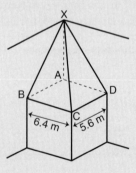

   MEG

7 The diagram shows a funnel and a cylinder for collecting rain. The radius of the cylinder and the radius of the top of the funnel are both 8 cm, while the radius of the lower end of the funnel is 0.25 cm.

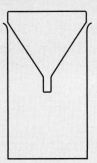

(i) During a cloud burst 4 cm of rain fell in 10 minutes. Calculate, to 3 significant figures,
   (a) the volume of water which is collected in the cylinder in this time
   (b) the speed in cm/s at which the water emerged from the lower end of the funnel, assuming this to be constant for these 10 minutes.

(ii) In order that small amounts of rain can be measured more accurately, the rain collected can be poured into a second cylinder which has a radius of 3 cm.

In a certain period the depth of rain collected in the large cylinder was estimated to be 0.6 cm, and when this water was poured into the small cylinder the depth was 5.1 cm. Assuming the second depth to be accurate, calculate how much rain (in centimetres) fell in this period, and calculate the percentage error in the first reading.

MEI

8 A floating toy is in the shape of a circular pyramid of height 20 cm. The top section protruding above the water is of height 4 cm and volume 50 cm^3.

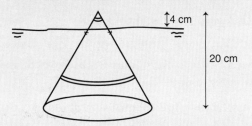

Find the volume of the cone beneath the water level.

9 In a survey, 1000 people were asked to guess the weight of a turkey.

Weight (kg)	Frequency, f
5–10	80
10–20	360
20–30	380
30–40	120
40–45	60

a Calculate the frequency densities for each group and construct a histogram to display the results.

b From your histogram, estimate the probability that a member of the sample chosen at random had guessed a weight of between 14 kg and 24 kg.

c Calculate the mean guess per person.

10 In triangle ABC, AC = 8.9 cm, BC = 12.4 cm and ∠BAC = 120°. Calculate ∠ABC.

11 You have been given the coordinates of three points, O(0, 0, 0), A(0, 3, 2) and B(−5, 3, 2). Calculate these.

   a OA   **b** OB   **c** ∠BOA

Financial arithmetic

Wages and salaries

A **wage** is calculated at a certain rate for the number of hours per week and is usually paid weekly. Overtime – hours worked over and above the normal hours each week – is usually paid at a higher rate.

A **salary** is a fixed annual sum of money, usually paid each month.

(*Note*: 'per annum' means 'per year', and is often shortened to 'p.a.'.)

Example 1

The manager of a shoe shop earns a salary of £17 000 p.a.; an assistant, Brian, earns an hourly rate of £5.20 per hour for a 40-hour week, with overtime paid at 'time and a half'.

a Calculate Brian's pay for a 50-hour week.

Brian's wage = pay for normal time + pay for overtime
$$= 40 \times £5.20 + 10 \times (1.5 \times £5.20)$$
$$= £208 + £78$$
$$= £286$$

b Calculate the manager's pay per week.

Manager's weekly pay $= £17 000 \div 52$
$$= £326.92$$

c How many hours per week would Brian have to work to earn as much as the manager?

Normal time pay $= £208$
Overtime needed $= £326.92 - £208$
$$= £118.92$$
Overtime rate $= 1.5 \times £5.20 = £7.80$
Overtime hours $= £118.92 \div £7.80$
$$= 15.25$$

Brian must work a total of $55\frac{1}{4}$ hours to earn as much as his manager.

Income tax and VAT

All governments collect money from their citizens and businesses through **taxation** to pay for public services: health, transport, policing, defence, etc.

Income tax is paid on the money earnt (*direct* taxation), and **value added tax** (**VAT**) is paid on the money spent (*indirect* taxation). There are many other taxes too, such as capital gains tax, corporation tax and inheritance tax. *Everyone* pays tax!

The philosophy of some governments is that wealthy people, who earn and spend more, should pay higher taxes than poorer people. Each year the Treasury predicts and calculates next year's expenditure and then adjusts the taxation rates so that enough money is collected to pay for everything.

Calculating income tax

A percentage of income is taken by the government as income tax. The higher the income, the higher the percentage rate!

Key Points

♦ **Gross income** = total income before tax and other deductions.

♦ **Personal allowance** = the earnings that are 'tax-free' (£4535 in April 2001).

♦ **Taxable income** = the earnings that are taxed
= total income − personal allowance.

♦ **Net income** = income that remains after tax and other deductions have been taken out.

Tax rates in the UK vary according to an individual's earnings, as shown in this table and graph, for the tax year 2001/2002.

Tax	Rates	Band of taxable income
Starting rate	10%	£0–£1880 per annum
Basic rate	22%	£1881–£29 400 per annum
Higher rate	40%	Over £29 400 per annum

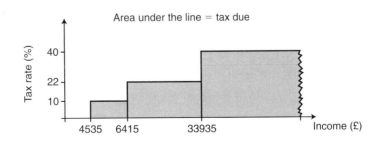

Area under the line = tax due

Example 2

Mrs Singh earns a gross salary of £37 500 p.a.

a Use the year 2001 tax rates to calculate her annual income tax bill.

b What percentage of her gross salary is deducted as tax?

Her income tax is deducted from her salary evenly each month.

c Calculate her net monthly pay, after deduction of income tax.

Note: Mrs Singh will also have to pay National Insurance contributions which will be a further deduction from her gross pay. NI is ignored in this example.

a Deduct personal allowance from gross salary to calculate the taxable income:

taxable income = £37 500 − £4535 = £32 965

Calculate the tax in each income band as shown in this table.

Starting rate: 10%	Basic rate: 22%	Higher rate: 40%
£1880	£29 400 − £1880 = £27 520	£32 965 − £29 400 = £3565
Tax = 10% of £1880	Tax = 22% of £27 520	Tax = 40% of £3565
$= \frac{10}{100} \times 1880 = £188$	$= \frac{22}{100} \times 27\,520 = £6054.40$	$= \frac{40}{100} \times 3565 = £1426$

Total annual tax = £188 + £6054.40 + £1426 = £7668.40

b $\frac{7668.40}{37\,500} \times 100\% = 20.4\%$

20.4% of her gross salary is deducted in income tax.

c Net annual salary $\quad = £37\,500 − £7668.40 = £29\,831.60$

$\therefore \quad$ Net monthly salary $= £29\,831.60 \div 12 = £2485.97$

Calculating value added tax (VAT)

VAT is included in the price that is paid for an article. In 2001, the standard rate of VAT on most products was $17\frac{1}{2}\%$, so the shopkeeper had to add $17\frac{1}{2}\%$ onto the original price to arrive at the selling price.

Some products like fruit, are zero-rated. Others are exempt and some, like fuel are at a lower rate.

Key Points

◆ To *add* $17\frac{1}{2}\%$ VAT to the original price, *multiply* by 1.175.

◆ To *subtract* $17\frac{1}{2}\%$ VAT from the selling price, *divide* by 1.175.

Example 3

Belinda wants to buy a bicycle and finds a good deal on the Internet. At bike4sale.com, the price is £98 + VAT. Calculate the total price.

Total cost = £98 × 1.175 = £115.15

Example 4

Postman Pat can claim back VAT on business expenses. At cycleshop.com, the price of a bicycle is £115 (including VAT). Calculate the price *excluding* VAT.

£115 ÷ 1.175 = £97.87

Exercise 44

1 Jim works a 40-hour week at £5.65 per hour. Calculate his weekly and annual gross pay.

2 Nina works a 35-hour week at £6.50 per hour. Calculate her weekly and annual gross pay.

3 Pam earns a gross salary of £15 800 p.a. On average, she works 50 hours per week. Calculate her hourly rate of pay.

4 Carl receives a gross salary of £14 650 p.a. Calculate his hourly rate of pay assuming that he works an average of 48 hours each week.

For Questions 5–8, refer to page 183 for information on tax rates and tax bands to calculate the annual income tax bill and net monthly pay on these gross salaries.

5 £20 000 p.a. **6** £27 000 p.a. **7** £40 000 p.a. **8** £57 000 p.a.

For Questions 9–12, use $17\frac{1}{2}\%$ as the rate of VAT.

9 A discount warehouse lists its prices 'excluding VAT'. Calculate the full prices of these.

  a An ink-jet printer at £94.72

  b Two pairs of designer jeans at £26 each

  c Six bottles of wine at £4.95 each

10 A mail-order shopping catalogue lists its prices 'excluding VAT'. Calculate the full prices of these.

  a A fountain pen at £15

  b Three wallets at £24.50 each

  c Eight boxes of Christmas cards at £2.99 each

11 A building contractor can put the following purchases down as business expenses and thus reclaim the VAT (which is included in the prices). Calculate his saving on each of these orders.

  a One hammer drill at £120   **b** Four boxes of nails at £3.50 each

  c Five double-glazed windows at £345 each

12 How much VAT is included in the price of these?

  a One litre of engine oil at £5.49   **b** 45 litres of petrol at 82.4 pence per litre

  c Four new tyres at £63.75 each

Exercise 44★

For Questions 1–6, use $17\frac{1}{2}\%$ as the VAT rate and the tax rates and tax bands given on page 183.

1 A radio presenter has signed a £100 000 p.a. contract.

   a Calculate the net salary per annum, after tax has been deducted.

   b Calculate the net pay per week.

   c What percentage of the gross salary is paid in income tax?

2 It is known that a professional footballer is 'on £4000 per week'.

   a Calculate his gross pay per annum.

   b Calculate the net salary per week, after tax has been deducted.

   c What percentage of the gross salary is paid in income tax?

3 A senior teacher earns a gross salary of £36 000 p.a.

   a Calculate her annual income tax bill and her monthly 'take-home pay'.

   She spends all her money and pays VAT on everything she buys.

   b Calculate the proportion of her gross earnings that is deducted as tax.

4 An office supervisor earns a monthly gross salary of £2100.

   a Calculate her monthly income tax bill and her annual net pay.

   She spends all her money and pays VAT on everything she buys.

   b Calculate the proportion of her gross earnings that is deducted as tax.

5 A person has 15% of his gross salary deducted in income tax. How much does he earn?

6 A person has 20% of her gross salary deducted in income tax. How much does she earn?

Use this information in Questions 7 and 8.

In September 2000, there were widespread protests, led by the truck drivers and farmers, against the British Government about the high price of petrol. A special 'fuel tax' is added to the untaxed price of a litre of petrol before VAT is added to give the 'price at the pumps'. In September 2000, the 'fuel tax' was 48.82p per litre.

7 **a** Show how, for a litre of petrol, an 'untaxed price' of 20p gives a pump price of 80.9p.

   For this price calculate the total tax as a percentage of the

   b pump price   **c** untaxed price.

8 Assume that the 'pump price' is 85p per litre.

   a Calculate the 'untaxed price'.

   b Calculate a new figure for fuel tax which would result in a 10% reduction of this 'pump price'.

Savings, credit and loans

Banks and building societies make their profit by buying and selling money. They 'buy it' from savers and pay them interest; they 'sell it' to borrowers and charge them a higher interest. The rates that banks advertise for savers and borrowers are, in fact, the prices that the bank or the customer pays for borrowing money. The banks will make their prices look as competitive and attractive as possible, so it is important to read the small print. Rates can be misleading!

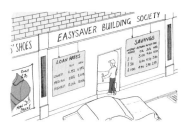

Savings accounts

Banks pay compound interest, quoted at an annual rate (with or without tax deducted).

Example 5

Julia places £500 in a savings account that pays a gross interest rate of 6%.

a How much will Julia have in her account after four years?

To add 6%, multiply by 1.06

$\therefore$ savings $= 500 \times (1.06)^4 = £631.24$

b Tax is deducted from the *interest* at 22% to give a net interest rate. Calculate the net interest rate.

To deduct 22% from the interest, calculate how much is kept.

$\therefore$ 78% of 6% $= 0.78 \times 6\% = 4.68\%$

$\therefore$ net interest rate is 4.68%

c How much will Julia have in her account after four years at the net rate?

To calculate at a rate of 4.68%, multiply by 1.0468 four times (once for each year).

$\therefore$ savings $= £500 \times (1.0468)^4 = £600.38$

Credit cards

Credit cards enable you to buy goods and then pay for them later. You receive a 'statement of your account' at the end of each month. You can pay the account in full without charge. If you do not pay the full amount, interest is added at a monthly rate to the amount that is not paid off.

Example 6

Rita's credit card account is £380 and the monthly interest charge is 1.5%. She only pays off £50.

a Calculate the interest on the balance.

Balance $= £380 - £50 = £330$

1.5% of £330 $= 0.015 \times £330 = £4.95$

b Calculate the interest charge as an annual rate.

To add 1.5%, multiply by 1.015.

For 12 months, multiply by $(1.015)^{12} = 1.1956$

$\therefore$ interest rate is 19.56% (not $12 \times 1.5\% = 18\%$)

Credit plans and loans

A credit plan is a loan arranged by a shop or business to enable you to buy their goods. The interest on the loan is calculated using simple interest and then the monthly repayments are calculated to pay off the lump sum and interest over a fixed time period. However, the actual interest rate (APR) is much higher than the published rate because you do not borrow all the money for the whole time period. You will also be charged an 'arrangement fee' on top of the repayments.

Example 7

John is buying a car for £10 000. He pays a 20% deposit and takes out a credit plan to borrow the remainder over three years at 8.5% p.a. The arrangement fee is £80.

a Calculate the interest on the loan and the monthly repayments.

Deposit = 20% of £10 000 = £2000

∴ Loan = £10 000 − £2000 = £8000

Interest = 3 × 8.5% of £8000
= 3 × 0.085 × £8000 = £2040

Total to repay = £8000 + £2040 = £10 040

Monthly repayments = £10 040 ÷ 36 = £278.89

b Calculate the total cost of the car.

Total cost = £2000 + £10 040 + £80 = £12 120

c Ben negotiates a 5% discount off the list price by offering to pay the full price 'up-front'. What is the real extra cost of the credit plan?

Interest = £2040, fee = £80, discount = 5% of £10 000 = £500

∴ total cost of credit = £2040 + £80 + £500 = £2620

Key Points

In these two formulae, P is the principal sum, R is the rate of interest, n is the number of years and A is the amount earned after n years.

Compound interest $\quad A = P\left(1 + \dfrac{R}{100}\right)^{n}$ $\qquad$ **Simple interest** $\quad A = P\left(1 + \dfrac{Rn}{100}\right)$

Exercise 45

1 Calculate the interest in an account when interest is earned on these amounts.

   a £250 saved for one year at 8% p.a.

   b £1240 saved for four years at 10% p.a.

2 Calculate the final amount in an account when interest is earned on these amounts.

   a £600 saved for one year at 7.5% p.a.

   b £945 saved for three years at 12% p.a.

For Questions 3–8, calculate the monthly rates as annual rates. Give your answers correct to 2 decimal places.

3 1%	**4** 3%	**5** 2%
6 1.6%	**7** 2.5%	**8** 2.2%

For Questions 9–14, Calculate the annual rates as monthly rates. Give your answers correct to 2 decimal places.

9 15%	**10** 12%	**11** 20%
12 24%	**13** 30%	**14** 36%

15 Davina has £638 owing on her credit account. The charge on uncleared balances is 1.7% per month. She pays off £65. How much interest will be added to the account?

16 Fojir has £258.95 owing on his credit account and forgets to make a payment at the end of the month. £3.80 interest is added to his account. Calculate the interest charge as

   a a monthly rate

   b an annual rate

17 Damon is taking out a credit plan to buy a new car, which costs £12 400. He pays a deposit of 30% and decides to pay the rest over 36 months. The charge on the loan is calculated as simple interest at 7.75% p.a. and there is a fee of £65.

   a Calculate the monthly repayment.

   b Calculate the total cost of the car.

   c What is the true cost of the credit if the dealer offers a 10% discount for 'payment up-front'.

18 A television set is advertised at £799. Trevor decides to pay a 20% deposit and the remainder in 24 monthly payments. There is a fee of £20 for taking out a credit plan and the interest rate is 7% p.a..

   a Calculate the monthly repayment.

   b What is the total cost of the television set?

   c What is the true cost of Trevor's credit if Ellen bought the same television for £750?

Inflation and exchange rates

When prices rise, workers demand higher wages so that they can pay the higher prices. Of course, higher wages increase the cost of manufacturing goods and so that pushes prices up, which pushes wages up, ...

The **inflation rate** is the rate at which prices are rising. It is usually given as an annual rate, e.g. 4.3% p.a.

Low inflation generally means that a country has a strong economy. If a country has a strong economy, the international money dealers will buy that country's currency and that will push the exchange rate up.

The **exchange rate** is the price of buying and selling foreign currencies, e.g. £1 = $1.483, £1 = €1.74, £1 = 180 Japan yen.

When the exchange rate for the pound goes up, the pound will buy more dollars, euros or yen. A higher exchange rate will make exports more expensive and imports cheaper. This weakens the economy because manufacturers have to cut their profit margins and drop the prices of their exported goods. So the exchange rate falls back.

Politicians and economists argue and debate the cause and effect of these issues endlessly!

Exercise 45★

1 Calculate the interest gained on these building society tax-free savings accounts.
   a £200 saved for six months at 0.4% per month.
   b £75 saved for one year at 0.5% per month.

2 Calculate the interest gained on these savings accounts.
   a £150 saved for nine months at 0.2% per month.
   b £60 saved for one year at 0.35% per month.

3 £200 is saved for three years at 6.4% gross p.a. The interest is taxed at 22%.
   a Calculate the interest gained on this savings account.
   b Calculate the net interest rate.
   c Calculate how much is in the account *after* tax has been deducted each year.

4 Emilios saves £450 for two years in an account paying 5.9% gross interest p.a. The interest is taxed at 22%.
   a How much interest does he earn before tax is deducted?
   b Calculate the net interest rate.
   c Calculate how much is in the account *after* tax has been deducted each year.

5 Shilan invests in a savings account at 5.75% gross p.a. The rate of inflation is 4.7%. Comment on the 'buying power' of his savings in a year's time.

6 If inflation is 8%, calculate the minimum rate of gross interest that will make savings grow faster than prices.

7 When the exchange rate between Britain and America is £1 = $1.60, a British export Jaguar costs $40 000. Calculate the equivalent price in Britain.
Calculate its cost in America if the exchange rate moves to

   a £1 = $1.45   **b** £1 = $1.75

8 When the exchange rate between Germany and Britain was DM2.8 = £1, a new Mercedes cost £28 000 in Britain. Calculate the equivalent price in Germany.
What would you expect the same car to cost when

   a the exchange rate is DM3.2 = £1?   **b** the exchange rate is DM2.2 = £1?

9 Read this quotation for a new car.

   a Calculate the rate of simple interest used to obtain the 'total charge for credit'.

   b Calculate the monthly payments if the deposit had been £2000.

TraCar 1.25 LX 3-door	
On-the-road price	£10 050.00
Deposit	£3015.00
Balance	£7035.00
Total charge for credit*	£1811.08
Total amount payable	£11 861.09
36 monthly payments	£243.78
APR	16.9%
*Includes a finance facility fee of £70 payment with the first monthly payment.	

10 Read this quotation for a new computer.

   a Calculate the rate of simple interest used to obtain the 'total charge for credit'.

   b Calculate the monthly payments if the deposit had been £1100.

Bell Q853z Computer	
Installed price	£3650.00
Deposit	£750.00
Balance	£2900.00
Total charge for credit*	£537.50
Total amount payable	£4187.50
24 monthly payments	£141.98
APR	17.2%
*Includes a finance facility fee of £30 payable with the first monthly payment.	

Mortgages

A mortgage is a loan taken out from a bank or building society to purchase a house. The bank 'secures' the loan by keeping the deeds to the house until all the money is paid back. The bank may 'repossess' the house if you are unable to keep up the loan repayments. A typical mortgage loan might be for taken over 25 years. There are two main types of mortgages: endowment mortgages and repayment mortgages.

- With an **endowment mortgage**, you pay off the interest only on the loan, month by month, and separately make regular investments which will pay off the capital sum at the end of the loan period.

- With a **repayment mortgage** you pay monthly instalments which pay the interest and gradually reduce the capital sum. This is called a repayment mortgage.

Example 8

Mr and Mrs Trueman are buying a house for £60 000. They pay a deposit of £10 000 and take out a repayment mortgage of £50 000 over 25 years. The interest rate is 10% p.a. and the repayments are calculated annually.

a Show, on a spreadsheet, that 25 annual payments of £5508.40 are required to pay off the loan and calculate the monthly payments.

Set up the spreadsheet like this.

	A	B	C	D	E	F
1	Interest rate	Mult. factor	Annual payment	Capital	Plus interest	Minus payment
2	10%	1.10	5508.40	50000	=D2*B2	=E2-C2
3		=B2	=C2	=F2	=D3*B3	=E3-C3
4		=B3	=C3	=F3	=D4*B4	=E4-C4
⋮	Scroll down columns B, C, D, E and F					
26		=B3	=C3	=F25	=D26*B26	=E26-C26

Cell F26 contains 0.354 984, which is close to zero.
Monthly payment = £5508.40 ÷ 12 = £459.03

b Calculate the total cost of buying the house.

Total cost = £10 000 + (25 × £5508.40) = £147 710

c If house prices rise at an average rate of 5% p.a., calculate an estimate of the house value at the end of the mortgage.

House value after 25 years = £60 000 × 1.05^{25} = £203 000 (to 3 s.f.)
So, although the loan is expensive, it is a good investment!

d Use your spreadsheet to show how much of the capital sum is paid off in the first ten years.

Cell D12 contains £41 897.41.

∴   Capital paid off = £50 000 − £41 897.41 = £8102.59

Activity 27

Use the spreadsheet from Example 8 to investigate how changes in the interest rate affect the annual repayments.

For example, change cells A2 to 9%, B2 to 1.09 and then use the method of 'trial and improvement' in cell C2 to find the value that makes cell F26 close to 0.

Activity 28

In Example 8 and Activity 27 the remaining capital and the amount of interest was calculated on an *annual* basis, yet the loan is repaid with *monthly* payments. Monthly calculations rather than annual calculations make a significant difference.

Amend the spreadsheet from Example 8 to show that if the remaining capital and the amount of interest are calculated *monthly* then, at 10% p.a., the monthly repayments would be reduced from £459.03 to £439.25. (A saving of £6015 over 25 years!)
You will need to insert a column for the monthly interest rate (=1.10^(1/12)) and 300 rows.

Investigate, using other rates of interest.

Activity 29

Use these mortgage repayment formulae to *calculate* the repayments for your examples from Activities 27 and 28.

Interest rate p.a. $= r\%$
Amount borrowed $= £P$
Number of years $= n$
Annual repayment $= £A$
Monthly repayment $= £M$

Interest calculated annually	Interest calculated monthly
$R = 1 + \dfrac{r}{100}$	$R = \sqrt[12]{1 + \dfrac{r}{100}}$
$A = \dfrac{PR^n(R-1)}{(R^n-1)}$ $M = \dfrac{A}{12}$	$M = \dfrac{PR^{12n}(R-1)}{(R^{12n}-1)}$

Exercise 46 (Revision)

1   Calculate the annual gross salary of a part-time computer technician working an 18-hour week at £15.50 per hour.

2   Using $17\frac{1}{2}\%$ as the rate of VAT, calculate the VAT on these items.
   a   A new tyre advertised at £35.60 + VAT
   b   A new bicycle frame advertised at £65 incl. VAT

3   Use the tax rates and tax bands on page 183 to calculate the annual tax bill for
   a   a mechanic earning £24 500 p.a.   b   a doctor earning £53 000 p.a.

4 Calculate the interest earned on £500, invested for four years at 5.5% p.a.

5 Calculate 1.1% per month as an annual rate.

6 A computer is advertised at £900. Lesley decides to pay a 20% deposit and the remainder in 24 monthly payments. There is no 'setting-up fee'. Simple interest is added to the loan at the rate of 9% p.a. before the monthly payments are calculated.

   a Calculate the monthly payments.　　**b** Calculate the total cost of the computer.

Exercise 46★ (Revision)

1 Calculate the interest gained on an investment of £24 000 at 0.85% per month, over three years.

2 **a** Calculate 10% p.a. as a monthly rate, correct to 3 decimal places.

   b How many months would it take an investment to double at this interest rate?

3 A builder pays £5000 in income tax for the year 2000–2001. Use the tax rates given on page 183 to calculate his gross earnings.

4 Use the formula

$$A = \frac{PR^n(R-1)}{(R^n-1)}$$

where $r\%$ = interest rate p.a., $R = 1 + \dfrac{r}{100}$, £P = amount borrowed, n = number of years, and £A = annual repayment, to calculate the *monthly* repayment on a mortgage loan of £110 000 at 8% p.a. over 20 years.

5 Read this finance quotation for an alarm system.

FINANCE QUOTATION	
Spectra Alarm System	
Installation price:	£3995
Deposit:	£1000
Balance:	£2995
Total charge for credit: (including a finance facility fee of £50 payable with the first monthly payment)	£611.58
Total amount payable:	£4606.58
36 monthly payments:	£98.79
APR:	12.1%

   a Calculate the rate of simple interest used to obtain the 'total charge for credit'.

   b Use the same formula to calculate the monthly payments if the deposit had been £1500, rather than £1000.

Algebra 3

Solving quadratic equations

Quadratic equations can be written as $ax^2 + bx + c = 0$ where a, b and c are constants.

Solving quadratic equations by factorising

Quadratic equations with $a = 1$ can often be solved by factorizing.

Remember

There are three types of quadratic equations with $a = 1$.

- If $b = 0$ $x^2 - c = 0$
  - $\Rightarrow$ $x^2 = c$
  -               $x = \pm\sqrt{c}$

- If $c = 0$ $x^2 + bx = 0$
  - $\Rightarrow$ $x(x + b) = 0$
  -            $x = 0$ or $x = -b$

- If $b \neq 0$ and $c \neq 0$ $x^2 + bx + c = 0$
  - $\Rightarrow$ $(x + p)(x + q) = 0$
  -                    $x = -p$ or $x = -q$

where $p \times q = c$ and $p + q = b$.

If c is positive then p and q have the same sign as b.
If c is negative then p and q have opposite signs to each other.

Example 1

Solve these quadratic equations

a $x^2 - 81 = 0$
      $x^2 = 81$
        $x = -9$ or $x = 9$

b $x^2 - 7x = 0$
     $x(x - 7) = 0$
         $x = 0$ or $x = 7$

c $x^2 - 10x + 21 = 0$
   $(x - 7)(x - 3) = 0$
         $x = 7$ or $x = 3$

(*Note*: there are *two* solutions)

Exercise 47

Solve these equations by factorising.

1 $x^2 + 7x + 10 = 0$ **2** $x^2 + 7x + 12 = 0$ **3** $x^2 - 2x - 15 = 0$

4 $x^2 - 2x - 8 = 0$ **5** $x^2 - 6x + 9 = 0$ **6** $x^2 - 4x + 4 = 0$

7 $x^2 + 4x - 12 = 0$ **8** $x^2 + 5x - 24 = 0$ **9** $x^2 - 4x = 0$

10 $x^2 - 3x = 0$ **11** $x^2 - 36 = 0$ **12** $x^2 - 49 = 0$

Exercise 47★

Solve these equations by factorising.

1 $x^2 + 15x + 56 = 0$ **2** $x^2 + 15x + 54 = 0$ **3** $x^2 - 4x - 45 = 0$

4 $x^2 + 2x - 63 = 0$ **5** $x^2 - 14x + 49 = 0$ **6** $x^2 - 10x + 25 = 0$

7 $x^2 - 3x - 40 = 0$ **8** $x^2 + 3x - 180 = 0$ **9** $x^2 + 17x = 0$

10 $x^2 + 19x = 0$ **11** $x^2 - 121 = 0$ **12** $x^2 - 169 = 0$

More difficult quadratic equations

When $a \neq 1$, factorisation may be harder. *Always* take out any number factors first.

Example 2

Solve $12x^2 - 24x - 96 = 0$.

Take out the number factor, in this case 12. The resulting expression is then easier to factorise.

$$12x^2 - 24x - 96 = 0$$
$$12(x^2 - 2x - 8) = 0$$
$$12(x + 2)(x - 4) = 0$$
$$x = -2 \text{ or } x = 4$$

If there is no simple number factor, then the factorisation is harder.

Example 3

Solve $3x^2 - 13x - 10 = 0$.
$$3x^2 - 13x - 10 = 0$$
$$(3x + 2)(x - 5) = 0$$
$$x = -\frac{2}{3} \text{ or } x = 5$$

Exercise 48

Solve these equations by factorising.

1 $2x^2 - 10x + 12 = 0$ **2** $2x^2 + 14x + 20 = 0$ **3** $2x^2 - 5x + 2 = 0$

4 $2x^2 - 7x + 6 = 0$ **5** $2x^2 + 5x + 3 = 0$ **6** $2x^2 + 7x + 3 = 0$

7 $3x^2 + 9x + 6 = 0$ **8** $3x^2 + 12x - 15 = 0$ **9** $2x^2 - 18 = 0$

10 $2x^2 - 50 = 0$ **11** $3x^2 - 6x = 0$ **12** $3x^2 + 9x = 0$

13 $3x^2 + 7x + 2 = 0$ **14** $3x^2 + 14x + 8 = 0$ **15** $3x^2 - 5x - 2 = 0$

16 $3x^2 - 11x + 6 = 0$ **17** $4x^2 - 4x - 24 = 0$ **18** $4x^2 + 16x - 20 = 0$

19 $3x^2 + 8x + 4 = 0$ **20** $3x^2 + 10x - 8 = 0$ **21** $4x^2 + 13x + 3 = 0$

22 $4x^2 - 3x - 10 = 0$ **23** $6x^2 - 7x - 3 = 0$ **24** $6x^2 - 5x + 1 = 0$

25 $8x^2 + 6x + 1 = 0$ **26** $4x^2 + 3x - 1 = 0$ **27** $5x^2 - 27x + 10 = 0$

28 $4x^2 + 8x - 21 = 0$ **29** $10x^2 - 23x + 12 = 0$ **30** $10x^2 + 11x - 35 = 0$

Exercise 48★

Solve these equations by factorising.

1 $2x^2 - 6x + 4 = 0$ **2** $2x^2 + 16x + 30 = 0$ **3** $2x^2 - 7x + 6 = 0$

4 $2x^2 + 7x - 15 = 0$ **5** $3x^2 + 31x + 36 = 0$ **6** $3x^2 + 30x + 63 = 0$

7 $3x^2 = 17x + 28$ **8** $2x^2 = x + 15$ **9** $3x^2 - 48 = 0$

10 $4x^2 - 36 = 0$ **11** $7x^2 - 21x = 0$ **12** $8x^2 - 24x = 0$

13 $4x^2 + 40x + 100 = 0$ **14** $4x^2 - 24x + 32 = 0$ **15** $4x^2 = 29x - 7$

16 $4x^2 = 23x - 15$ **17** $x(6x - 13) = -6$ **18** $3x(2x - 9) = -30$

19 $9x^2 + 25 = 30x$ **20** $6x^2 + 2 = 7x$ **21** $x^2 + \dfrac{3x}{4} + \dfrac{1}{8} = 0$

22 $x^2 - 0.1x - 0.3 = 0$ **23** $4x^2 - \dfrac{5x}{3} - 1 = 0$ **24** $x^2 - 1.5x - 1 = 0$

25 $\dfrac{3x^2}{4} + \dfrac{9x}{2} + 6 = 0$ **26** $\dfrac{1}{x} - \dfrac{1}{x+1} = \dfrac{1}{x+4}$ **27** $x^3 - 4x^2 - 21x = 0$

28 $4x^4 - 5x^2 + 1 = 0$

Solving quadratic equations by completing the square

Completing the square means writing expressions like $x^2 + 10x$ as $(x + 5)^2 - 25$.

This can be checked by multiplying out the brackets:

$(x + 5)^2 - 25 = x^2 + 10x + 25 - 25 = x^2 + 10x$

Completing the square is done as follows:

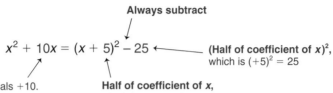

Always subtract

$x^2 + 10x = (x + 5)^2 - 25 \longleftarrow$ (Half of coefficient of x)^2, which is $(+5)^2 = 25$

Coefficient of x, equals $+10$.
The coefficient is the number in front of x

Half of coefficient of x, which is $+10 \div 2 = +5$

Example 4

Complete the square for these expressions.

a $x^2 + 12x = (x + 6)^2 - 36 \longleftarrow$ (Half of coefficient of x)$^2 = 6^2 = 36$

Coefficient of x equals 12

Half of coefficient of x equals 6

b $x^2 + 5x = \left(x + \frac{5}{2}\right)^2 - \frac{25}{4} \longleftarrow$ (Half of coefficient of x)$^2 = \left(\frac{5}{2}\right)^2 = \frac{25}{4}$

Coefficient of x equals 5

Half of coefficient of x equals $\frac{5}{2}$

c $x^2 - 6x = (x - 3)^2 - 9 \longleftarrow$ (Half of coefficient of x)$^2 = (-3)^2 = 9$

Coefficient of x equals -6

Half of coefficient of x equals -3

d $x^2 - 6x - 4 = (x - 3)^2 - 9 - 4 = (x - 3)^2 - 13$

Treat the $x^2 - 6x$ as in Example 4c, then incorporate the -4.

e $4 + 6x - x^2 = -[x^2 - 6x - 4] = -[(x - 3)^2 - 13] = 13 - (x - 3)^2$

Take out a factor -1 and then treat as in Example 4d.

Completing the square gives a neat way to solve quadratic equations. This should only be done when no simple factors can be found.

Example 5

Solve $x^2 - 12x - 40 = 0$ by completing the square.

$$x^2 - 12x - 40 = 0$$
$$\therefore \quad (x - 6)^2 - 36 - 40 = 0 \quad \text{(Completing the square)}$$
$$(x - 6)^2 = 76$$

Square root both sides to give

$$x - 6 = \sqrt{76} \qquad \text{or} \quad x - 6 = -\sqrt{76}$$
$$x = 6 + \sqrt{76} \quad \text{or} \qquad x = 6 - \sqrt{76}$$
$$x = 14.7 \qquad \text{or} \qquad x = -2.72 \text{ to 3 s.f.}$$

Example 6

Solve $20 - 8x - 2x^2 = 0$ by completing the square.

$$20 - 8x - 2x^2 = 0$$
$$\therefore \quad x^2 + 4x - 10 = 0 \quad \text{(Dividing both sides by } -2\text{)}$$
$$(x + 2)^2 - 4 - 10 = 0 \quad \text{(Completing the square)}$$
$$(x + 2)^2 = 14$$
$$x + 2 = \sqrt{14} \quad \text{or} \quad x + 2 = -\sqrt{14}$$
$$x = 1.74 \quad \text{or} \qquad x = -5.74 \quad \text{(to 3 s.f.)}$$

Exercise 49

Solve these equations by completing the square.

Give your answers correct to 3 significant figures.

1 $x^2 + 2x - 5 = 0$ **2** $x^2 + 6x - 8 = 0$ **3** $x^2 - 2x - 6 = 0$

4 $x^2 - 6x - 15 = 0$ **5** $x^2 + 4x = 8$ **6** $x^2 + 2x = 7$

7 $x^2 - 10x + 15 = 0$ **8** $x^2 + 12x + 34 = 0$ **9** $x^2 + 14x - 3 = 0$

10 $x^2 + 16x - 7 = 0$ **11** $x^2 - 20x - 33 = 0$ **12** $x^2 - 14x + 47 = 0$

13 $x^2 - 4x - 20 = 0$ **14** $x^2 - 8x - 10 = 0$ **15** $x^2 - 10x = 120$

16 $x^2 - 14x = 41$ **17** $x^2 + 3x - 2 = 0$ **18** $x^2 + x - 8 = 0$

19 $x^2 - 5x - 3 = 0$ **20** $x^2 - 7x + 9 = 0$

Exercise 49★

Solve these equations by completing the square.

Give your answers correct to 3 significant figures.

1 $x^2 - 6x + 1 = 0$ **2** $x^2 - 4x + 1 = 0$ **3** $x^2 - 16x + 3 = 0$

4 $x^2 - 12x - 25 = 0$ **5** $x^2 + 6x - 12 = 0$ **6** $x^2 + 4x + 2 = 0$

7 $x^2 - 13 = 6x$ **8** $x^2 + 14 = 8x$ **9** $x^2 - 2x = 1$

10 $x^2 - 6x = 2$ **11** $2x^2 - 16x + 4 = 0$ **12** $2x^2 + 8x - 6 = 0$

13 $2x^2 - 5x = 7$ **14** $2x^2 + 7x = 3$ **15** $x(5x + 12) = -5$

16 $x(3x + 8) = -2$ **17** $3 - 10x - 4x^2 = 0$ **18** $3 - 4x - 6x^2 = 0$

19 $7x^2 = 4 + 4x$ **20** $4x^2 = 3 + 6x$

Investigate

For what values of k does the equation $x^2 + 8x + k = 0$ have real solutions?

Completing the square can tell you other things about a quadratic function.

The quadratic formula

The quadratic formula is used to solve quadratic equations that may be awkward to solve by other means.

Key Point

If $ax^2 + bx + c = 0$ then $x = \dfrac{-b \pm \sqrt{b^2 - 4ac}}{2a}$

Example 7

Solve $3x^2 - 8x + 2 = 0$ giving your solution correct to 3 significant figures.

Here $a = 3$, $b = -8$ and $c = 2$.   *Note*: b is a negative number.

Substituting into the formula gives $-(-8) = +8$ $(-8)^2 = +64$

$$x = \frac{-(-8) \pm \sqrt{(-8)^2 - 4 \times 3 \times 2}}{2 \times 3} = \frac{8 \pm \sqrt{64 - 24}}{6}$$

So $x = \dfrac{8 + \sqrt{40}}{6} = 2.39$ or $x = \dfrac{8 - \sqrt{40}}{6} = 0.279$

> **Example 8**
>
> Solve $2.3x^2 + 3.5x - 4.8 = 0$ giving your solution correct to 3 significant figures.
>
> Here $a = 2.3$, $b = 3.5$ and $c = -4.8$. Substituting into the formula gives
>
> $$x = \frac{-3.5 \pm \sqrt{12.25 - 4 \times 2.3 \times (-4.8)}}{2 \times 2.3} = \frac{-3.5 \pm \sqrt{56.41}}{4.6}$$
>
> So $x = \dfrac{-3.5 + \sqrt{56.41}}{4.6} = 0.872$ or $x = \dfrac{-3.5 - \sqrt{56.41}}{4.6} = -2.39$
>
> The solutions are $x = 0.872$ or $x = -2.39$.

Exercise 50

Solve these equations using the quadratic formula.

Giving your solutions correct to 3 significant figures.

1 $x^2 + x - 8 = 0$ **2** $x^2 + 2x - 4 = 0$ **3** $x^2 - 2x - 7 = 0$

4 $x^2 - x - 3 = 0$ **5** $3x^2 + 6x + 2 = 0$ **6** $3x^2 + 7x + 3 = 0$

7 $4x^2 + x - 4 = 0$ **8** $3x^2 + 5x + 1 = 0$ **9** $x^2 + x = 5$

10 $x^2 + 2x = 7$ **11** $6x - 1 = x^2$ **12** $16x - 3 = x^2$

13 $8 + 3x - 7x^2 = 0$ **14** $1 + 5x - 3x^2 = 0$ **15** $8x = 2 + 5x^2$

16 $2x = 7x^2 - 3$

17 The length of a rectangle is $2\,\text{cm}$ more than the width. The area is $12\,\text{cm}^2$.
Find the length of the rectangle.

18 The height of a triangle is $3\,\text{cm}$ more than the width. The area is $10\,\text{cm}^2$.
Find the height of the triangle.

19 The height, $h\,\text{m}$, of a rocket above the ground is given after t seconds by $h = 40t - 5t^2$.
When is the rocket $50\,\text{m}$ high?

20 The distance, $d\,\text{m}$, that a scooter has rolled down a hill after t seconds is given by
$d = 2t + t^2$. Find how long it takes to travel $100\,\text{m}$.

Exercise 50★

Solve these equations using the quadratic formula.

Give your solutions correct to 3 significant figures.

1 $x^2 + 13x + 4 = 0$ **2** $x^2 + 12x + 6 = 0$ **3** $x^2 - 6x + 7 = 0$

4 $x^2 - 7x + 5 = 0$ **5** $3x^2 - 5x = 2$ **6** $3x^2 - 2x = 1$

7 $x(5x - 8) = -1$ **8** $x(5x + 2) = 1$ **9** $3x^2 = 7x + 2$

10 $4x^2 = 8x + 3$ **11** $10 + 3x - 2x^2 = 0$ **12** $5 - 2x - 4x^2 = 0$

13 $2.3x^2 - 12.6x + 1.3 = 0$ **14** $3.7x^2 - 9.4x + 2.8 = 0$

15 $x(x + 1) + (x - 1)(x + 2) = 3$ **16** $x(x + 1) + (x + 2)(x + 3) = 4$

17 The perimeter of a rectangular room is $13.5\,\text{m}$ and the length of the diagonal is $5\,\text{m}$.
Find the dimensions of the room.

18 The area of a rectangular lawn is $30\,\text{m}^2$. During landscaping the length was decreased by 1m and the width increased by 1m, but the area did not change.
Find the original dimensions of the lawn.

19 The sum of the first n integers $1 + 2 + 3 + 4 + \cdots + n = \frac{1}{2}n(n + 1)$.
How many numbers must be taken to have a sum greater than one million?

20 An n-sided polygon has $\frac{1}{2}n(n - 3)$ diagonals.
How many sides has a polygon with 665 diagonals?

For Questions 21–23, solve the equation using the quadratic formula.

21 $1 + \dfrac{5}{x} = \dfrac{12}{x^2}$

22 $\dfrac{2}{x - 2} + \dfrac{4}{x + 1} = 3$

23 $\dfrac{1}{x} - \dfrac{1}{x + 1} = \dfrac{1}{9x + 4}$

24 O is the origin, A is the point $(p, 5)$ and B is the point $(12, 0)$.
Find the values of p such that angle OAB is a right angle. Produce a spreadsheet that uses the quadratic formula to give the solutions to a quadratic equation.

Proof of the quadratic formula

This proves the quadratic formula for the case when $a = 1$, i.e. for the quadratic equation $x^2 + bx + c = 0$.

$$x^2 + bx + c = 0$$

$$\Rightarrow \quad \left(x + \frac{b}{2}\right)^2 - \left(\frac{b}{2}\right)^2 + c = 0 \qquad \text{(Completing the square)}$$

$$\left(x + \frac{b}{2}\right)^2 = \left(\frac{b}{2}\right)^2 - c$$

$$\left(x + \frac{b}{2}\right)^2 = \frac{b^2}{4} - c$$

$$\left(x + \frac{b}{2}\right)^2 = \frac{b^2 - 4c}{4}$$

$$x + \frac{b}{2} = \frac{\pm\sqrt{b^2 - 4c}}{2} \qquad \text{(Taking the square root of both sides)}$$

$$x = \frac{-b \pm \sqrt{b^2 - 4c}}{2}$$

Activity 30

♦ Modify the proof to prove the *general* quadratic formula, i.e. when $a \neq 1$.

The quadratic formula provides an easy way of finding how many solutions there are to a quadratic equation.

Activity 31

♦ Use the graphs to find how many solutions there are to each of these equations.

$$x^2 + 8x + 15 = 0 \qquad x^2 + 8x + 16 = 0 \qquad x^2 + 8x + 17 = 0$$

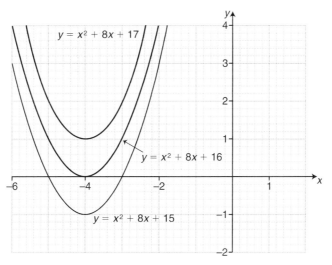

♦ For each of the quadratic equations, work out the values of $b^2 - 4ac$.

♦ Try to find a rule involving $b^2 - 4ac$ that tells you how many solutions a quadratic equation has.

Exercise 51

State how many solutions there are to these equations. Do *not* solve them.

1 $x^2 - 2x + 1 = 0$ **2** $x^2 - 9 = 0$

3 $x^2 + 4 = 0$ **4** $x^2 + 2x + 1 = 0$

5 $x^2 - 2x + 5 = 0$ **6** $x^2 - 4x + 4 = 0$

7 $x^2 + 6x + 1 = 0$ **8** $x^2 - 2x - 3 = 0$

9 $x^2 - x + 1 = 0$ **10** $x^2 + 8x + 12 = 0$

Exercise 51 ★

State how many solutions there are to these equations. Do *not* solve them.

1 $x^2 - 3 = 0$ **2** $x^2 + 3x + 3 = 0$

3 $x^2 - x - 1 = 0$ **4** $4x^2 - 4x + 5 = 0$

5 $4x^2 - 4x + 1 = 0$ **6** $2x^2 + 3x + 2 = 0$

7 $4x^2 - 7x + 2 = 0$ **8** $2x^2 - 4x + 9 = 0$

9 $3x^2 + 8x + 3 = 0$ **10** $9x^2 + 6x + 1 = 0$

Solving simultaneous equations, one linear and one nonlinear

Graphically, this corresponds to the intersection of a straight line and a curve.

Activity 32

♦ Use this graph to solve the simultaneous equations $x + 2y = 10$ and $x^2 + y^2 = 25$.

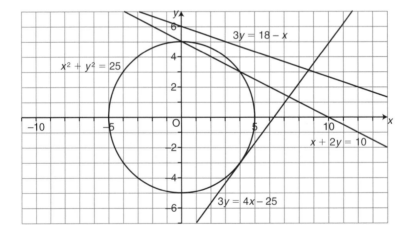

♦ Use the graph to solve the simultaneous equations $3y = 4x - 25$ and $x^2 + y^2 = 25$.

What is the connection between the line $3y = 4x - 25$ and the circle $x^2 + y^2 = 25$?

♦ Are there any real solutions to the simultaneous equations $3y = 18 - x$ and $x^2 + y^2 = 25$?

Drawing graphs is one way of solving simultaneous equations. Sometimes they can be solved algebraically. Example 9 shows how to solve the first pair from Activity 32.

Example 9

Solve the simultaneous equations $x + 2y = 10$ and $x^2 + y^2 = 25$.

Make x the subject of the linear equation:

$$x = 10 - 2y$$

Substitute this into the nonlinear equation:

$$(10 - 2y)^2 + y^2 = 25$$

Simplify and solve the equation:

$$100 - 40y + 4y^2 + y^2 = 25$$
$$5y^2 - 40y + 75 = 0$$
$$y^2 - 8y + 15 = 0$$
$$(y - 3)(y - 5) = 0$$
$$y = 3 \text{ or } y = 5$$

When $y = 3$, $x = 4$ (using the equation $x = 10 - 2y$).
When $y = 5$, $x = 0$ (using the equation $x = 10 - 2y$).

So the solutions are $x = 0$, $y = 5$ and $x = 4$, $y = 3$.

The algebraic method is preferred because it is more accurate.

Remember

♦ *Always* substitute the linear equation into the nonlinear equation.
♦ Look at the equations carefully and see which is the easier unknown to eliminate.
♦ When one unknown has been found, find the other using the linear equation.
♦ Pair the solutions correctly.

Example 10

Solve the simultaneous equations $x + y = 4$ and $x^2 + 2xy = 2$.

Substituting for y in the second equation will make the working easier.

Make y the subject of the linear equation:

$$y = 4 - x$$

Substitute this into the nonlinear equation:

$$x^2 + 2x(4 - x) = 2$$

Simplify:

$$x^2 + 8x - 2x^2 = 2$$
$$x^2 - 8x + 2 = 0$$

Solve this equation using the formula:

$$x = 0.258 \text{ or } x = 7.74 \text{ (to 3 s.f.)}$$

Using $y = 4 - x$ gives $y = 3.74$ or $y = -3.74$ (to 3 s.f.)

So the solutions are $x = 0.258$ and $y = 3.74$ or $x = 7.74$ and $y = -3.74$, to 3 s.f.

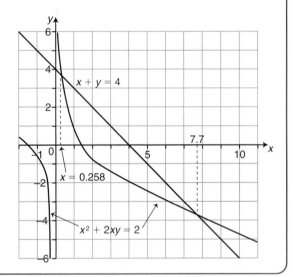

Exercise 52

For Questions 1–14, solve the simultaneous equations, giving your answers correct to 3 significant figures where appropriate.

1 $y = x + 1$, $y = x^2 - 2x + 3$

2 $y = x - 1$, $y = x^2 + 2x - 7$

3 $y = 2x - 1$, $y = x^2 + 4x - 6$

4 $y = 3x + 1$, $y = x^2 - x + 2$

5 $2x + y = 1$, $x^2 + y^2 = 2$

6 $x + 2y = 2$, $x^2 + y^2 = 1$

7 $x - 2y = 1$, $xy = 3$

8 $3x + y = 4$, $xy = -4$

9 $x + y = 2$, $3x^2 - y^2 = 1$

10 $x + y = 3$, $x^2 - 2y^2 = 4$

11 $x - 2y = 3$, $x^2 + 2y^2 = 3$

12 $2x + y = 2$, $4x^2 + y^2 = 2$

13 $x - y = 2$, $x^2 + xy - 3y^2 = 5$

14 $x + y = 4$, $2x^2 - 3xy + y^2 = 4$

15 The rim of my bicycle wheel has a radius of 30 cm, and the inner hub has a radius of 3 cm. The spokes are tangents to the inner hub. The diagram shows just one spoke. The x and y axes are positioned with the origin at the centre of the wheel as shown.

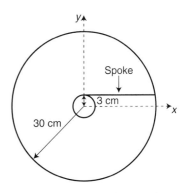

a Write down the equation of the rim.

b Write down the equation of the spoke.

c Solve the equations simultaneously.

d What is the length of the spoke?

16 The shape of the cross-section of a vase is given by $y^2 - 24y - 32x + 208 = 0$, with units in cm. The vase is 20 cm high. Find the radius of the top of the vase.

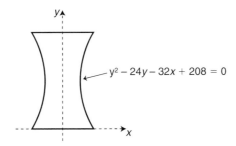

Exercise 52★

Solve these simultaneous equations, giving your answers correct to 3 significant figures where appropriate.

1 $y = 4x + 2$, $y = x^2 + x - 5$

2 $y = 1 - 3x$, $y = x^2 - 7x + 3$

3 $2x + y = 2$, $3x^2 - y^2 = 3$

4 $x + 2y = 1$, $x^2 + 2y^2 = 3$

5 $y - x = 4$, $2x^2 + xy + y^2 = 8$

6 $x + y = 3$, $x^2 + 3xy - 2y^2 = 8$

7 $x + y = 1$, $\dfrac{x}{y} + \dfrac{y}{x} = 2.5$

8 $x - y = 10$, $\dfrac{1}{y} - \dfrac{1}{x} = 5$

9 Find the points of intersection of the circle $x^2 - 6x + y^2 + 4y = 12$ and the line $4y = 3x - 42$. What is the connection between the line and the circle?

10 a Find the intersection points A and B of the line $4y + 3x = 22$ and the circle $(x - 2)^2 + (y - 4)^2 = 25$.

b Find the distance AB.

c What is the relationship between AB and the circle?

11 The lines $y = 2x$ and $2y + x = 20$ intersect the circle $(x - 4)^2 + (y - 3)^2 = 25$ at a common point, B.

a Find the coordinates of B and the other two points (A and C) where the lines intersect the circle.

b Find the angle between the two lines.

c What is the relationship between AC and the circle?

For Questions 12–14, solve the simultaneous equations.

12 $xy = 12, (x - 1)(y + 2) = 15$ **13** $x^2 - y^2 = 16, x + y = 2$

14 $\dfrac{1}{x} + \dfrac{1}{y} = (x - 4)(y - 4) = 2$

15 The design of some new spectacle frames is shown in the diagram. They consist of two circular rims, both 2 cm in radius, which are held 2 cm apart by a curved bridge piece and a straight length of wire AB.
Axes are set up as shown, and AB is 1.5 cm above the x-axis.

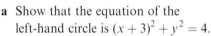

a Show that the equation of the left-hand circle is $(x + 3)^2 + y^2 = 4$.

b Find the equation of the right-hand circle.

c Write down the equation of the line AB.

d Find the coordinates of A and B and the length of the wire AB.

16 A rocket is launched from the surface of the Earth. The surface of the Earth can be modelled by the equation $x^2 + y^2 = 6400^2$ where the units are in km.

The path of the rocket can be modelled by the equation $y = 8000 - \dfrac{x^2}{2500}$.

Find the coordinates of where the rocket takes off and where it lands.

Exercise 53 (Revision)

1 Solve these quadratic equations by factorising.

a $x^2 + x - 12 = 0$ **b** $5x^2 - 5x - 30 = 0$ **c** $3x^2 + x - 2 = 0$

2 If $y = x^2 + 4x + 8$ find, by completing the square, the minimum value of y and sketch the graph of y against x.

3 Use the quadratic formula to solve these equations.

    a $x^2 - 2x - 4 = 0$ **b** $3x^2 - 5x + 1 = 0$

4 A cereal packet is a cuboid with height 12 cm. The depth of the box is 4 cm more than the width, and the volume is 480 cm^3. Find the width of the box.

5 Solve these simultaneous equations.

    a $y = x + 2$, $y = x^2 + 4x - 8$ **b** $y = 1 - x$, $x^2 + y^2 = 4$

6 Robin Hood is designing a new bow in the shape of an arc of a circle of radius 2 m. Robin wants the distance between the string and the bow to be 30 cm. Use axes as shown in the diagram.

    a Find the equation of the circle.

    b Write down the equation of AB.

    c Find the coordinates of A and B and the length of string Robin needs.

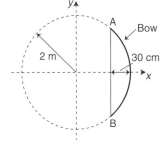

Exercise 53★ (Revision)

1 Solve these quadratic equations by factorising.

    a $x^2 + x - 72 = 0$ **b** $7x^2 = 14x + 168$ **c** $2x(4x + 7) = 15$

2 If $y = x^2 - 12x + 33$ find, by completing the square, the minimum value of y and sketch the graph of y against x.

3 Use the quadratic formula to solve these equations.

    a $3x^2 = 7x + 5$ **b** $2.1x^2 + 8.4x - 4.3 = 0$

4 Pete can cycle 15 km/h faster than he can walk. When he cycles the 4 km to school, he takes 36 minutes less than when he walks. Find his speed of walking.

5 Solve these simultaneous equations.

    a $y = 2x - 1$, $y = 2x^2 + 7x - 13$ **b** $x + y = 2$, $2x^2 - x + y^2 = 6$

6 The path of the comet Fermat is an ellipse with equation $x^2 + 36y^2 = 324$ where the units are in au (1 au, called an astronomical unit, is the distance from the Earth to the Sun). The comet can be detected by eye at a distance of 3 au from the Earth and the equation of this circle is $(x - 17.5)^2 + y^2 = 9$.

Find the coordinates of the points where the comet can be seen from the Earth.

Graphs 3

Function notation

A letter can be used to stand for a rule. For example, let f stand for a rule.

If x is input, the output is $f(x)$:

Now, let the rule in the box be 'double the input and then add 1'.

If 5 is input, the output is 11:

f has operated on 5 to give 11, so write $f(5) = 11$.

If x is input, the output is $2x + 1$:

f has operated on x to give $2x + 1$, so write $f(x) = 2x + 1$.

If $(x - 3)$ is input, the output is $2(x - 3) + 1$,
which simplifies to $2x - 5$:

f has operated on $(x - 3)$ to give $2x - 5$, so write $f(x - 3) = 2x - 5$.

Example 1

If $f(x) = x^2 + 3x$, find $f(4)$, $f(2x)$, $2f(x)$, $f(x) - 1$ and $f(x - 1)$

f is the rule 'add together the square of the input and three times the input'.

$f(4) = 4^2 + 3 \times 4 = 16 + 12 = 28$
$f(2x) = (2x)^2 + 3(2x) = 4x^2 + 6x$
$2f(x) = 2(x^2 + 3x) = 2x^2 + 6x$
$f(x) - 1 = x^2 + 3x - 1$
$f(x - 1) = (x - 1)^2 + 3(x - 1) = x^2 - 2x + 1 + 3x - 3 = x^2 + x - 2$

Exercise 54

1 If $f(x) = 2x + 1$, find

   a $f(3)$ **b** $f(-2)$ **c** $f(x + 2)$ **d** $f(x) + 2$

2 If $f(x) = 3x - 2$, find

   a $f(2)$ **b** $f(-1)$ **c** $f(x + 1)$ **d** $f(x) + 1$

3 If $f(x) = 4x - 3$, find

   a $f(1)$ **b** $f(-4)$ **c** $f(2x)$ **d** $2f(x)$

4 If $f(x) = 2x - 4$, find

   a $f(4)$ **b** $f(-2)$ **c** $f(4x)$ **d** $4f(x)$

5 If $f(x) = 3 - x$, find

   a $f(-3)$ **b** $f(-x)$ **c** $f(-3x)$ **d** $-3f(x)$

6 If $f(x) = 5 - x$, find

   a $f(-5)$ **b** $f(-x)$ **c** $f(-5x)$ **d** $-5f(x)$

7 If $f(x) = x^2 + 2x$, find

   a $f(-1)$ **b** $f(x - 1)$ **c** $f(x - 1) + 1$ **d** $1 - f(x - 1)$

8 If $f(x) = x^2 - x$, find

   a $f(-2)$ **b** $f(x + 1)$ **c** $f(x + 1) + 1$ **d** $1 - f(x + 1)$

Exercise 54★

1 If $f(x) = x^2 + 1$, find

   a $f(-2)$ **b** $f(x + 2)$ **c** $f(x) + 2$ **d** $f(x + 2) + 2$

2 If $f(x) = x^2 + 2$, find

   a $f(-1)$ **b** $f(x + 1)$ **c** $f(x) + 1$ **d** $f(x + 1) + 1$

3 If $f(x) = 2x^2 - 2$, find

   a $f(-x)$ **b** $-f(x)$ **c** $f(2x)$ **d** $2f(x)$

4 If $f(x) = 4x^2 - 4$, find

   a $f(-x)$ **b** $-f(x)$ **c** $f(4x)$ **d** $4f(x)$

5 If $f(x) = 3x - x^2$, find

   a $f(3x)$ **b** $3f(x)$ **c** $3f(-x)$ **d** $f(-3x)$

6 If $f(x) = 2x - x^2$, find

   a $f(2x)$ **b** $2f(x)$ **c** $2f(-x)$ **d** $f(-2x)$

7 If $f(x) = \dfrac{1}{x^2}$, find

   a $\dfrac{1}{f(x)}$ **b** $f\left(\dfrac{1}{x}\right)$ **c** $\dfrac{1}{f(1/x)}$

8 If $f(x) = \dfrac{1}{x}$, find

   a $\dfrac{1}{f(x)}$ **b** $f\left(\dfrac{1}{x}\right)$ **c** $\dfrac{1}{f(1/x)}$

Graphs of functions

To picture how a function behaves, you can draw a graph.

Example 2

Draw the graph of $f(x) = x^2 + 3x$ for $-4 \leqslant x \leqslant 1$.

First make a table of values. The graph of $y = f(x)$ can now be drawn.

x	-4	-3	-2	-1	0	1
x^2	16	9	4	1	0	1
$3x$	-12	-9	-6	-3	0	3
$f(x)$	4	0	-2	-2	0	4

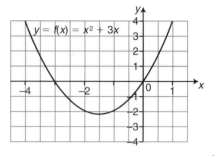

Investigate

♦ Find functions for which $f(x) = f(-x)$ or $f(x) = -f(-x)$.

♦ What symmetries do the graphs of these functions possess?

Standard graphs

As well as straight line graphs, you should remember the standard graphs.

Remember

$y = f(x) = x^2$　　　　$y = f(x) = x^3$　　　　$y = f(x) = \dfrac{1}{x}$

$y = f(x) = \cos x$
$y = f(x) = \sin x$

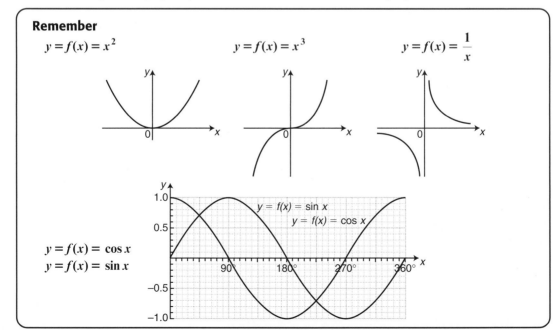

Transforming graphs

When writing equations of graphs, y and $f(x)$ can be interchanged when y is a function of x. However, it is useful to use $f(x)$ notation when describing transformations.

Vertical translations

This diagram shows the graphs of $y = x^2$, $y = x^2 - 1$, $y = x^2 - 2$ and $y = x^2 + 1$, all plotted on one set of axes.

The transformation from the graph of $y = f(x) = x^2$ to the other three graphs is a vertical translation.

The transformation of the graph of $y = f(x)$ to the graph of $y = f(x) + a$ is a vertical translation of a.

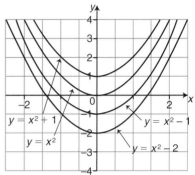

Activity 33

◆ What are the transformations from the graph of $f(x) = x^2$ to the graph $f(x) = x^2 - 3$ and to $f(x) = x^2 + 2$?

◆ Plot these graphs for $-3 \leqslant x \leqslant 3$ to check your answers.

Horizontal translations

The diagram shows the graphs of $y = x^2$, $y = (x - 1)^2$, $y = (x - 2)^2$ and $y = (x + 1)^2$ all plotted on one set of axes.

The transformation from the graph of $y = f(x) = x^2$ to the other three graphs is a horizontal translation.

The transformation of the graph of $y = f(x)$ to the graph of $y = f(x - a)$ is a horizontal translation of a.

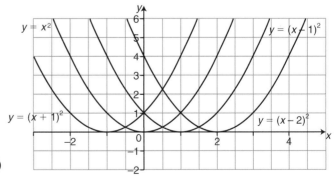

The transformation of the graph of $y = f(x)$ to the graph of $y = f(x + a)$ is a horizontal translation of $-a$ as $f(x + a) = f(x - -a)$.

Activity 34

◆ What are the transformations from the graph of $f(x) = x^2$ to the graphs $f(x) = (x - 3)^2$ and to $f(x) = (x + 2)^2$?

◆ Plot these graphs for $-4 \leqslant x \leqslant 4$ to check your answers.

Exercise 55★

For Questions 1 to 6, sketch the graphs in each question on one set of axes.

1 **a** $f(x) = x^3$ **b** $f(x) = (x + 1)^3$ **c** $f(x) = x^3 + 1$

2 **a** $f(x) = x^3$ **b** $f(x) = (x - 1)^3$ **c** $f(x) = x^3 - 1$

3 **a** $f(x) = \dfrac{1}{x}$ **b** $f(x) = \dfrac{1}{x} - 1$ **c** $f(x) = \dfrac{1}{(x - 1)}$

4 **a** $f(x) = \dfrac{1}{x}$ **b** $f(x) = \dfrac{1}{x} + 1$ **c** $f(x) = \dfrac{1}{(x + 1)}$

5 **a** $f(x) = \sin x$ **b** $f(x) = \sin(x - 30°)$ **c** $f(x) = \sin x - 1$

6 **a** $f(x) = \cos x$ **b** $f(x) = \cos(x + 30°)$ **c** $f(x) = \cos x + 1$

7 Suggest equations for these graphs.

a

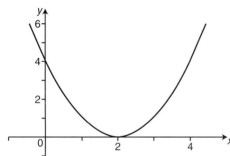

b

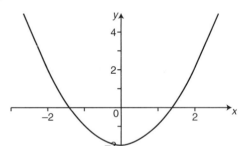

8 Suggest equations for these graphs.

a

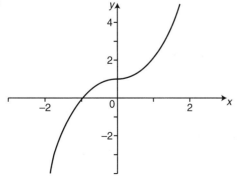

b

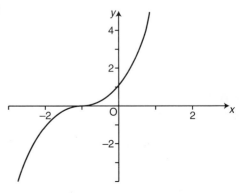

Reflections in the *x*-axis

These three graphs show a function $f(x)$ together with the function $-f(x)$, both plotted on the same axes.

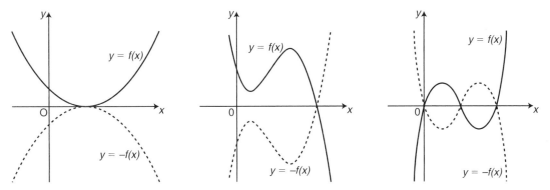

In each case, the transformation from $f(x)$ to $-f(x)$ is a reflection in the *x*-axis.

Activity 35

Sketch these graphs (sketch each pair on one set of axes).

♦ $f(x) = x^2, f(x) = -x^2$ ♦ $f(x) = x^3, f(x) = -x^3$

♦ $f(x) = 1 + x, f(x) = -(1 + x)$

Reflections in the *y*-axis

These three graphs show a function $f(x)$ and the function $f(-x)$ plotted on the same axes.

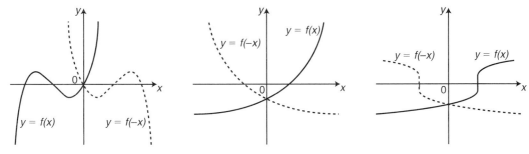

In each case, the transformation from $f(x)$ to $f(-x)$ is a reflection in the *y*-axis.

Activity 36

Sketch these graphs (sketch each pair on one set of axes).

♦ $f(x) = x^3, f(x) = (-x)^3$ ♦ $f(x) = \dfrac{1}{x}, f(x) = \dfrac{1}{(-x)}$

♦ $f(x) = 1 + x, f(x) = 1 + (-x)$

Stretches parallel to the y-axis

Activity 37

◆ Copy and complete this table.

x	0°	30°	60°	90°	120°	150°	180°	210°	240°	270°	300°	330°	360°
sin x	0	0.50	0.87	1.00	0.87	0.50	0	−0.50	−0.87	−1.00	−0.87	−0.50	0
2 sin x													
3 sin x													

◆ Draw, on one set of axes, the graphs of $f(x) = \sin x$, $f(x) = 2\sin x$ and $f(x) = 3\sin x$.

◆ Note that the transformation from the graph of $f(x) = \sin x$ to $f(x) = 2\sin x$ is a stretch parallel to the y-axis ($\updownarrow$) with scale factor 2.
Also note that the transformation from the graph of $f(x) = \sin x$ to $f(x) = 3\sin x$ is a stretch parallel to the y-axis ($\updownarrow$) with scale factor 3.
The transformation of the graph of $f(x)$ to the graph of $kf(x)$ where k is any *positive* number is a stretch parallel to the y-axis ($\updownarrow$) with scale factor k.
If k is *negative*, say $k = -a$, the transformation is a reflection in the x-axis followed by a stretch parallel to the y-axis ($\updownarrow$) with scale factor $+a$.

◆ *Sketch* these graphs (sketch each pair on one set of axes).
  ▶ $y = x^2$, $y = 3x^2$
  ▶ $y = x^3$, $y = 2x^3$
  ▶ $y = x + 1$, $y = 2(x + 1)$

Stretches parallel to the x-axis

These two graphs show a function $f(x)$ and the function $f(2x)$ plotted on the same axes.

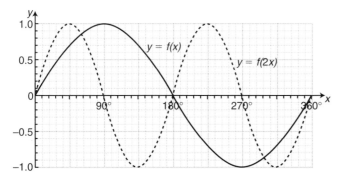
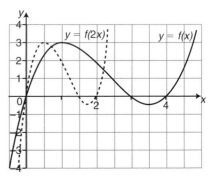

In each case the transformation from $f(x)$ to $f(2x)$ is a stretch with scale factor $\frac{1}{2}$ parallel to the x-axis ($\longleftrightarrow$).

The next two graphs show a function $f(x)$ together with the function f, $\left(\frac{1}{2}x\right)$, both plotted on the same axes. In each case, the transformation from $f(x)$ to $f\left(\frac{1}{2}x\right)$ is a stretch parallel to the x-axis ($\longleftrightarrow$) with scale factor 2.

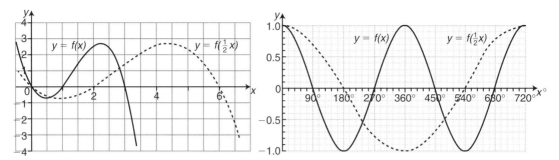

The transformation of the graph of $f(x)$ to the graph of $f(kx)$ where k is any *positive* number is a stretch parallel to the x-axis with scale factor $1/k$. If k is *negative*, say $k = -a$ the transformation is a reflection in the y-axis, followed by a stretch parallel to the x-axis with scale factor $1/a$.

> **Remember**
> ◆ A stretch parallel to the y-axis ($\updownarrow$) leaves the x-axis unchanged and stretches out the values along the y-axis.
> ◆ A stretch parallel to the x-axis ($\longleftrightarrow$) leaves the y-axis unchanged and stretches out the values along the x-axis.

Activity 38

Sketch these graphs (sketch each pair on one set of axes).
- $y = x^3$, $y = (2x)^3$
- $y = x^3$, $y = \left(\frac{1}{2}x\right)^3$
- $y = x + 1$, $y = 2x + 1$

Key Points

Function	Transformation
◆ $f(x) + a$	Translation $\begin{pmatrix} 0 \\ a \end{pmatrix}$
◆ $f(x - a)$	Translation $\begin{pmatrix} a \\ 0 \end{pmatrix}$
◆ $-f(x)$	Reflection in the x-axis
◆ $f(-x)$	Reflection in the y-axis
◆ $af(x)$	One-way stretch, parallel to y-axis, with scale factor a
◆ $f(ax)$	One-way stretch, parallel to x-axis, with scale factor $1/a$

Exercise 56

For Questions 1–4, sketch all three graphs on one set of axes.

1 Describe the transformations from $f(x) = x + 1$ to

    a $f(x) = -(x + 1)$ **b** $f(x) = -x + 1$

2 Describe the transformations from $f(x) = 2 - x$ to

    a $f(x) = 2 + x$ **b** $f(x) = -(2 - x)$

3 Describe the transformations from $f(x) = \cos x$ to

    a $f(x) = \cos 2x$ **b** $f(x) = \frac{1}{2}\cos x$

4 Describe the transformations from $f(x) = \sin x$ to

    a $f(x) = \sin\frac{1}{2}x$ **b** $f(x) = 2\sin x$

This diagram shows the graph of $f(x)$.
In each of Questions 5–14, copy the diagram and sketch the required function.

5 $-f(x)$ **6** $f(-x)$ **7** $2f(x)$

8 $f(2x)$ **9** $\frac{1}{2}f(x)$ **10** $f\left(\frac{1}{2}x\right)$

11 $-2f(x)$ **12** $f(-2x)$ **13** $-\frac{1}{2}f(x)$

14 $f\left(-\frac{1}{2}x\right)$

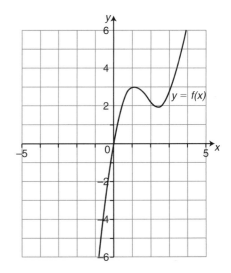

$y = f(x)$

Exercise 56★

1 Describe the transformations from $f(x) = x - 1$ to

   a $f(x) = 2(x - 1)$ b $f(x) = \frac{1}{2}x - 1$

   Sketch all three graphs on one set of axes.

2 Describe the transformations from $f(x) = x + 2$ to

   a $f(x) = \frac{1}{2}x + 2$ b $f(x) = 2(x + 2)$

   Sketch all three graphs on one set of axes.

3 The diagram shows several functions.

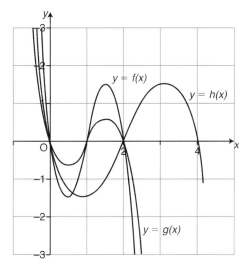

   a Express $g(x)$ in terms of $f(x)$.

   b Express $h(x)$ in terms of $f(x)$.

4 The curve $f(x)$ passes through the three points A$(6, 0)$, B$(0, 4)$ and C$(-2, 3)$.
   Find the corresponding points that

   a the curve $f(2x)$ passes through   b the curve $\frac{1}{2}f(x)$ passes through.

5 The curve $f(x)$ passes through the three points A$(0, 2)$, B$(3, 0)$ and C$(2, -4)$.
   Find the corresponding points that

   a the curve $f\left(\frac{1}{2}x\right)$ passes through

   b the curve $2f(x)$ passes through.

6 What is the equation when $f(x) = x^3$ is:

   a reflected in the x-axis?

   b reflected in the y-axis?

7 What is the equation when $f(x) = \dfrac{1}{x}$ is:

   a reflected in the x-axis?

   b reflected in the y-axis?

8 **a** Express $g(x)$ in terms of $f(x)$.

   b Express $h(x)$ in terms of $f(x)$.

   c Express $j(x)$ in terms of $f(x)$.

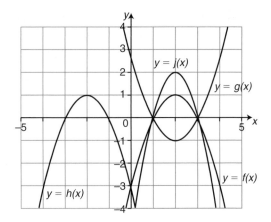

Exercise 57 (Revision)

1 If $f(x) = 2x - 1$, find

   a $f(2)$ **b** $f(x + 1)$ **c** $f(-x)$ **d** $-f(x)$

2 If $f(x) = x^2 - 2x$, find

   a $f(x - 1)$ **b** $f(-x)$ **c** $f(x^2)$

3 Find the equation when $y = 2x + 1$ is

   a reflected in the y-axis   **b** translated by 1 parallel to the x-axis

   c translated by 2 parallel to the y-axis

4 Sketch these curves.

   a $f(x) = (x - 2)^2$ **b** $f(x) = x^2 - 2$ **c** $f(x) = \sin 2x$

5 The curve $f(x)$ passes through the point $(2, 3)$. Find the corresponding point that

   a $f(x) + 1$ passes through   **b** $f(x + 1)$ passes through.

6 The diagram shows $f(x)$. Copy the diagram and sketch these curves on it.

   a $f(-x)$

   b $f(x + 1)$

   c $f\left(\frac{1}{2}x\right)$

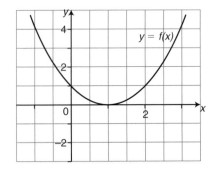

7 Mr Gauss, a mathematics teacher, is trying to set a question for his class. He wants a quadratic curve with a maximum at the point $(0, 4)$.

   a Suggest a suitable equation that Mr Gauss might use.

   b Where does this equation intersect the x-axis?

Mr Gauss wants to stretch the curve by a scale factor of 2 parallel to the x-axis.

   c What is the new equation?

   d Where does this curve intersect the x-axis?

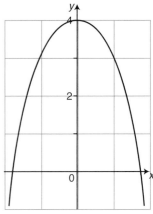

Exercise 57★ (Revision)

1 If $f(x) = x - \dfrac{1}{x}$, find

   a $f(2)$ **b** $f(x^2)$ **c** $f(-x)$ **d** $f\left(\dfrac{1}{x}\right)$

2 If $f(x) = x^2 + x$, find p if $f(-p) = f(2p)$.

3 Find the equation when $y = x^2 - x$ is

   a reflected in the x-axis   **b** reflected in the y-axis

   c translated by the vector $\begin{pmatrix} -1 \\ 0 \end{pmatrix}$.

4 Find the equation when $y = \cos x$ is

   a stretched with scale factor $\frac{1}{2}$ parallel to the y-axis

   b stretched with scale factor $\frac{1}{2}$ parallel to the x-axis.

5 Sketch these graphs

   a $f(x) = -x^3$ **b** $f(x) = \dfrac{1}{x-1}$ **c** $f(x) = \cos x - 1$

6 The diagram shows $f(x)$. Copy the diagram and sketch these curves on it.

   a $-f(x)$

   b $\frac{1}{2}f(2x)$

   c $2f\left(\frac{1}{2}x\right)$

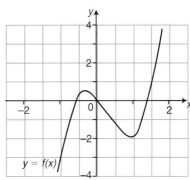

7 Dave is a keen sea fisherman and wants to be able to predict the depth of water at his favourite fishing site. He decides to model the depth of the water using the sine function. The diagram shows his first attempt, where the *x*-axis represents time in minutes and $f(x)$ is the depth in metres.

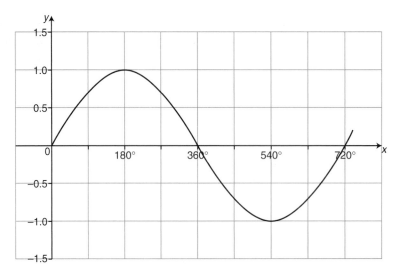

a Write down the transformation of the sine function that will produce the graph of Dave's first attempt.

b Write down the function that will produce the graph of Dave's first attempt.

The water depth actually varies between 1 m and 5 m as shown in the next diagram, so Dave tries to improve his model.

c Describe the transformation from the first graph to the second graph.

d Write down the function that will produce the second graph.

e What depth of water does this model predict for a time of 2 hours?

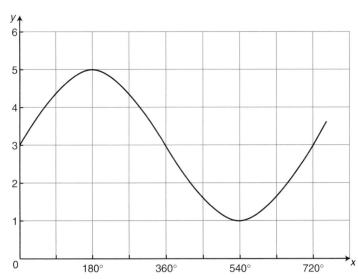

Shape and space 3

Vectors

A **vector** has both size and direction. In contrast, a **scalar** has size but no direction. Vectors are very useful tools in mathematics and physics, helping to make calculations more direct. In 1881, American mathematician J. W. Gibbs published the book *Vector Analysis*, which established vectors as they are known today.

Activity 39

Identify these quantities as vector or scalar quanities:

- ▶ Volume
- ▶ Acceleration
- ▶ A pass in hockey
- ▶ Area

- ▶ Temperature
- ▶ Velocity
- ▶ Price
- ▶ Rotation of 180°

- ▶ Force
- ▶ Length
- ▶ Density
- ▶ 10 km on a bearing of 075°

Notation

In this book, vectors are written as bold letters (**a**, **p**, **x**, ...) or capitals covered by an arrow ($\overrightarrow{AB}$, $\overrightarrow{PQ}$, $\overrightarrow{XY}$, ...). In other books, you might find vectors written as bold italic letters (*a*, *p*, *x*, ...). When hand writing vectors, they are written with a wavy or straight underline ($\underset{\sim}{a}$, $\underset{\sim}{p}$, $\underset{\sim}{x}$, or $\underline{a}$, $\underline{p}$, $\underline{x}$).

On coordinate axes, a vector can be described by a **column vector**, which can be used to find the **magnitude** and angle of the vector.

Example 1

a Express vector **s** as a column vector.

$$\mathbf{s} = \begin{pmatrix} 3 \\ 4 \end{pmatrix}$$

b Find the magnitude of vector **s**.

Length of $\mathbf{s} = \sqrt{3^2 + 4^2} = \sqrt{25} = 5$

c Calculate the size of angle x.

$\tan x = \frac{4}{3} \Rightarrow x = 53.1°$ (to 3 s.f.)

Example 2

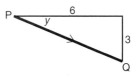

a Express vector $\overrightarrow{PQ}$ as a column vector

$$\overrightarrow{PQ} = \begin{pmatrix} 6 \\ -3 \end{pmatrix}$$

b Find the magnitude of vector $\overrightarrow{PQ}$.

Length of $\overrightarrow{PQ} = \sqrt{6^2 + 3^2}$

$= \sqrt{45}$

$= 6.71$ (to 3 s.f.)

c Calculate the size of angle y.

$\tan y = \frac{3}{6} \Rightarrow y = 26.6°$ (to 3 s.f.)

Activity 40

Karen and Keith play golf. Their shots to the hole are shown as vectors.

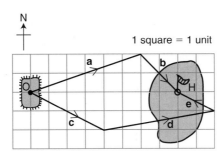

1 square = 1 unit

♦ Copy and complete this table by using the grid.

Vector	Column vector	Magnitude (to 3 s.f.)	Bearing
a	$\begin{pmatrix} 6 \\ 2 \end{pmatrix}$	6.32	072°
b			
c			
d			
e			

♦ Write down the vector $\overrightarrow{OH}$ and state if there is a connection between $\overrightarrow{OH}$ and the vectors **a**, **b** and the vectors **c**, **d**, **e**.

Vector geometry

Parallel and equivalent vectors

Two vectors are **parallel** if they have the same direction but not necessarily equal size.

For example, these vectors **a** and **b** are parallel.

$$\mathbf{a} = \begin{pmatrix} 3 \\ 2 \end{pmatrix} \qquad \mathbf{b} = \begin{pmatrix} 6 \\ 4 \end{pmatrix}$$

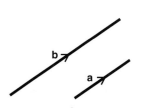

Two vectors are **equivalent** if they have the same direction and size.

Addition of vectors

The result of adding a set of vectors is the vector representing their total effect. This is the **resultant** of the vectors.

To add a number of vectors, they are placed end to end so that the next vector starts where the last one finished. The resultant vector joins the *start* of the first vector to the *end* of the last one.

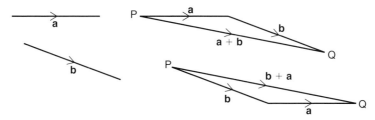

Vector $\overrightarrow{PQ} = \mathbf{a} + \mathbf{b} = \mathbf{b} + \mathbf{a}$

Multiplication of a vector by a scalar

When a vector is multiplied by a scalar, its length is multiplied by this number but its direction is unchanged, unless the scalar is *negative*, in which case the direction is *reversed*.

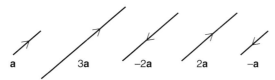

Example 3

Given vectors **a**, **b** and **c** as shown, draw the vector **r** where $\mathbf{r} = \mathbf{a} + \mathbf{b} - \mathbf{c}$.

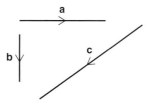

Here is the resultant of $\mathbf{a} + \mathbf{b} - \mathbf{c} = \mathbf{r}$.

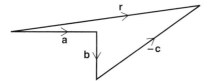

Example 4

ABCDEF is a regular hexagon with centre O.
$\overrightarrow{AB} = \mathbf{x}$ and $\overrightarrow{BC} = \mathbf{y}$. Express the vectors $\overrightarrow{ED}$,
$\overrightarrow{DE}$, $\overrightarrow{FE}$, $\overrightarrow{AC}$, $\overrightarrow{FA}$ and $\overrightarrow{AE}$ in terms of $\mathbf{x}$ and $\mathbf{y}$.

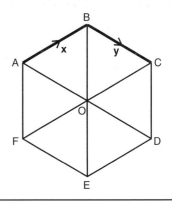

$\overrightarrow{ED} = \mathbf{x}$	$\overrightarrow{DE} = -\mathbf{x}$
$\overrightarrow{FE} = \mathbf{y}$	$\overrightarrow{AC} = \mathbf{x} + \mathbf{y}$
$\overrightarrow{FA} = \mathbf{x} - \mathbf{y}$	$\overrightarrow{AE} = 2\mathbf{y} - \mathbf{x}$

Exercise 58

Use this diagram to answer Questions 1–4.

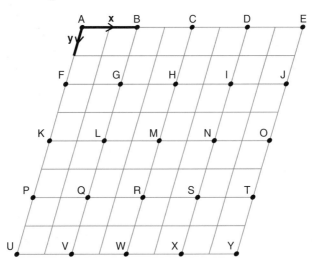

For Questions 1 and 2, express each vector in terms of $\mathbf{x}$ and $\mathbf{y}$.

1   **a** $\overrightarrow{XY}$ **b** $\overrightarrow{EO}$ **c** $\overrightarrow{WC}$ **d** $\overrightarrow{TP}$

2   **a** $\overrightarrow{KC}$ **b** $\overrightarrow{VC}$ **c** $\overrightarrow{CU}$ **d** $\overrightarrow{AS}$

For Questions 3 and 4, write the vector formed when the vectors given are added to point H as capital letters (e.g. $\overrightarrow{HO}$).

3   **a** $2\mathbf{x}$ **b** $\mathbf{x} + 2\mathbf{y}$ **c** $2\mathbf{y} - \mathbf{x}$ **d** $2\mathbf{x} + 2\mathbf{y}$

4   **a** $4\mathbf{y} + 2\mathbf{x}$ **b** $4\mathbf{y} - 2\mathbf{x}$ **c** $\mathbf{x} - 2\mathbf{y}$ **d** $2\mathbf{x} + 6\mathbf{y}$

In Questions 5–10, express each vector in terms of **x** and **y**.

5 ABCD is a rectangle.

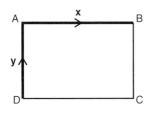

Find

a $\overrightarrow{DC}$ **b** $\overrightarrow{DB}$

c $\overrightarrow{BC}$ **d** $\overrightarrow{AC}$

6 ABCD is a trapezium.

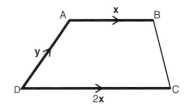

Find

a $\overrightarrow{AC}$ **b** $\overrightarrow{DB}$

c $\overrightarrow{BC}$ **d** $\overrightarrow{CB}$

7 ABCD is a parallelogram.

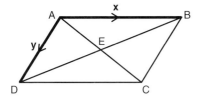

Find

a $\overrightarrow{DC}$ **b** $\overrightarrow{AC}$

c $\overrightarrow{BD}$ **d** $\overrightarrow{AE}$

8 ABCD is a rhombus.

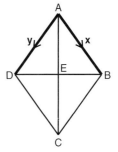

Find

a $\overrightarrow{BD}$ **b** $\overrightarrow{BE}$

c $\overrightarrow{AC}$ **d** $\overrightarrow{AE}$

9

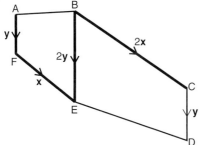

Find

a $\overrightarrow{AB}$ **b** $\overrightarrow{AD}$

c $\overrightarrow{CF}$ **d** $\overrightarrow{CA}$

10 ABC is an equilateral triangle, with $\overrightarrow{AC} = 2\mathbf{x}$, $\overrightarrow{AB} = 2\mathbf{y}$.

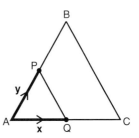

Find

a $\overrightarrow{PQ}$ **b** $\overrightarrow{PC}$

c $\overrightarrow{QB}$ **d** $\overrightarrow{BC}$

11 The gear stick of a car is shown. The lever can only shift along the grooves shown to reach each gear. N is neutral and R is reverse.

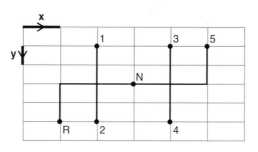

Express these gear changes in terms of **x** and **y**.

a 1st to 4th   **b** 3rd to 2nd

c N to R   **d** 2nd to 5th

12 A rectangular biscuit tin OABCDEFG is shown. $\overrightarrow{OA} = \mathbf{x}$, $\overrightarrow{AB} = \mathbf{y}$ and $\overrightarrow{OD} = \mathbf{z}$

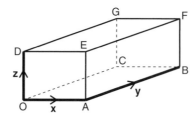

An ant crawls these direct journeys in search of crumbs. Express each journey as a vector in terms of **x**, **y** and **z**.

a $\overrightarrow{OE}$ **b** $\overrightarrow{OB}$ **c** $\overrightarrow{OF}$ **d** $\overrightarrow{EC}$

Example 5

In $\triangle OAB$, the mid-point on AB is M.
$\overrightarrow{OA} = \mathbf{x}$, $\overrightarrow{OB} = \mathbf{y}$, $\overrightarrow{OD} = 2\mathbf{x}$ and $\overrightarrow{OC} = 2\mathbf{y}$.

a Express $\overrightarrow{AB}$, $\overrightarrow{OM}$ and $\overrightarrow{DC}$ in terms of **x** and **y**.

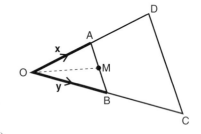

$$\overrightarrow{AB} = \overrightarrow{AO} + \overrightarrow{OB}$$
$$= -\mathbf{x} + \mathbf{y}$$
$$= \mathbf{y} - \mathbf{x}$$
$$\overrightarrow{DC} = \overrightarrow{DO} + \overrightarrow{OC}$$
$$= -2\mathbf{x} + 2\mathbf{y}$$
$$= 2\mathbf{y} - 2\mathbf{x}$$
$$= 2(\mathbf{y} - \mathbf{x})$$

$$\overrightarrow{OM} = \overrightarrow{OA} + \overrightarrow{AM}$$
$$= \overrightarrow{OA} + \tfrac{1}{2}\overrightarrow{AB}$$
$$= \mathbf{x} + \tfrac{1}{2}(\mathbf{y} - \mathbf{x})$$
$$= \mathbf{x} + \tfrac{1}{2}\mathbf{y} - \tfrac{1}{2}\mathbf{x}$$
$$= \tfrac{1}{2}\mathbf{x} + \tfrac{1}{2}\mathbf{y}$$
$$= \tfrac{1}{2}(\mathbf{x} + \mathbf{y})$$

b How are AB and DC related?
$\overrightarrow{DC} = 2\overrightarrow{AB}$, so AB is parallel to DC and half its magnitude.

Exercise 58★

In Questions 1–10, each vector should be expressed in terms of **x** and **y**, where $\overrightarrow{OA} = $ **x** and $\overrightarrow{OB} = $ **y**.

1 M is the mid-point of AB.

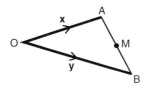

Find

a $\overrightarrow{AB}$ **b** $\overrightarrow{AM}$ **c** $\overrightarrow{OM}$

2 The ratio of AM:MB = 1:2.

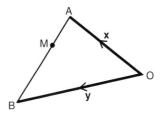

Find

a $\overrightarrow{AB}$ **b** $\overrightarrow{AM}$ **c** $\overrightarrow{OM}$

3 A and B are the mid-points of OD and OC respectively.

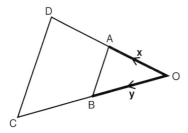

a Find $\overrightarrow{AB}$, $\overrightarrow{OD}$ and $\overrightarrow{DC}$.

b How are AB and DC related?

4 The ratio of OA:AD = 1:2 and B is the mid-point of OC.

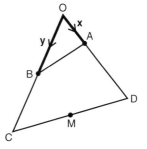

a Find $\overrightarrow{AB}$, $\overrightarrow{OD}$ and $\overrightarrow{DC}$.

b M is the mid-point of CD. Find $\overrightarrow{OM}$.

5 The ratio of OA:OC = 1:2 and OB:OD = 1:2.

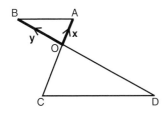

a Find $\overrightarrow{AB}$, $\overrightarrow{OC}$, $\overrightarrow{OD}$ and $\overrightarrow{DC}$.

b How are AB and DC related?

6 OABC is a parallelogram. The ratio of OD:DC = 1:2.

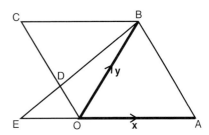

Find $\overrightarrow{AB}$, $\overrightarrow{OD}$, $\overrightarrow{BD}$, $\overrightarrow{OE}$ and $\overrightarrow{DE}$.

7 OABCDE is a regular hexagon.

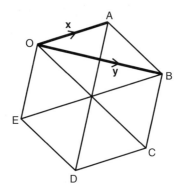

Find $\overrightarrow{AB}$, $\overrightarrow{BC}$, $\overrightarrow{AD}$ and $\overrightarrow{BD}$.

8 ABP is an equilateral triangle.

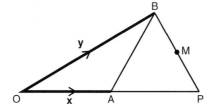

a Find $\overrightarrow{OP}$, $\overrightarrow{AB}$ and $\overrightarrow{BP}$.

b M is the mid-point of BP. Find $\overrightarrow{OM}$.

9 OM:MA = 2:3 and AN = $\frac{3}{5}$ AB.

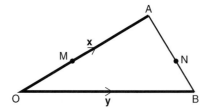

a Find $\overrightarrow{MA}$, $\overrightarrow{AB}$, $\overrightarrow{AN}$ and $\overrightarrow{MN}$.

b How are OB and MN related?

10 OM:MB = 1:2 and AN = $\frac{1}{3}$ AB.

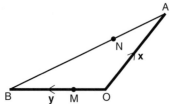

a Find $\overrightarrow{AB}$ and $\overrightarrow{MN}$.

b How are OA and MN related?

More addition, subtraction and multiplication

Vectors can be added, subtracted and multiplied using their components.

Example 6

$$\mathbf{s} = \begin{pmatrix} 1 \\ 2 \end{pmatrix}, \mathbf{t} = \begin{pmatrix} 3 \\ 0 \end{pmatrix} \text{ and } \mathbf{u} = \begin{pmatrix} -2 \\ 5 \end{pmatrix}$$

a Express as column vectors: $\mathbf{p} = \mathbf{s} + \mathbf{t} + \mathbf{u}$, $\mathbf{q} = \mathbf{s} - 2\mathbf{t} - \mathbf{u}$ and $\mathbf{r} = 3\mathbf{s} + \mathbf{t} - 2\mathbf{u}$

b Sketch the resultants $\mathbf{p}$, $\mathbf{q}$ and $\mathbf{r}$ accurately.

c Find their magnitudes.

a Calculation	b Sketch	c Magnitude
$\mathbf{p} = \mathbf{s} + \mathbf{t} + \mathbf{u}$ $= \begin{pmatrix} 1 \\ 2 \end{pmatrix} + \begin{pmatrix} 3 \\ 0 \end{pmatrix} + \begin{pmatrix} -2 \\ 5 \end{pmatrix}$ $= \begin{pmatrix} 2 \\ 7 \end{pmatrix}$		Length of $\mathbf{p}$ $= \sqrt{2^2 + 7^2}$ $= \sqrt{53}$ $= 7.3$ to 1 d.p.
$\mathbf{q} = \mathbf{s} - 2\mathbf{t} - \mathbf{u}$ $= \begin{pmatrix} 1 \\ 2 \end{pmatrix} - 2\begin{pmatrix} 3 \\ 0 \end{pmatrix} - \begin{pmatrix} -2 \\ 5 \end{pmatrix}$ $= \begin{pmatrix} 1 \\ 2 \end{pmatrix} + \begin{pmatrix} -6 \\ 0 \end{pmatrix} + \begin{pmatrix} 2 \\ -5 \end{pmatrix}$ $= \begin{pmatrix} -3 \\ -3 \end{pmatrix}$		Length of $\mathbf{q}$ $= \sqrt{3^2 + 3^2}$ $= \sqrt{18}$ $= 4.2$ to 1 d.p.
$\mathbf{r} = 3\mathbf{s} + \mathbf{t} - 2\mathbf{u}$ $= 3\begin{pmatrix} 1 \\ 2 \end{pmatrix} + \begin{pmatrix} 3 \\ 0 \end{pmatrix} - 2\begin{pmatrix} -2 \\ 5 \end{pmatrix}$ $= \begin{pmatrix} 3 \\ 6 \end{pmatrix} + \begin{pmatrix} 3 \\ 0 \end{pmatrix} + \begin{pmatrix} 4 \\ -10 \end{pmatrix}$ $= \begin{pmatrix} 10 \\ -4 \end{pmatrix}$		Length of $\mathbf{r}$ $= \sqrt{10^2 + 4^2}$ $= \sqrt{116}$ $= 10.8$ to 1 d.p.

Exercise 59

1 Given that $\mathbf{p} = \begin{pmatrix} 2 \\ 3 \end{pmatrix}$ and $\mathbf{q} = \begin{pmatrix} 4 \\ 5 \end{pmatrix}$

simplify and express $\mathbf{p} + \mathbf{q}$, $\mathbf{p} - \mathbf{q}$ and $2\mathbf{p} + 3\mathbf{q}$ as column vectors.

2 Given that $\mathbf{u} = \begin{pmatrix} 1 \\ 2 \end{pmatrix}$, $\mathbf{v} = \begin{pmatrix} -4 \\ 3 \end{pmatrix}$ and $\mathbf{w} = \begin{pmatrix} 2 \\ -5 \end{pmatrix}$

simplify and express $\mathbf{u} + \mathbf{v} + \mathbf{w}$, $\mathbf{u} + 2\mathbf{v} - 3\mathbf{w}$ and $3\mathbf{u} - 2\mathbf{v} - \mathbf{w}$ as column vectors.

3 Given that $\mathbf{p} = \begin{pmatrix} 1 \\ 2 \end{pmatrix}$ and $\mathbf{q} = \begin{pmatrix} 3 \\ 4 \end{pmatrix}$

simplify and express $\mathbf{p} + \mathbf{q}$, $\mathbf{p} - \mathbf{q}$ and $2\mathbf{p} + 5\mathbf{q}$ as column vectors.

4 Given that $\mathbf{s} = \begin{pmatrix} 1 \\ -3 \end{pmatrix}$, $\mathbf{t} = \begin{pmatrix} 2 \\ 3 \end{pmatrix}$ and $\mathbf{u} = \begin{pmatrix} 4 \\ -5 \end{pmatrix}$

simplify and express $\mathbf{s} + \mathbf{t} + \mathbf{u}$, $2\mathbf{s} - \mathbf{t} + 2\mathbf{u}$ and $2\mathbf{u} - 3\mathbf{s}$ as column vectors.

5 Two vectors are defined as $\mathbf{v} = \begin{pmatrix} 3 \\ 1 \end{pmatrix}$ and $\mathbf{w} = \begin{pmatrix} 1 \\ 4 \end{pmatrix}$.

Express $\mathbf{v} + \mathbf{w}$, $2\mathbf{v} - \mathbf{w}$ and $\mathbf{v} - 2\mathbf{w}$ as column vectors, find the magnitude and draw the resultant vector triangle for each vector.

6 Two vectors are defined as $\mathbf{p} = \begin{pmatrix} 2 \\ -1 \end{pmatrix}$ and $\mathbf{q} = \begin{pmatrix} 3 \\ 5 \end{pmatrix}$.

Express $\mathbf{p} + \mathbf{q}$, $3\mathbf{p} + \mathbf{q}$ and $\mathbf{p} - 3\mathbf{q}$ as column vectors, find the magnitude and draw the resultant vector triangle for each vector.

7 Chloe, Leo and Max enter an orienteering competition. Each decides to take a different route described by these column vectors, where the units are in km:

$$\mathbf{s} = \begin{pmatrix} 1 \\ 1 \end{pmatrix} \qquad \mathbf{t} = \begin{pmatrix} 2 \\ 3 \end{pmatrix}$$

They all start from the same point P, and take 3 hours to complete their routes:

Chloe $\qquad \mathbf{s} + 2\mathbf{t}$
Leo $\qquad 2\mathbf{s} + \mathbf{t}$
Max $\qquad 5\mathbf{s} - \mathbf{t}$

a Express each journey as a column vector.

b Find the length of each journey, and hence calculate the average speed of each orienteer in km/hour.

8 Use the information in Question 7 to answer this question.

Chloe, Leo and Max were all aiming to be at their first marker position Q, which is at position vector $\begin{pmatrix} 1 \\ 5 \end{pmatrix}$ from point P.

a Find how far each of them was from Q after their journeys.

b Calculate the bearing of Q from each of the orienteers after their journeys.

Exercise 59★

1 Given that $\mathbf{p} = \begin{pmatrix} 2 \\ 1 \end{pmatrix}$ and $\mathbf{q} = \begin{pmatrix} 3 \\ -1 \end{pmatrix}$

find the magnitude and bearing of the vectors $\mathbf{p} + \mathbf{q}$, $\mathbf{p} - \mathbf{q}$ and $2\mathbf{p} - 3\mathbf{q}$.

2 Given that $\mathbf{r} = \begin{pmatrix} 1 \\ -3 \end{pmatrix}$ and $\mathbf{s} = \begin{pmatrix} 4 \\ 1 \end{pmatrix}$

find the magnitude and bearing of the vectors $2(\mathbf{r} + \mathbf{s})$, $3(\mathbf{r} - 2\mathbf{s})$ and $(4\mathbf{r} - 6\mathbf{s})\sin 30°$.

3 Given that $\mathbf{t} + \mathbf{u} = \begin{pmatrix} 1 \\ 1 \end{pmatrix}$ where $\mathbf{t} = \begin{pmatrix} m \\ 3 \end{pmatrix}$, $\mathbf{u} = \begin{pmatrix} 2 \\ n \end{pmatrix}$ and m and n are constants, find the values of m and n.

4 Given that $2\mathbf{v} - 3\mathbf{w} = \begin{pmatrix} 2 \\ -3 \end{pmatrix}$ where $\mathbf{v} = \begin{pmatrix} 5 \\ -m \end{pmatrix}$, $\mathbf{w} = \begin{pmatrix} n \\ 4 \end{pmatrix}$ and m and n are constants, find the values of m and n.

5 These vectors represent journeys undertaken by yachts in km.
Express each one in column vector form.

a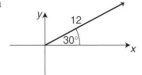

b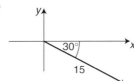

6 These vectors represent journeys undertaken by crows in km.
Express each one in column vector component form.

a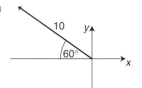

b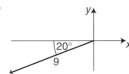

7 $\mathbf{s} = \begin{pmatrix} 2 \\ 3 \end{pmatrix}$ and $\mathbf{t} = \begin{pmatrix} -6 \\ 1 \end{pmatrix}$

   a If $m\mathbf{s} + n\mathbf{t} = \begin{pmatrix} -16 \\ 6 \end{pmatrix}$, solve this vector equation to find the constants m and n.

   b If $p\mathbf{s} + \mathbf{t} = \begin{pmatrix} 0 \\ q \end{pmatrix}$, solve this vector equation to find the constants p and q.

8 The centre spot of a hockey pitch O is the origin of coordinates, with the x-axis passing across the pitch, and the y-axis passing up the centre. All units are in metres.

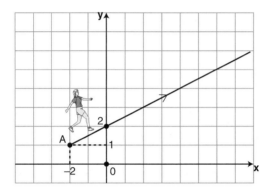

At $t = 0$, Anne is at A. When $t = 1$, Anne is at $(0, 2)$. Anne's position after t seconds is shown by the vector starting at point A.

   a Explain why after t seconds Anne's position vector $\mathbf{r}$ is given by

$$\mathbf{r} = \begin{pmatrix} -2 \\ 1 \end{pmatrix} + t\begin{pmatrix} 2 \\ 1 \end{pmatrix}$$

   b Find Anne's speed in m/s.

At $t = 0$, Fleur, who is positioned on the centre spot, O, hits the ball towards Anne's path so that Anne receives it 5 s after setting off.

The position vector of the ball hit by Fleur, $\mathbf{s}$, is given by

$$\mathbf{s} = (t - 3)\begin{pmatrix} a \\ b \end{pmatrix}$$

   c Find the value of constants a and b and hence the speed of the ball in m/s.

Activity 41

A radar tracking station O is positioned at the origin of x and y axes, where the x-axis points due East and the y-axis points due North. All the units are in km.

A helicopter is detected t minutes after midday with position vector $\mathbf{r}$, where

$$\mathbf{r} = \begin{pmatrix} 12 \\ 5 \end{pmatrix} + t\begin{pmatrix} -3 \\ 4 \end{pmatrix}$$

♦ Copy and complete this table and use it to plot the course of the helicopter.

Time	12:00 $t = 0$	12:01 $t = 1$	12:02 $t = 2$	12:03 $t = 3$	12:04 $t = 4$
r	$\begin{pmatrix} 12 \\ 5 \end{pmatrix}$				

♦ Calculate the speed of this helicopter in km/hour correct to 1 decimal place, and its bearing.

♦ An international boundary is described by the line $y = 5x$.
 ▸ Draw this boundary on your graph.
 ▸ Estimate the time the helicopter crosses the boundary by careful inspection of your graph.
 ▸ Considering the helicopter's position vector

$$\mathbf{r} = \begin{pmatrix} x \\ y \end{pmatrix}$$

 express x and y in terms of t and use these equations with $y = 5x$ to find the time when the boundary is crossed, correct to the nearest second.

Exercise 60 (Revision)

1 Given that $\mathbf{p} = \begin{pmatrix} 3 \\ 4 \end{pmatrix}$ and $\mathbf{q} = \begin{pmatrix} -2 \\ 1 \end{pmatrix}$

 simplify $\mathbf{p} + \mathbf{q}$, $\mathbf{p} - \mathbf{q}$ and $3\mathbf{p} - 2\mathbf{q}$ as column vectors and find the magnitude of each vector.

2 Given that $\mathbf{r} = \begin{pmatrix} 2 \\ -5 \end{pmatrix}$ and $\mathbf{s} = \begin{pmatrix} 3 \\ 4 \end{pmatrix}$

 simplify $\mathbf{r} + \mathbf{s}$, $\mathbf{r} - \mathbf{s}$ and $3\mathbf{s} - 2\mathbf{r}$ as column vectors and find the magnitude of each vector.

3 In terms of vectors **x** and **y**, find these vectors.

   a $\overrightarrow{AB}$ **b** $\overrightarrow{AC}$ **c** $\overrightarrow{CB}$

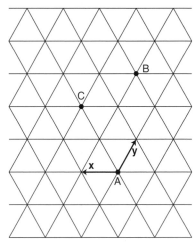

4 If $\overrightarrow{OA} = \mathbf{v}$ and $\overrightarrow{OB} = \mathbf{w}$ and M is the mid-point of AB.
Find these vectors in terms of **v** and **w**.

   a $\overrightarrow{AB}$ **b** $\overrightarrow{AM}$ **c** $\overrightarrow{OM}$

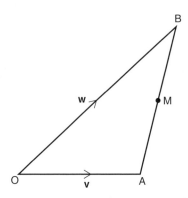

5 ABCDEF is a regular hexagon. Vectors $\overrightarrow{OA} = \mathbf{x}$ and $\overrightarrow{OB} = \mathbf{y}$.
Find these vectors in terms of **x** and **y**.

   a $\overrightarrow{AB}$ **b** $\overrightarrow{FB}$ **c** $\overrightarrow{FD}$

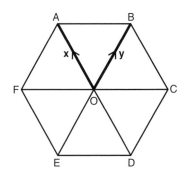

Exercise 60★ (Revision)

1 Given that $2\mathbf{p} - 3\mathbf{q} = \begin{pmatrix} 5 \\ 15 \end{pmatrix}$ where $\mathbf{p} = \begin{pmatrix} 4 \\ m \end{pmatrix}$, $\mathbf{q} = \begin{pmatrix} n \\ -3 \end{pmatrix}$ and m and n are constants, find the values of m and n.

2 If $\mathbf{r} = \begin{pmatrix} 4 \\ -1 \end{pmatrix}$, $\mathbf{s} = \begin{pmatrix} 3 \\ 7 \end{pmatrix}$ and $m\mathbf{r} + n\mathbf{s} = \begin{pmatrix} 7 \\ 37 \end{pmatrix}$, find constants m and n.

3 In the diagram, OXYZ is a parallelogram. M is the mid-point of XY.

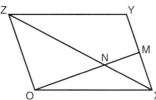

   a Given that $\overrightarrow{OX} = \begin{pmatrix} 8 \\ 0 \end{pmatrix}$ and $\overrightarrow{OZ} = \begin{pmatrix} -2 \\ 6 \end{pmatrix}$,

   write down the vectors $\overrightarrow{XM}$ and $\overrightarrow{XZ}$.

   b Given that $\overrightarrow{ON} = v\overrightarrow{OM}$, write down in terms of v the vector $\overrightarrow{ON}$.

   c Given that $\overrightarrow{ON} = \overrightarrow{OX} + w\overrightarrow{XZ}$, find in terms of w the vector $\overrightarrow{ON}$.

   d Solve two simultaneous equations to find v and w.

4 ABCD is a parallelogram in which $\overrightarrow{AB} = \mathbf{x}$ and $\overrightarrow{BC} = \mathbf{y}$. AE:ED = 1:2.

   a Express in terms of $\mathbf{x}$ and $\mathbf{y}$, $\overrightarrow{AC}$ and $\overrightarrow{BE}$.

   b AC and BE intersect at F, such that $\overrightarrow{BF} = v\overrightarrow{BE}$.

   (i)   Express $\overrightarrow{BF}$ in terms of $\mathbf{x}$, $\mathbf{y}$ and v.

   (ii) Show that $\overrightarrow{AF} = (1 - v)\mathbf{x} + \tfrac{1}{3}v\mathbf{y}$.

   (iii) Use this expression for $\overrightarrow{AF}$ to find the value of v.

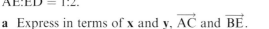

5 A shooting star's position vector $\mathbf{r}$, t seconds after being detected on radar, is given by

   $$\mathbf{r} = \begin{pmatrix} 12 \\ 7 \end{pmatrix} + t\begin{pmatrix} -11 \\ 3 \end{pmatrix}$$

   where the units are in km.

   a Find the position vector $\mathbf{r}$ of the star after $t = 0$, $t = 1$, $t = 2$ and $t = 3$ seconds.

   b Plot the star's route across the radar screen for the first 3 seconds.

   c Calculate its speed in km/hour correct to 3 significant figures, and its bearing.

Handling data 3

More probability

The rules of probability are quite simple; more challenging questions require a deeper understanding and an efficient use of these laws.

Multiplication ('and') rule

If two events A and B can occur without being affected by one another (for example, a dice is thrown and it starts to rain!), they are **independent**.

Example 1

A coin is flipped and a dice is thrown. Find the probability that the result is a tail and a multiple of three.

Event T is a tail thrown: $p(\text{T}) = \frac{1}{2}$

Event M is a multiple of three is rolled: $p(\text{M}) = \frac{2}{6}$

Probability of T and M: $p(\text{T and M}) = p(\text{T}) \times p(\text{M})$

$$= \frac{1}{2} \times \frac{2}{6}$$

$$= \frac{1}{6}$$

Addition ('or') rule

If two events A and B *cannot* occur at the same time (for example, a card drawn from a pack cannot be an Ace and a Queen) they are called **mutually exclusive**.

Key Point

If A and B are mutually exclusive:

$$p(A \text{ or } B) = p(A) + p(B)$$

This makes sense, as adding fractions produces a larger fraction and the condition of one or other event happening implies a greater chance.

Example 2

A card is randomly selected from a pack of 52 playing cards.

4 aces

4 queens

Find the probability that either an Ace or a Queen is selected.

Event A is an Ace is picked out: $p(A) = \frac{4}{52}$

Event Q is a Queen is picked out: $p(Q) = \frac{4}{52}$

Probability of A or Q: $p(A \text{ or } Q) = p(A) + p(Q)$

$$= \frac{4}{52} + \frac{4}{52}$$
$$= \frac{8}{52}$$
$$= \frac{2}{13}$$

Probability tree diagrams

Tree diagrams can be used to show all possible outcomes of a sequence of events. Together with the 'and' and 'or' rules, they can make problems easier to solve.

Example 3

Ghost Boy is an albino koala bear in San Diego Zoo. Albinos are born without melanin in their skin, which results in them having a very pale complexion and white fur in this case.

The probability of a koala having the albino gene is $\frac{1}{75}$. The albino gene must be inherited from *both* parents, but then only one out of four cubs produced by a pair of albino-gene carriers is an albino cub.

Find the probability of two randomly paired koalas producing an albino cub like Ghost Boy.

Let event C represent an albino-gene carrier and event $\overline{C}$ be a non-albino-gene carrier.

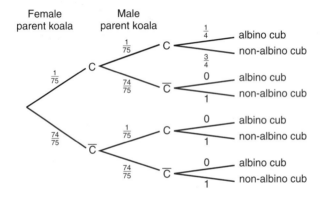

Let event A be that an albino koala cub is born. Then

$$p(A) = p(C) \times p(C) \times \frac{1}{4}$$

$$= \frac{1}{75} \times \frac{1}{75} \times \frac{1}{4}$$

$$= \frac{1}{22\,500}$$

Clearly, Ghost Boy is a rare creature!

Note: Only part of the tree diagram needed to be drawn to work out the probabilities. It is not always necessary to draw *all* the branches, this can overcomplicate the picture. A selection of branches may be sufficient to solve a problem, but you must ensure that all 'routes' are included.

Exercise 61

Use tree diagrams in these questions where appropriate.

1 Two normal six-sided dice have their spots covered and replaced by the letters U, V, W, X, Y and Z, with one letter on each face. If two such dice are thrown, calculate the probability that they show:

a two vowels   **b** a vowel and a consonant.

2 Six small plastic tiles are placed in a bag and jumbled up. Each tile has a single letter on it, the letters being B, O and Y. There are two 'B's, two 'O's and two 'Y's.

a If one tile is removed at a time without replacement and the letters are placed in order from left to right, calculate the probability that the word formed is

(i) BOY   (ii) YOB   (iii) BOB.

b If two letter 'S's are placed in the bag from the start, what is the probability that after four selections, the word BOYS is *not* formed?

3 Teresa loves playing tennis. If the day is sunny, the probability that she plays tennis is 0.7. If it is not a sunny day, the probability that she plays tennis is 0.4. Also, the probability that Saturday will not be sunny is 0.15. Use a tree diagram to find the probabilities of these outcomes

a Teresa plays tennis on Saturday.

b Teresa does not play tennis on Saturday.

4 The probability of the Gatwick Express train to Victoria Station arriving late is 0.3. The probability that it arrives on time is 0.6. What is the probability that the train

a is early?   **b** is not late?   **c** is on time for two days in a row?

d is late on a given Friday, but not late on the next two days?

e is late exactly once over a period of three days in a row?

5 A box contains five distinctly different pairs of gloves. Kiril is in a hurry and randomly selects two gloves without replacement. What is the probability that

a the gloves are both right-handed?

b the gloves will be a right- and a left-handed glove?

c they will be a matching pair?

6 A drawer contains four pairs of black socks, three pairs of blue, two pairs of green, one pair of yellow and one odd red sock. Two socks are randomly selected without replacement. What is the probability that

a they are both black?

b they are both the same colour?

c one of the socks is a red one?

Example 4

Female elephants are called cows; male elephants are called bulls.

The probability that a particular elephant gives birth to a cow is $\frac{3}{5}$.

Use a tree diagram to find the probability that from three births she has produced exactly two bulls.

Let event C be the birth of a cow, and event B the birth of a bull. Consider a series of three births, being careful only to plot the paths required. There are three combinations that result in exactly two bulls from three births: BBC, BCB or CBB.

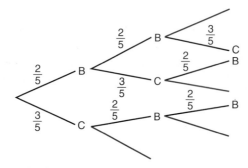

Note: Only part of the tree diagram is needed.

$$p(\text{exactly 2 bulls from 3 births}) = p(\text{BBC}) + p(\text{BCB}) + p(\text{CBB})$$
$$= \left(\frac{2}{5} \times \frac{2}{5} \times \frac{3}{5}\right) + \left(\frac{2}{5} \times \frac{3}{5} \times \frac{2}{5}\right) + \left(\frac{3}{5} \times \frac{2}{5} \times \frac{2}{5}\right)$$
$$= \frac{12}{125} \quad + \quad \frac{12}{125} \quad + \quad \frac{12}{125}$$
$$= \frac{36}{125}$$

Alternatively, because multiplication is commutative (independent of the order), one combination could have been considered (BBC say) and multiplied by 3, as the fractions do not change.

Exercise 61 ★

1 A bag contains three bananas, four pears and five kiwi-fruits. One piece of fruit is randomly withdrawn from the bag and eaten before the next is taken. Use a tree diagram to find these probabilities:

   a That the first two fruits picked out are pears

   b That the second fruit picked out is a pear

   c That the first three fruits withdrawn are all different

   d That neither of the first two fruits picked out is a banana, but the third is a banana.

2 A box contains three £1 coins, five 50p coins and four 20p coins. Two are selected randomly from the bag without replacement. What is the probability that:

a the two coins are of equal value?

b the two coins will total less than £1?

c at least one of the coins will be a 50p coin?

3 Mr and Mrs Hilliam plan a family of four children. If babies of either sex are equally likely and assuming that only single babies are born, what is the probability of the Hilliam children being

a four girls?   **b** three girls?   **c** at least one girl?

4 A new technique is 80% successful in detecting cancer in infected patients. If cancer is detected, an appropriate operation has a 75% success rate, the first time it is attempted. If this operation is unsuccessful, it can be repeated only twice more, with success rates of 50% and 25% respectively. What is the probability of an infected patient

a being operated on successfully once?

b being cured at the third operation?

c being cured?

5 A bag X contains ten coloured discs of which four are white and six are red. A bag Y contains eight coloured discs of which five are white and three are red. A disc is drawn at random from X and placed in Y. A second disc is now drawn at random from X and placed in Y.

a Using a tree diagram, show that the probability that the two discs drawn are both red is $\frac{1}{3}$.

b Copy and complete this table.

Outcome		Probability
Bag X	**Bag Y**	
4R + 4W	5R + 5W	$\frac{1}{3}$
5R + 3W		
	3R + 7W	

c A disc is now drawn at random from the ten in Y and placed in X, so that there are now nine discs in each bag. Find the probability that there are:

(i) four red discs in bag X

(ii) seven red discs in bag X

(iii) six red discs in bag X

(iv) five red discs in bag X

6 Two gamblers, Omar and Yosef, decide to play a simple game with a single fair die. The winner is the first player to roll a six! Omar goes first. What is the probability that:

a Omar wins the game?   **b** Yosef wins the game?

Activity 42

The randomised response questionnaire technique was pioneered in America to find out the proportion of people who have participated in antisocial, embarrassing or illegal activities. Most people would not answer questions truthfully, but this method involves responding truthfully depending on the scores on two dice. There is no reason for anyone *not* to tell the truth, because each person can keep their dice score to themselves.

Two dice are used for each person: one black, one white. The black dice is rolled first. If it is even, the survey question must be answered truthfully. If it is odd, the white dice is rolled and the respondent must answer the question, 'Is the white dice number even?' truthfully.

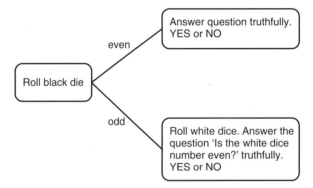

The number of respondents who answer YES is noted.

If 60 people responded to the question, 'Do you copy your homework?' and 24 answered 'yes', it is possible to estimate how many of this sample of 60 cheat with their homework.

♦ Show that the proportion of the group who copy homework is probably $\frac{3}{20}$

♦ Set a suitable question (not of an embarrassing nature!) which people may be reluctant to admit openly to answering truthfully and then carry out your own randomised response survey. Why would you wish to make your sample size as large as practicable?

Double six!!!

Scoring two sixes on two dice is a highly desirable score to obtain in many games played throughout the world. Backgammon and Monopoly are two examples where scoring the magical double six score gives the player a great advantage.

How many rolls of a single dice would you expect to make before you obtain a six?

♦ Gather data to examine this problem practically by copying and completing the table.

Number of throws to obtain a six, x	Frequency, f
1	
2	
3	
4	
5	
6	
7	
⋮	

♦ Calculate the mean value of x.

♦ Use a simple computer application to simulate rolling the dice many more times and compare your answers.

♦ Try to investigate (by spreadsheet?) the result by producing a series that sums to give the mean value of x.

♦ Compare all your answers and comment.

How many rolls of two dice would you expect before you obtain a double six?

♦ Use a simple computer application to simulate this practical many times.

♦ Try to investigate (by spreadsheet?) the result be producing a series that sums to give the mean value of x.

♦ Compare your answers and comment.

Exercise 62 (Revision)

1   Gina and Iona are involved in a Ski Instructor Test. They are only allowed one re-test should they fail the first. Their probabilities of passing are as shown.

	Gina	Iona
P(pass on 1st test)	0.7	0.4
P(pass on 2nd test)	0.9	0.6

These probabilities are independent of each other. Calculate the probability that:

a Iona becomes a ski instructor at the second attempt

b Gina passes at her first attempt whilst Iona fails her first test

c only one of the girls becomes a ski instructor, assuming that a re-test is taken if the first test is failed.

2   Melissa is growing apple and pear trees for her orchard. She plants seeds in her greenhouse, but forgets to label the seedling pots. She knows that the types of apple and pear trees are in the numbers shown.

	Eating	Cooking
Apple	24	76
Pear	62	38

She picks out an apple seedling at random.

a Estimate the probability that it is an eater.

b Estimate the probability that it is a cooker.

She picks out an eater seedling at random.

c Estimate the probability that it is an apple.

d Estimate the probability that it is a pear.

e She picks out three seedlings at random without replacement. Find the probability that she ends up with at least one eating apple seedling.

3   The probability that a seagull lays a certain number of eggs is as shown.

Number of eggs	Probability
0	0.1
1	0.2
2	0.3
3	0.2
4	0.1
5 or more	0.1

What is the probability that

a a seagull lays more than four eggs?

b a seagull lays no eggs?

c two seagulls lay a total of at least four eggs?

4 A football player works out from his previous season's results the probabilities of him scoring goals in a game.

Number of goals	Probability
0	0.4
1	0.3
2	0.2
3 or more	0.1

Assume that these probabilities apply to the current season.

a Find the probability that in a game he scores at most two goals.

b Find the probability that in a game he scores four goals.

c What is the probability that in two games he scores at least three goals?

Exercise 62★ (Revision)

1 Christmas lights are produced in a large batch such that one-fifth are defective. If lights are removed in turn from this large batch, find the probability from the first three lights of

   a one defective   **b** two defectives   **c** at least one defective

2 Batteries are made on a factory production line such that 15% are faulty. If batteries are removed for quality control, find the probability from the first three batteries of

   a no defectives   **b** two defectives   **c** at least two defective

3 A veterinary surgeon has three independent tests A, B and C for the presence of a virus in a cow. Tests are performed in the order A, B, C.

Probabilities of a positive test depending on the presence of the virus			
	Test A	**Test B**	**Test C**
Virus present	$\frac{2}{3}$	$\frac{4}{5}$	$\frac{5}{6}$
Virus *not* present	$\frac{1}{5}$	$\frac{1}{6}$	$\frac{1}{7}$

a Find the probability that two tests will be positive and one negative on an infected cow.

b If two positive tests is the minimum criterion for indicating an infected cow, find the probability that:

   (i)   after three tests on an infected cow, the criterion is *not* met

   (ii) after three tests on an uninfected cow, the criterion *is* met.

4 In a multiple choice test Karen has not revised and has no idea of the correct answer. She guesses the answers and has a probability of p of obtaining the right option. From the first three questions the probability of her getting only one correct is 0.243. Find p.

Numeracy practice 3

Skills practice

Number

Work out these.

1 2.67×0.7 **2** 4.97×0.3 **3** $5.8 \div 0.2$ **4** $93 \div 0.3$

5 35.6×1.4 **6** 48.7×1.3 **7** $40.8 \div 12$ **8** $68.4 \div 12$

9 $45 - 0.01$ **10** $6.3 - 0.001$ **11** $3^5 - 3^4$ **12** $4^4 - 4^3$

13 $\sqrt{1.44}$ **14** $\sqrt{0.81}$ **15** $10^3 \div 10^4$ **16** $10^2 \div 10^4$

17 $3^{-2} \times 6^3$ **18** $6^{-2} \times 3^3$ **19** $2^{\frac{1}{3}} \times 2^{\frac{1}{3}} \times 2^{\frac{1}{3}}$ **20** $3^{\frac{1}{2}} \times 3^{\frac{1}{2}}$

21 $163.2 \div 17$ **22** $101.4 \div 13$ **23** $6^4 \div 3^4$ **24** $4^4 \div 2^4$

Give your answer to these in standard form.

25 $(2.4 \times 10^5) \times (1.5 \times 10^{-3})$ **26** $(4.5 \times 10^5) \times (1.4 \times 10^{-7})$

27 $(2.4 \times 10^4) \div (1.6 \times 10^{-3})$ **28** $(3.6 \times 10^{-5}) \div (1.5 \times 10^3)$

Algebra

Simplify these

1 $3x^2 - 6x^2 + 2x^2$ **2** $x^2 - 4x^2 + 3x^2$ **3** $4xy^2 \times 2x^2y$

4 $3yx^2 \times 4xy^2$ **5** $\dfrac{4ba^2}{2ab^2}$ **6** $\dfrac{6xy^3}{3x^2y}$

7 $x - (x^2 - 2) + x^2$ **8** $p - (p^3 + 3) + 3$ **9** $\dfrac{a}{3} + \dfrac{a}{2}$

10 $\dfrac{a}{2} + \dfrac{a}{6}$ **11** $\dfrac{x}{2y} \times \dfrac{y^2}{3}$ **12** $\dfrac{a^2}{2b} \times \dfrac{2b^2}{a}$

Solve these for x.

13 $\dfrac{19}{x} = 3.8$ **14** $\dfrac{17}{x} = 3.4$ **15** $8.7 - 2x = 7.8$

16 $12.6 - 2x = 9.5$ **17** $3(x - 5) = 2(8 - x)$ **18** $5(x - 6) = 2(3 - 2x)$

19 $\dfrac{2x^2 - 4}{2} = 23$ **20** $\dfrac{3x^2 + 12}{4} = 15$ **21** $0 = x^2 - 5x - 14$

22 $0 = x^2 - 6x + 9$

Substitute $a = 3.2$ and $b = -0.8$ to find the value of these.

23 $\dfrac{a^2}{a} - b$ **24** $\dfrac{b^2}{b} + a$ **25** $(a - b)^3$ **26** $(b - a)^3$

Challenges

1 **a** Factorise $3x^2 - 27y^2$ and hence find the three factors of 2 999 973.

   b Use factors to find the exact value of $824\,931^2 - 824\,939 \times 913\,823$.

2 These circles are concentric and the 20 cm line is a tangent to the inner circle.

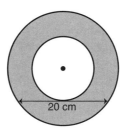

   Find the shaded area.

3 Copy and complete the cross-number. (No answer can begin with zero.)

Across
1A $6D \times 5$
4A $6A + 7A$

Down
2D 7A squared
3D A multiple of 6D
5D $3D \times 2$

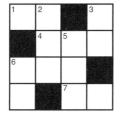

4 Find an estimate of the probability of a motorist having to wait at a certain set of traffic lights near to your home or school.

5 In the multiplication sums, each letter represents a different number.
Find the number that each letter represents. (There are two possibilities for part **a**.)

  a
```
  THING
      H ×
  ─────
  SHAWL
```

  b
```
  - - - -
     YD ×
  ───────
   CDXY
  XBYDB
  ──────
  XCSYCY
```

6 The diagram shows a sailing boat with two masts of height 12 m and 8 m.

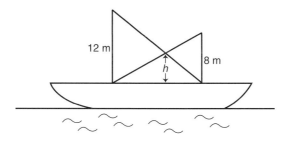

   Use similar triangles to find the height h above the deck where the two supporting wires cross.

Fact finder: Mount Vesuvius

There have been many volcanic eruptions and earthquakes of catastrophic proportions in the world's history, many of which have been far more powerful than Italy's Mount Vesuvius.

In **1815**, **92 000** people died due to the Tambora volcano's eruption in Indonesia, and in **1976**, **242 000** people perished when an earthquake shook Tangshan in eastern China.

However, the eruption of Vesuvius in AD **79** has become infamous due to the extraordinary documentation of the event and its impact on the towns of Pompei and Herculaneum. The instability of the area is due to the northward movement of the African tectonic plate at **3 cm per year**. The eruption lasted three days, during which time the sky was dark with dust and ash ejected **17 km** into the air covering nearby villages and towns in just a few hours. Pompei (population **20 000**) was covered with **7 m** of hot ash while Herculaneum (population **5000**) was hit by a rapid mud-flow **25 m** deep, which captured people and animals as they tried to escape. During the eruption, **4 km³** of magma and **10⁶ m³** of lapilli (fine ash) were spewed out in **24 hours** causing **3600** lives to be lost.

Many artefacts were perfectly preserved in Herculaneum due to the protection of the deep mud-flow. These are kept in the Naples Museum, where they have inspired poets, philosophers and scientists over the years.

The present-day summit of **1281 m** would have been dwarfed by the height of the volcano in the year **700 AD** of **3000 m**. Since **1631** there have been major eruptions from Vesuvius in **1760**, **1794**, **1858**, **1861**, **1872**, **1906**, **1929**, **1933** and **1944**.

The top of the crater today is an enormous circular chasm **600 m** in diameter and **200 m** deep. Walking around the summit takes about **one hour** and vapour can still be seen escaping from fumaroles (cracks), some of which have temperatures of **500°C** indicating that Vesuvius is still active. If the volcano were to erupt to the same strength as in **79 AD**, it would require the evacuation of about **600 000** people. Vesuvius is modelled as a right-circular pyramid whose top has been blown off. Its cross-section is as shown.

NOT TO SCALE

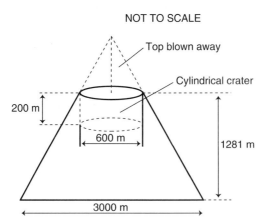

Exercise

1 How many years elapsed between the infamous volcanic destruction of Pompei and the Tambora eruption?

2 What percentage of the population of Pompei and Herculaneum perished due to the volcanic activity?

3 How many years will the African tectonic plate take to shift one mile northwards? (1 mile ≈ 1600 m)

4 What is the percentage decrease in the height of Vesuvius from that in the year AD 700?

5 Given that C degrees Celsius is related to F degrees Fahrenheit by the formula $C = 5(F - 32)/9$, find the temperature around some of the fumaroles in the crater of Vesuvius today in degrees Fahrenheit.

6 Calculate the speed a tourist travels, in m/s, walking around the top of the crater of Vesuvius.

7 Given that the approximate areas of Herculaneum and Pompei are half a square mile and four square miles respectively, calculate an estimate in m^3 in standard form to three significant figures of these:

   a the volume of hot mud-flow that filled Herculaneum

   b the volume of hot ash that fell on Pompei.

8 a Since 1631, what is the average number of years between major volcanic activities in Vesuvius?

   b Using these data, when would you reasonably expect the next eruption of Vesuvius?

9 Calculate in m^3/s, in standard form correct to 3 significant figures the rate at which magma was thrown out from Vesuvius in AD 79.

10 a Given that the average density of magma from Vesuvius in AD 79 was approximately $4500 \, kg/m^3$, calculate the mass of magma spilled out in tonnes per second.

   b Compare your answer in a to an average family car of mass 1 tonne. (1 tonne = 1000 kg)

11 Calculate an estimate of the volume of Mount Vesuvius in m^3 in standard index form correct to 3 significant figures. $\left(\text{Volume of cone} = \frac{1}{3}\pi r^2 h\right)$

12 Calculate an estimate of the area of the slopes of Mount Vesuvius in km^2 correct to 3 significant figures. (Curved surface area of cone $= \pi r l$)

Navigation

A radar tracking station O is taken as the origin of coordinates, with the x-axis pointing due East and the y-axis pointing due North, all units being in km.

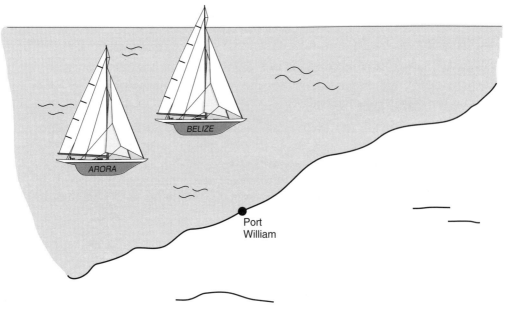

1 Two yachts, Arora (A) and Belize (B), are first detected on the radar at noon.

Their position vectors, $\mathbf{r} = \begin{pmatrix} x \\ y \end{pmatrix}$ relative to O, t hours after noon are:

$$\mathbf{r}_A = \begin{pmatrix} -7 \\ 1 \end{pmatrix} + t\begin{pmatrix} 10 \\ 6 \end{pmatrix} \quad \text{and} \quad \mathbf{r}_B = \begin{pmatrix} 1 \\ 1 \end{pmatrix} + t\begin{pmatrix} 5 \\ 7 \end{pmatrix}$$

   a Copy and complete this table and use it to plot the course of both yachts during the time period shown. (Scales: x and y axes 1 cm to 2 km.)

t (h)	0	2	3
$\mathbf{r}_A$	$\begin{pmatrix} -7 \\ 1 \end{pmatrix}$		
$\mathbf{r}_B$	$\begin{pmatrix} 1 \\ 1 \end{pmatrix}$		

   b Calculate the speeds of both yachts in km/hour correct to 3 significant figures.

   c Mark on your graph the position where the paths of the yachts cross with the letter P. Does this point indicate a collision?

2 Part of the coastline is given by the equation $2y = x - 12$, valid for $12 \leqslant x \leqslant 28$. Draw the coastline on your graph, indicating Port William at position $(16, 2)$.

3 Due to an approaching storm the coastguard radios orders to both yachts to change direction immediately to dock at Port William. The position vector of Arora relative to O, u hours after 3pm, is given by

$$\mathbf{r}_A = \begin{pmatrix} 23 \\ 19 \end{pmatrix} + u \begin{pmatrix} -3.5 \\ -8.5 \end{pmatrix}$$

  a What time does Arora dock at Port William?

  b Belize heads directly for Port William, arriving at the same time as Arora. Write down its position vector relative to O, u hours after 3 p.m.

  c Plot the courses of both yachts to Port William on your graph and calculate the speeds of the yachts in km/hour correct to 3 significant figures.

4 **Investigate** the closest distance between Arora and Belize between noon and 3 p.m. and the time at which this occurs.

5 At 3 p.m., Yacht Corsica signals a distress call from $(-2, 23)$. A rescue helicopter H heads directly for this position. Its position vector relative to O is given by

$$\mathbf{r}_H = \begin{pmatrix} 24 \\ -3 \end{pmatrix} + u \begin{pmatrix} -15 \\ 15 \end{pmatrix}$$

Calculate the time at which the helicopter arrives at Corsica.

6 If $\mathbf{r}_H = \begin{pmatrix} a \\ b \end{pmatrix} + u \begin{pmatrix} c \\ d \end{pmatrix}$

investigate the relationship between a, b, c, d and the helicopter's

  a speed

  b bearing

  c distance moved u hours after 3 p.m.

Summary 3

Financial arithmetic

♦ Taxation (net income is that which remains after tax and other deductions)

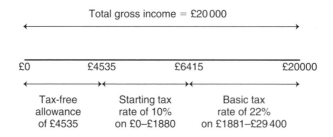

Taxable income = £20 000 − £4535 = £15 465

Tax at starting rate = 10% of £1880 = £188

Tax at basic rate = 22% of (£15 465 − £1880) = £2988.70

Net income = £20 000 − £188 − £2988.70 = £16 823.30

♦ Percentages
To add VAT at, say 17.5%, to the original price: multiply by 1.175.
To subtract VAT at, say 17.5%, from the total price: divide by 1.175.

♦ Compound percentage formula: $A = P\left(1 + \dfrac{R}{100}\right)^n$

Loans
When money is borrowed, on credit cards, mortgages, loans, etc., interest is charged. The money borrowed and the interest have to be repaid over an agreed period of time.

Algebra

Solving quadratic equations by factorising

$x^2 - 2x - 8 = 0$ (Factorise)

$(x + 2)(x - 4) = 0$

$\Rightarrow \qquad (x + 2) = 0 \qquad$ or $\quad (x - 4) = 0$

$\Rightarrow \qquad\qquad x = -2 \quad$ or $\qquad x = 4$

Solving quadratic equations by completing the square

$x^2 + 4x - 2 = 0$ (Completing the square)

$(x + 2)^2 - 4 - 2 = 0$

$(x + 2)^2 = 6$

$x + 2 = \pm\sqrt{6}$

$\therefore \quad x = \sqrt{6} - 2 = 0.449$ or $x = -\sqrt{6} - 2 = -4.45$ (to 3 s.f.)

Solving quadratic equations by the formula

If $ax^2 + bx + c = 0$ then

$$x = \frac{-b \pm \sqrt{b^2 - 4ac}}{2a}$$

$x^2 + 4x - 2 = 0 \qquad a = 1, b = 4, c = -2$

$$\therefore \quad x = \frac{-4 \pm \sqrt{16 + 8}}{2}$$

so $\quad x = \dfrac{-4 + \sqrt{24}}{2}$ or $x = \dfrac{-4 - \sqrt{24}}{2}$

giving $x = 0.449$ or $x = -4.45$ (to 3 s.f.)

Solving simultaneous equations, one linear and one nonlinear

$$y = 2x^2 - x - 4 \qquad ①$$
$$y = 2 - x \qquad\qquad ②$$

From ②

$$x = (2 - y) \qquad ③$$

Substituting ③ into ①

$$y = 2(2 - y)^2 - (2 - y) - 4$$
$$\therefore \quad 0 = 2y^2 - 8y + 2$$

Using the formula, $y = 3.732$ or $y = 0.2679$ (to 4 s.f.)

Using $x = 2 - y$ gives $x = -1.73$ or $x = 1.73$ (to 3 s.f.)

So solutions are $x = -1.73$, $y = 3.73$ or $x = 1.73$, $y = 0.268$.

UNIT 3 ◆ Summary 3

Functions

♦ Notation. If $f(x) = x^2 - x$ then $f(2) = 2^2 - 2 = 2$ and
$f(-3) = (-3)^2 - (-3) = 9 + 3 = 12$.

♦ Graphs of functions. To draw the graph of $f(x) = x^2 - x$, plot $f(x)$ against x.

Function	Transformation
♦ $f(x) + a$	Translation $\begin{pmatrix} 0 \\ a \end{pmatrix}$
♦ $f(x - a)$	Translation $\begin{pmatrix} a \\ 0 \end{pmatrix}$
♦ $-f(x)$	Reflection in the x-axis
♦ $f(-x)$	Reflection in the y-axis
♦ $af(x)$	One-way stretch, parallel to y-axis, with scale factor a
♦ $f(ax)$	One-way stretch, parallel to x-axis, with scale factor $1/a$

Vector notation

Vectors have magnitude and direction and can be written as bold letters: **v**, **u**, ..., with capitals covered by an arrow: $\overrightarrow{OP}$, $\overrightarrow{OQ}$, ... or on coordinate axes as column vectors

$\begin{pmatrix} 3 \\ -1 \end{pmatrix}$, $\begin{pmatrix} 0 \\ 6 \end{pmatrix}$, ...

Multiplication of a vector by a scalar

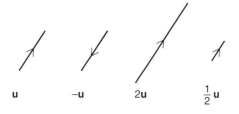

u   −**u**   2**u** $\frac{1}{2}$**u**

Vector geometry

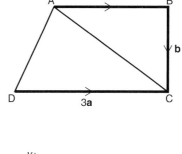

♦ $\overrightarrow{AC} = \overrightarrow{AB} + \overrightarrow{BC} = 2\mathbf{a} + \mathbf{b}$

∴ $\overrightarrow{AD} = \overrightarrow{AC} + \overrightarrow{CD}$

$= 2\mathbf{a} + \mathbf{b} + (-3\mathbf{a}) = \mathbf{b} - \mathbf{a}$

AB is parallel to DC. ∴ ABCD is a trapezium

Ratio of AB:DC = 2:3. ∴ 2DC = 3AB

♦ $\overrightarrow{OD} = \begin{pmatrix} 3 \\ 0 \end{pmatrix}$, $\overrightarrow{DC} = \begin{pmatrix} -2 \\ 4 \end{pmatrix}$, $\overrightarrow{CA} = \begin{pmatrix} -2 \\ -2 \end{pmatrix}$

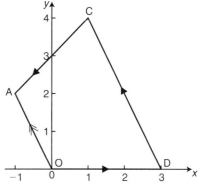

∴ $\overrightarrow{OA} = \overrightarrow{OD} + \overrightarrow{DC} + \overrightarrow{CA}$

$= \begin{pmatrix} 3 \\ 0 \end{pmatrix} + \begin{pmatrix} -2 \\ 4 \end{pmatrix} + \begin{pmatrix} -2 \\ -2 \end{pmatrix}$

$= \begin{pmatrix} -1 \\ 2 \end{pmatrix}$

Probability

◆ The **probability** of an event E happening, $p(E)$

$$p(E) = \frac{\text{number of desired outcomes}}{\text{total number of possible outcomes}}$$

(Impossible) $0 \leqslant p(E) \leqslant 1$ (Certain)

◆ The probability of an event not happening is $p(\bar{E})$.

$$p(E) + p(\bar{E}) = 1$$

Relative frequency

Experimental probability is measured by

$$\textbf{relative frequency} = \frac{\text{number of successes}}{\text{total number of trials}}$$

Independent events

If A and B are **independent** events

$$p(A \; and \; B) = p(A) \times p(B)$$

$$p(A \; or \; B) = p(A) + p(B)$$

To calculate the probability of an event occurring, it is necessary to consider *all* the ways in which that event can happen.

A bag contains three white and one black marble. Three marbles are removed from the bag individually, being replaced before each selection. Find the probability that from the three marbles there are at least two black marbles.

Let B and W be the number of black and white marbles respectively.

$$p(B \geqslant 2) + p(B < 2) = 1$$

so $\quad p(B \geqslant 2) = 1 - p(B < 2)$

$$= 1 - p(B \leqslant 1)$$

$$= 1 - p(B = 0 \text{ or } B = 1)$$

$$= 1 - [p(B = 0) + p(B = 1)]$$

$$p(B = 0) = p(W = 3) = \left(\tfrac{3}{4}\right)^3 = \tfrac{27}{64}$$

$$p(B = 1) = \left(\tfrac{1}{4}\right)\left(\tfrac{3}{4}\right)^2 \times 3 = \tfrac{27}{64}$$

$$p(B \geqslant 2) = 1 - \left(\tfrac{27}{64} + \tfrac{27}{64}\right)$$

so $\quad p(B \geqslant 2) = \tfrac{10}{64} = \tfrac{5}{32}$

Examination practice 3

Paper 3A (Non-calculator)

1 The area of the rectangle is $126\,\text{cm}^2$.

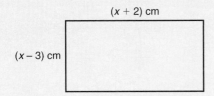

(x + 2) cm

(x − 3) cm

   a Form an equation and show that it simplifies to

$$0 = x^2 - x - 132$$

   b Solve this equation for x and hence find the perimeter of the rectangle.

2 If $f(x) = x^2 - 2x$ find:

   a $f(2)$

   b $f(-x)$

   c $f(x + 1)$

   d $f\left(\dfrac{1}{x}\right)$

3 OACB is a parallelogram. M is the mid-point of OB and N is the mid-point of OA.

$\overrightarrow{OM} = \mathbf{m}$

$\overrightarrow{ON} = \mathbf{m}$

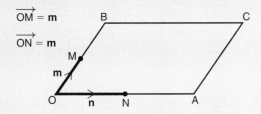

   Express these vectors in terms of $\mathbf{m}$ and $\mathbf{n}$.

   a $\overrightarrow{OA}$ b $\overrightarrow{OB}$

   c $\overrightarrow{AB}$ d $\overrightarrow{NM}$

   e What can you deduce about $\overrightarrow{NM}$ and $\overrightarrow{AB}$?

4 Sketch the graph of $f(x) = \sin x$. On the same axes sketch the curve of $f(x + 90°)$.

5 Mr Jaipur earns a gross salary of £25 000 p.a. He has a tax-free allowance of £4500.

   If the starting rate of tax is at 10% on the first £1500 of taxable income and the basic rate of tax is at 25% on the remainder, find the amount of tax he has to pay on a year's salary.

6 AEBO is a rectangle and OBDC is a parallelogram.

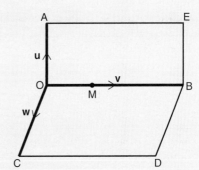

$\overrightarrow{OA} = \mathbf{u}$, $\overrightarrow{OB} = \mathbf{v}$, $\overrightarrow{OC} = \mathbf{w}$ and OM:MB = 1:2.

Express in terms of $\mathbf{u}$, $\mathbf{v}$, $\mathbf{w}$ in their simplest forms:

   a $\overrightarrow{OM}$

   b $\overrightarrow{AM}$

   c $\overrightarrow{MD}$

   d the ratio AM:MD.

7 On each day that I go to work, the probability that I leave home before 0800 is 0.2. The probability that I leave home after 0810 is 0.05.

The probability that I am late for work depends upon the time I leave home.

The probabilities are given in the table below.

Time of leaving home	Before 0800	Between 0800–0810	After 0810
Probability of being late	0.01	0.1	0.2

I work 200 days each year. Estimate how many times I would expect to be late for work in a year.

NEAB

8 The diagram shows several functions.

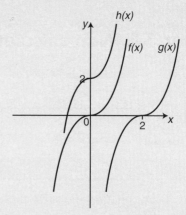

a Express in terms of $f(x)$:
   (i) $h(x)$
   (ii) $g(x)$

b If $f(x) = x^3$ find the equation of the functions:
   (i) $f(3x)$
   (ii) $3f(x)$

Paper 3B (Calculator)

Where appropriate give your answers correct to 3 significant figures.

1   Solve for x by completing the square:

$$x^2 - 4x - 10 = 0$$

2   This is a sketch graph of $y = f(x)$, where

$$f(x) = (x+3)(x-2)(x-4)$$

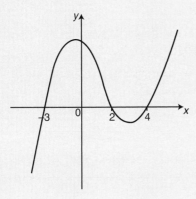

a   Calculate the value of $f(0)$.

b   Copy the sketch graph and, on the same axes, sketch the graph of $y = f(-x)$.

c   Describe fully the single geometric transformation which maps the graph of $y = f(x)$ onto the graph of $y = f(-x)$.

The equation $f(x) = f(-x)$ has a solution $x = 0$. It also has a positive solution x such that $n < x < n + 1$, where n is a positive integer.

d   Write down the value of n.

LONDON

3   The figure represents a rectangular garden 25 metres long and 15 metres wide. The lawn is surrounded on three sides by a flower bed of width x metres.

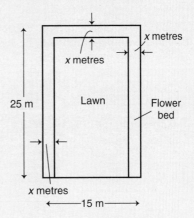

a   Write down the dimensions of the lawn in terms of x.

b   (i)   The area of the lawn is 200 m^2. Show that

$$2x^2 - 65x + 175 = 0$$

   (ii)   Solve the equation for x, the width of the flower bed.

4   Mr and Mrs Wupong-Smith arrange from their bank a mortgage of £200 000 to buy a house. To repay this loan *together with the interest* they agree to pay £31 952.29 each year over a period of 20 years.

a   Work out the total amount they pay in 20 years.

b   How much interest do they pay?

c   Work out the total amount of interest as a percentage of the total amount repaid.

5   Calculate the points of intersection of the parabola $y = 2x^2 + x - 3$ and the straight line $y = 2 - x$.

6 The position of a point is determined by its position vector $\begin{pmatrix} x \\ y \end{pmatrix}$ relative to the origin O. A and B have position vectors $\overrightarrow{OA} = \begin{pmatrix} 20 \\ 15 \end{pmatrix}$ and $\overrightarrow{OB} = \begin{pmatrix} 30 \\ 40 \end{pmatrix}$.

a Write down $\overrightarrow{AB}$.

b Calculate the magnitude of the vector $\overrightarrow{BA}$.

c Calculate the angle that the vector $\overrightarrow{BA}$ makes with the x-axis.

d X is the mid-point of AB. Write $\overrightarrow{OX}$ as a column vector.

7 A man travels to work by car but walks from his place of work to a café for lunch.

If it is raining when he leaves home in the morning, the probability that it is raining at lunchtime is $\frac{5}{6}$. If it is not raining when he leaves in the morning, the probability that it is raining at lunchtime is $\frac{1}{8}$.

If it is raining when he leaves home in the morning, the probability that he takes his umbrella with him is $\frac{3}{4}$. If not, the probability that he takes an umbrella is $\frac{1}{5}$.

The probability that it is raining in the morning when he leaves home is $\frac{1}{3}$.

Calculate the probabilities of the following events, showing clearly (where appropriate) the fractions added or multiplied to arrive at your results.

a It is not raining when the man leaves home, and he does not take an umbrella.

b It is raining when he leaves home, but he does not take an umbrella.

c It is not raining when he leaves home, he does not take an umbrella, but it is raining at lunchtime.

d It is raining at lunchtime and he is without an umbrella.

MEI

8 In the figure, OACB is a parallelogram.

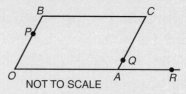

NOT TO SCALE

$\overrightarrow{OP} = \frac{2}{3}\overrightarrow{OB}$, $\overrightarrow{AQ} = \frac{1}{4}\overrightarrow{AC}$, $\overrightarrow{AR} = \frac{3}{5}\overrightarrow{OA}$

Denote the vector $\overrightarrow{OA}$ by **a**, the vector $\overrightarrow{OB}$ by **b**.

a Write down, in terms of **b**, the vector $\overrightarrow{OP}$.

b Write down, in terms of **a** and **b**, the vector $\overrightarrow{OQ}$.

c Deduce the vector $\overrightarrow{PQ}$.

d Write down the vector $\overrightarrow{OR}$.

e Deduce the vector $\overrightarrow{QR}$.

f Say, with reasons, whether PQR is a straight line.

MEI

Number 4 (Revision)

Each section of this unit starts with a summary of topics covered in *Book 1*.
The revision exercises then test *all* topics of *Book 1* and Units 1–3 of *Book 2*.

Fractions and ratio

Fractions

To change $\frac{1}{8}$ into a decimal: divide 1 by 8 $\qquad$ 0.125

To change $\frac{7}{20}$ into a percentage: multiply by 100% $\qquad$ $\frac{7}{20} \times 100\% = 35\%$

To simplify $\frac{15}{1.2}$: multiply top and bottom by 10 $\qquad$ $\frac{150}{12} = \frac{25}{2} = 12.5$

Ratio

Divide 105 hours in the ratio 3:4. The sum of the ratios is $3 + 4 = 7$. One part $= \frac{105}{7} = 15$
hours, three parts $= 3 \times 15 = 45$ hours, and four parts $= 4 \times 15 = 60$ hours.

Simple recurring decimals

$\frac{1}{7} = 1 \div 7 = 0.142\,857\,142\,8571\ldots$ and this is written as $0.\dot{1}42\,85\dot{7}$

Fractions that produce terminating decimals have 2 and/or 5 as the only factors in their
denominator, for example $\frac{3}{5}, \frac{3}{8}, \frac{7}{10}, \frac{3}{20}$. Fractions with prime numbers as factors in their
denominator recur, e.g. $\frac{1}{6}, \frac{1}{15}$.

Calculator

Significant figures
34.779 to 3 s.f. = 34.8
0.0659 to 2 s.f. = 0.066

Decimal places
2.0765 to 2 d.p. = 2.08
0.052 96 to 3 d.p. = 0.053

Check that you agree with these two calculations.

$\left(\dfrac{34.2 - 12.6}{3.1 - 2.9}\right)^5 = 1.47 \times 10^{10}$ (to 3 s.f.) $\qquad$ $\sqrt{\dfrac{4.35 \times 10^5}{6.47 \times 10^{-7}}} = 8.20 \times 10^5$ (to 3 s.f.)

Directed numbers
$3 + (-4) = 3 - 4 = -1$ $\qquad$ $6 \times (-2) = -12$
$3 - (-4) = 3 + 4 = 7$ $\qquad$ $(-6) \times (-2) = 12$
$(-3) + (-4) = -3 - 4 = -7$ $\qquad$ $6 \div (-2) = -3$
$(-3) - (-4) = -3 + 4 = 1$ $\qquad$ $(-6) \div (-2) = 3$

Order of operations
BIDMAS: **B**rackets, **I**ndices, **D**ivision/**M**ultiplication, **A**ddition/**S**ubtraction

Multiples of 6 are 6, 12, 18, 24, 30 . . .
Factors of 18 are 1, 2, 3, 6, 9 and 18. These are the only numbers that divide exactly into 18.
Prime numbers are 2, 3, 5, 7, 11, . . . Prime numbers have no factors apart from 1 and themselves.
Prime factors of 18 are 2 and 3. These are the only primes that divide exactly into 18.

Highest common factor (HCF) and lowest common multiple (LCM)

Find the HCF of 18 and 48.
Prime factors of 18 are $2 \times 3 \times 3$. Prime factors of 48 are $2 \times 2 \times 2 \times 2 \times 3$. Common factors to both numbers are 2 and 3. Thus highest common factor of 18 and 48 is $2 \times 3 = 6$.

Find the LCM of 18 and 48.
The lowest number that both numbers divide into must contain 2, 3 and 3 as well as 2, 2, 2, 2 and 3. Thus the lowest common multiple of 18 and 48 is $2 \times 2 \times 2 \times 2 \times 3 \times 3 = 144$.

Proportion

♦ If a passenger jet uses 600 gallons of fuel *every* hour, the number of gallons used is **directly proportional** to the time. So, the jet would use half as much fuel in half an hour.

The jet uses 600 gallons in 1 hour. (Divide both sides by 600)

$\therefore$ it uses 1 gallon in $\dfrac{1}{600}$ hours   (Change to seconds)

$\qquad$ 1 gallon in $\dfrac{1}{600} \times 3600 \, \text{s} = 6 \, \text{s}$

♦ A **density** of $11 \, \text{g/cm}^3$ means that 11 g of a substance has a volume of $1 \, \text{cm}^3$. So, $2 \, \text{cm}^3$ has a mass of 22 g.

♦ To **find the best buy**, find, for each item, either the cost of 1 g (in pence per gram), or the weight you can buy for 1 penny (in grams per penny).

♦ BT spent £159 308 000 on advertising in 2000. How much did BT spend on advertising per second in that year?

$$\text{Amount spent per second} = \frac{\text{total cost in year 2000}}{\text{seconds in that year}} = \frac{£159\,308\,000}{365 \times 24 \times 60 \times 60} = £5.05$$

Percentages

Simple percentages

The **original quantity** is always represented on a **number line** by 100%.

For a **loss** of 30%, the selling price x is given by $\dfrac{x}{70} = \dfrac{60}{100}$. The selling price x is £42.

For a **profit** of 30%, the selling price y is given by $\dfrac{60}{100} = \dfrac{y}{130}$. The selling price y is £78.

Multiplying factor method

For a **loss** of 30%, selling price $x = 60 - \left(60 \times \frac{30}{100}\right) = 60\left(1 - \frac{30}{100}\right) = 60 \times \frac{70}{100} = £42$

For a **profit** of 30%, selling price $y = 60 + \left(60 \times \frac{30}{100}\right) = 60\left(1 + \frac{30}{100}\right) = 60 \times \frac{130}{100} = £78$

Inverse percentages

A laptop computer is sold by Computer Warehouse for £850 to give a profit of 25%. Find the original price paid by the shop.

Let x = original price.

Method 1 (ratio line)

$$\frac{x}{100} = \frac{£850}{125}$$

$$\Rightarrow \quad x = \frac{£850}{125} \times 100$$

$$\Rightarrow \quad x = £680$$

Method 2 (multiplying factor)

$x \times 1.25 = £850 \quad \Rightarrow \quad x = \dfrac{£850}{1.25} \quad \Rightarrow \quad x = £680$

Compound percentages

◆ To increase/decrease a number by $R\%$, multiply by $\left(1 \pm \dfrac{R}{100}\right)$.

£50 *increased* by 14% $= £50 \times (1.14) = £57$.
£50 *decreased* by 14% $= £50 \times (0.86) = £43$.

◆ To increase/decrease a number by $R\%$, n successive times, multiply by $\left(1 \pm \dfrac{R}{100}\right)^n$.

£50 increased by 14% per year for 3 successive years $= £50 \times (1.14)^3 = £74.08$.
£50 decreased by 14% per year for 3 successive years $= £50 \times (0.86)^3 = £31.80$.

Indices and standard form

Index form

$10\,000\,000 = 10^7$ To display 10^7 on a calculator: 10 7

Standard form

Numbers are written as $a \times 10^n$, where $1 \leqslant a < 10$ and n is an integer.

$67\,000 = 6.7 \times 10^4$ To display 6.7×10^4 on a calculator: 6.7 $\boxed{\text{EXP}}$ 4

When adding or subtracting, make sure terms have matching indices.

$(7.93 \times 10^8) + (4.2 \times 10^6) = 7.93 \times 10^8 + 0.042 \times 10^8 = 7.972 \times 10^8$

$(7.93 \times 10^{-4}) - (4.2 \times 10^{-5}) = 79.3 \times 10^{-5} - 4.2 \times 10^{-5} = 75.1 \times 10^{-5}$

When using a square root, make sure the index is an even number.

$\sqrt{(4.9 \times 10^{15})} = \sqrt{(49 \times 10^{14})} = \sqrt{49} \times \sqrt{10^{14}} = 7 \times 10^7$

Where appropriate, give the final answer in standard form too.

Estimation using standard form

$793\,000\,000 \times 4\,200\,000 \approx 8 \times 10^8 \times 4 \times 10^6 = 8 \times 4 \times 10^{(8+6)} = 32 \times 10^{14} \approx 3 \times 10^{15}$

$(7.93 \times 10^{-4}) \div (4.2 \times 10^{-6}) \approx (8 \times 10^{-4}) \div (4 \times 10^{-6}) = 8 \div 4 \times 10^{(-4--6)}$
$$= 2 \times 10^2 = 200$$

Rules of indices

Question	Working	Rule	Calculator	Answer
$4^5 \times 4^4$	$4^{5+4} = 4^9$	Add indices	4 $\boxed{x^y}$ 9 $\boxed{=}$	262 144
$3.1^7 \div 3.1^3$	$3.1^{7-3} = 3.1^4$	Subtract indices	3.1 $\boxed{x^y}$ 4 $\boxed{=}$	92.3521
$(1.05^4)^6$	1.05^{24}	Multiply indices	1.05 $\boxed{x^y}$ 24 $\boxed{=}$	3.23 to 3 s.f.

Limits of accuracy

This carpet's dimensions are 2 m × 5 m (to the nearest metre).
What are the limits of accuracy for the carpet's perimeter and its area?
The largest possible dimensions are 2.5 m by 5.5 m.
The smallest possible dimensions are 1.5 m by 4.5 m.

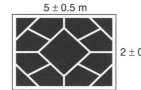

Largest perimeter $= 2 \times 2.5\,\text{m} + 2 \times 5.5\,\text{m} = 16\,\text{m}$
Smallest perimeter $= 2 \times 1.5\,\text{m} + 2 \times 4.5\,\text{m} = 12\,\text{m}$
So, the *exact* perimeter is between 12 m and 16 m.

Largest area $= 2.5\,\text{m} \times 5.5\,\text{m} = 13.75\,\text{m}^2$
Smallest area $= 1.5\,\text{m} \times 4.5\,\text{m} = 6.75\,\text{m}^2$
So, the *exact* area is between $6.75\,\text{m}^2$ and $13.75\,\text{m}^2$.

Exercise 63 (Revision)

Where appropriate, give your answers correct to 3 significant figures.

1 Blood comprises 8% of the weight of a human. Amy weighs 40 kg.
Find the weight of her blood.

2 In the year 2000, fifty Chinese students set a new domino record when 2.7 million dominoes fell in 7 minutes. On average how many dominoes fell per second?

3 Find 2.5% of 4×10^4.

4 A garden seat is bought for £80. When it is sold, a loss of £12 is made.
Find this loss as a percentage.

5 The length of a bacterium is 0.003 05 mm. Write this number in standard form.

6 Divide £26.60 in the ratio 4:3.

7 Work out these.

   a $4\frac{1}{5} \div \frac{7}{15}$ b $8\frac{3}{7} - 6\frac{4}{5}$

8 Express 945 as a product of prime factors, using indices where necessary.

9 Work out these.

   a 3.82×1.5 b $72.8 \div 13$

10 Use standard form to work out an estimate of the following, and give your answer in standard form correct to 1 significant figure.

   a $(6 \times 10^7) \times (8 \times 10^{-4})$ b $(3 \times 10^6) \div (7 \times 10^4)$

11 Four identical machines produce 1000 identical clamps in 1 hour.
How many clamps can one machine produce in 8 hours?

12 Change $0.5\dot{4}\dot{3}$ to a fraction in its lowest terms.

13 Work out these.

   a $2^{-4} \div 2^{-3}$ b $(5^3)^{\frac{1}{3}}$ c $(8)^{-\frac{1}{3}}$

14 Simplify these.

   a $2\sqrt{3} + 2\sqrt{3}$ b $2\sqrt{3} \div 2\sqrt{3}$ c $2\sqrt{3} \times 2\sqrt{3}$

15 The largest volcano eruption in the last 10 000 years was at Thera in 1520 BC. It brought about the end of the Minoan civilisation in Greece.

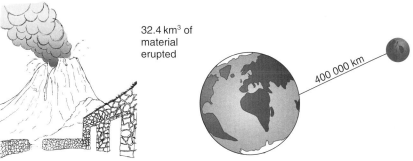

32.4 km³ of material erupted

400 000 km

The volume erupted by Thera equals that of a 400 000 km column that reaches from the Earth to the Moon. If this column has a square cross-section, find its width.

16 In the UK, in the 1990s, the poorest half of the population paid 11% income tax compared with 20% in the 1970s. Find this decrease as a percentage.

17 A rare stamp, bought for $500, increases in value at 5% per annum. Find its value after 6 years.

18 A CD is bought for £13, which includes VAT at 17.5%.
What was the price before VAT was added?

19 Work out these correct to 3 significant figures and show a rough check.

a $\dfrac{12.8}{4.5 + 8.1}$ 　　　　**b** $\sqrt{7.8^2 + 3.7^2 - 2 \times 7.8 \times 3.7 \cos 47°}$ 　　　　**c** $10^4 \times 9^{-4}$

20 The largest sewage works in the world is near Washington DC in the USA. It treats 740 million gallons per day. Using 1 gallon ≈ 4.55 litres, find the rate of treatment in

a gallons per second 　　　　**b** m^3 per second

21 On dry roads a car travelling at 30 mph slows at a constant rate and stops in 23 m.
How long does this take? (1 mile ≈ 1.609 km)

22 If $a = 9.7$ to 2 significant figures and $b = 3.4$ to 2 significant figures, find

a the maximum value of $a - b$ 　　　　**b** the minimum value of $a \div b$

Exercise 63★ (Revision)

Where appropriate give all answers correct to 3 significant figures.

1 The cockroach, which has been around for 100 million years, is the fastest insect on six legs and can travel 1 metre in 1 second. How fast is this in km/hour?

2 A car travels from X to Y at an average speed of 60 mph and returns to X at a speed of 40 mph. What is its average speed for the whole journey?

3 Which is the larger result, and by how much: to increase 45 kg by 10% or reduce 56 kg by 10%?

4 In 1990, 1 in 4 of the population were likely to develop cancer.
In 2000, the proportion rose to 3 in 10. Find the percentage increase.

5 A grain of sand weighs 10^{-4} g. How many million grains make up 1 kg?

6 Simplify the ratio 234 : 1092.

7 What is the highest prime factor of 442?

8 Work out these.

a 2.35×0.14 　　　　**b** $1.462 \div 0.17$

9 Use standard form to work out an estimate of the following, and give your answer in standard form correct to 1 significant figure.

a $(8.23 \times 10^{-3}) + (2.32 \times 10^{-4})$ 　　　　**b** $\sqrt{8.3 \times 10^{-5}}$

10 Three identical machines produce 40 identical tyres in 1 hour.
How many tyres can be produced by two machines in 6 hours?

11 Work out $0.\dot{2} + 0.\dot{2}85714$ as a fraction.

12 Solve these for x.

   a $x^{\frac{1}{3}} = 6$ **b** $(x^{-6})^{-\frac{1}{3}} = 169$ **c** $(x)^{-\frac{2}{3}} = \frac{1}{9}$

13 Simplify $\dfrac{3\sqrt{10}}{\sqrt{40}}$

14 Express these with rational denominators.

   a $\dfrac{5}{\sqrt{2}}$ **b** $\dfrac{3}{2+\sqrt{3}}$

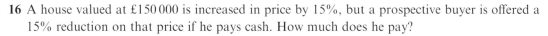

15 A telescope on Earth can just locate Pluto, a distance of 5.59×10^9 km.
Use the formula $V = 4R^3$ to work out the approximate volume, V, of space that can be viewed from Earth, where R is the distance to Pluto.

16 A house valued at £150 000 is increased in price by 15%, but a prospective buyer is offered a 15% reduction on that price if he pays cash. How much does he pay?

17 Between 1970 and 1990, developing countries with 'open economies' grew by 4.5% per year. The old communist countries, with 'closed economies', grew by just 0.7% per year. When would each have doubled?

18 In the UK, the number of air passengers has grown at 4.9% per annum since 1960. In 1960, there were 22 million. How many were there in 2000?

19 Work out these correct to 3 significant figures and show a rough check.

   a $23 \div 4.5^{\frac{3}{2}}$ **b** $48.5 - \left(\dfrac{1}{0.67}\right)^{-3}$ **c** $(0.3)^{\frac{4}{3}} \times (0.3)^{-\frac{5}{2}}$

20 A pair of shoes is sold for £67. If this price includes VAT at 17.5%, how much is the VAT?

21 The blades on a wind farm generator are 32 m long and rotate once every 4 seconds. Find the speed of the tip of a blade in mph. (1 mile ≈ 1.609 km)

22 If $a = 6.7 \pm 0.03$, $b = 8.1 \pm 0.05$ and $c = 0.05 \pm 0.02$, find the maximum value of

   $\dfrac{b - a}{c}$

23 The human gut has an area of about two tennis courts and on this lives about 100 trillion bacteria. (One trillion is 10^{12}.)

   a Taking the area of a tennis court as $260 \, m^2$, calculate the number of bacteria per cm^2.

   b Assume that each bacterium is in the shape of a cube and that a single layer covers the gut with no gaps. If these cubes were placed, touching each other, in a straight line, how long would the line be?

24 Given that $11\,111 \times 11\,111 = 123\,454\,321$ find the *exact* value of

$$\frac{999\,999\,999 \times 999\,999\,999}{1+2+3+4+5+6+7+8+9+8+7+6+5+4+3+2+1}$$

Formulae

Pythagoras' theorem
$a^2 = b^2 + c^2$

Triangle
Area of triangle $= \frac{1}{2} \times b \times h$

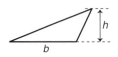

Parallelogram
Area of parallelogram $= b \times h$

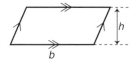

Trapezium
Area of trapezium $= \dfrac{h}{2}(a + b)$

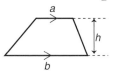

Circle
Area of circle $= \pi r^2$
Circumference of circle $= 2\pi r$

Speed
$\text{Speed} = \dfrac{\text{distance}}{\text{time}}$

Prism

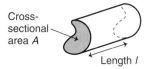

Cylinder

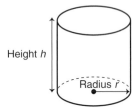

Volume $= A \times l$

Volume $= \pi r^2 h$
Total surface area $= 2\pi r^2 + 2\pi rh$

Solving problems using formulae

A metal cylindrical prism of height h cm and radius R cm has a central cylindrical hole of radius r cm removed from it. The volume V cubic centimetres of the remaining shape is given by $V = \pi R^2 h - \pi r^2 h = \pi(R^2 - r^2)h$.

Find the volume correct to 3 significant figures when $R = 10$ cm, $r = 8$ cm and $h = 6$ cm.

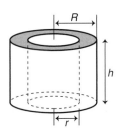

Facts	$R = 10$ cm, $r = 8$ cm, $h = 6$ cm, $V = ?$ cm^3
Equation	$V = \pi(R^2 - r^2)h$
Substitution	$V = \pi \times (10^2 - 8^2) \times 6$ cm^3
Working	$V = 679$ cm^3 (to 3 s.f.)

Simplifying

$4ac$ means $4 \times a \times c$.

$2s \times 3t = 6st$

$y^2 \times y = y^3$

$3ab \times 5b = 15ab^2$

Only add or subtract **like terms**.

$a - 3b + 2a - 2b = a + 2a - 3b - 2b = 3a - 5b$

$2c^2b + cb^2 - c^2b = c^2b + cb^2$

Multiply each term inside **brackets** by the term outside.

$4(2a - 3b) = 8a - 12b$

$2d - (3 - 4d) = 2d - 3 + 4d = 6d - 3$

Simplifying fractions

$$\frac{5a}{\cancel{12}^{\,6}} \times \frac{\cancel{2}^{\,1}b}{3} = \frac{5ab}{18}$$

$$\frac{5a}{12} \div \frac{2b}{3} = \frac{5a}{\cancel{12}_{\,4}} \times \frac{\cancel{3}^{\,1}}{2b} = \frac{5a}{8b}$$

$$\frac{5a}{12} + \frac{2b}{3} = \frac{5a + 8b}{12}$$

$$\frac{5a}{12} - \frac{2b}{3} = \frac{5a - 8b}{12}$$

Rearranging formulae

Identical process to solving equations: **perform the same operation to both sides** of the formula.

Making x the subject

$\dfrac{ax^2 - b}{c} = dx^2$ (Multiply both sides by c)

$ax^2 - b = cdx^2$ (Add b to both sides)

$ax^2 = cdx^2 + b$ (Subtract cdx^2 from both sides)

$ax^2 - cdx^2 = b$ (Factorise the left-hand side)

$(a - cd)x^2 = b$ (Divide both sides by $(a - cd)$)

$x^2 = \dfrac{b}{(a - cd)}$ (Square root both sides)

$x = \sqrt{\dfrac{b}{(a - cd)}}$

Indices

$$a^m \times a^n = a^{m+n}$$

$$a^m \div a^n = a^{m-n}$$

$$(a^m)^n = a^{mn}$$

$$a^0 = 1 \qquad (a \neq 0)$$

Solving equations

The way to solve equations is to isolate the unknown letter by systematically doing the same operation to both sides.

$3x + 4 = 2(x + 3)$ (Expand brackets)
$3x + 4 = 2x + 6$ (Collect like terms)
$3x - 2x = 6 - 4$ (Simplify)
$x = 2$
Check: $3 \times 2 + 4 = 2(2 + 3)$

$3(x + 4) - (x - 7) = 25$ (Expand brackets)
$3x + 12 - x + 7 = 25$ (Simplify)
$2x + 19 = 25$ (Subtract 19)
$2x = 6$ (Divide by 2)
$x = 3$
Check: $3(3 + 4) - (3 - 7) = 25$

Quadratic equations

Solve this for x.

$3x^2 - 4 = 71$ (Add 4 to both sides)

$3x^2 = 75$ (Divide both sides by 3)

$x^2 = 25$ (Square root both sides)

$x = \pm 5$

Equations with square roots

Solve this for y.

$\dfrac{\sqrt{y + 3}}{4} - 2 = 1$ (Multiply both sides by 4)

$\sqrt{(y + 3)} - 8 = 4$ (Add 8 to both sides)

$\sqrt{(y + 3)} = 12$ (Square both sides)

$y + 3 = 144$ (Subtract 3 from both sides)

$y = 141$

Equations with fractions

Solving for x.

$\dfrac{2(x - 3)}{3} - \dfrac{x - 1}{2} = 4$ (Multiply both sides by $3 \times 2 = 6$)

$4(x - 3) - 3(x - 1) = 24$ (Simplify)

$4x - 12 - 3x + 3 = 24$

$x - 9 = 24$ (Add 9 to both sides)

$x = 33$

Simultaneous equations

$x + 2y = 5$ (1)
$3x - 4y = 25$ (2)

$3 \times (1) \Rightarrow$ $3x + 6y = 15$ (3)
$(3) - (2) \Rightarrow$ $10y = -10$
$\Rightarrow$ $y = -1$
In (1) $x - 2 = 5$
$\Rightarrow$ $x = 7$
In (2) $21 - (-4) = 25$

Trial and improvement

Solving $x^3 + x = 24$ to 1 decimal place using trial and improvement.

x	$x^3 + x$	Comment
2	10	Too small
3	30	Too big
2.5	18.125	Too small so try 2.7
2.7	22.4 …	Too small so try 2.8
2.8	24.8 …	Too big so try 2.75
2.75	23.5	So $x = 2.8$ (to 1 d.p.)

Quadratics and factorising

Expanding brackets

First **O**utside **I**nside **L**ast

$(x+3)(x-1) = \quad x^2 \quad -x \quad +3x \quad -3 = x^2 + 2x - 3$

Factorising quadratics

This is the process of working backwards from $x^2 + 2x - 3$ to give $(x+3)(x-1)$. The factors of x^2 are x and x, and the factors of -3 are $+3$ and -1 or -3 and $+1$. Always check your answer by expanding the brackets.

Solving quadratics by factors

$x^2 + 2x - 3 = 0 \Rightarrow (x+3)(x-1) = 0$.

$\therefore$ *either* $(x+3) = 0$, so $x = -3$, *or* $(x-1) = 0$, so $x = 1$.

Factorising using the difference of two squares: $a^2 - b^2 = (a+b)(a-b)$

$4a^2 - b^2 = (2a)^2 - (b)^2 = (2a - b)(2a + b)$

Simple factorising

$2x^3 + 6x^5 = 2x^3(1 + 3x^2)$

$9xy^3 + 15x^3yz - 12x^2y^2 = 3xy(3y^2 + 5x^2z - 4xy)$

Inequalities

These are solved in a similar way to equations, except when both sides are multiplied or divided by a negative number. In that case, **the inequality is reversed**.

Solve the inequality showing the result on a number line.

$2(x-3) \leqslant 5(x-3)$ (Expand brackets)

$2x - 6 \leqslant 5x - 15$ (Add 15 to both sides)

$2x + 9 \leqslant 5x$ (Subtract $2x$ from both sides)

$9 \leqslant 3x$ (Divide both sides by 3)

$3 \leqslant x$

Therefore $x \geqslant 3$

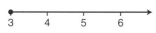

A solid circle means $\leqslant$ or $\geqslant$. An open circle means $<$ or $>$.

Exercise 64 (Revision)

Where appropriate, give answers correct to 3 significant figures.

1 Simplify these.

   a $(2x)^2 \times 2x^2$ **b** $(2x)^2 \div (2x^2)$ **c** $\dfrac{3x}{4} \div \dfrac{x^2}{6}$

2 Solve these.

   a $2(x-1) + 12 = 3(x+2)$ **b** $\dfrac{2x^2 - 5}{3} = 9$ **c** $(2+x)^2 = 9$

3 Find the value of x in these.

   a

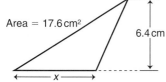

   b

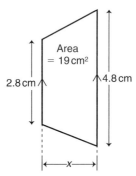

   c

4 Solve the inequality $x \leqslant 6 + 3x$ and represent your answer on a number line.

5 David is three years older than Tariq, who is five years older than Carl. If their combined age is 40, find their ages.

6 Factorise these and check your answer by expanding the brackets.

   a $3a^2b - 6ab^3$ **b** $x^2 - 6x - 7$ **c** $a^2 - b^2$

7 Simplify these.

   a $\dfrac{3x + x^2}{3x}$ **b** $a^{-2} \div a$ **c** $(b^{-2})^{\frac{1}{2}}$

8 I think of a number. I then square it and add three times the original number and the answer is 70. Let the original be x.

   a Write down an equation involving x.

   b Solve the equation to find the original number.

9 Sue and Issy are late for their maths lesson. To placate the teacher, they each pick him a bunch of flowers comprising daisies and dandelions. Sue picks x daisies and y dandelions, a total of 17 flowers. Issy picks three times as many daisies as Sue, and twice as many dandelions, a total of 44. Find the total number of daisies and dandelions picked.

10 A fierce dog is tethered by a rope 15 metres long to a post 6 metres from a straight path. For what distance along the path is one in danger?

11 Make x the subject in each of these.

   a $V = \pi x^2$ **b** $\dfrac{a + x}{b} - c = d$ **c** $ax + bx = d$

12 Solve $x^2 + 2x = 120$, by completing the square.

13 A formula for volume is $V = 4\pi(4ab^x + r^y)$. Find x and y.

14 Solve these simultaneous equations: $y = 10x - 3$, $y = x^2 - 3x$.

15 The area of this rectangle is $4\,\text{m}^2$. Find, by trial and improvement, its perimeter.

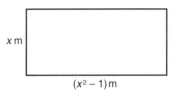

16 You know that a varies directly as the square root of b. If $a = 2$ when $b = 1$, find

   a the formula for a in terms of b

   b a when $b = 9$

   c b when $a = 2.6$

17 Find the area of the shaded regions.

   a 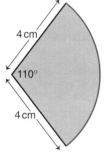   **b**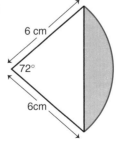

18 The height of the Great Pyramid of Giza is 481.1 feet and the perimeter of its square base is 3020 feet.

   a Investigate the belief that the ratio of the base perimeter to the height is 2π.

   b Find its volume.

   c Find the volume of an exact model of height 10 feet.

Exercise 64★ (Revision)

Where appropriate give answers correct to 3 significant figures.

1 Simplify these.

   a $(2x^2)^2 \times 3x \times x^3$

   b $\dfrac{12x^2}{5y} \div \dfrac{6x^3}{10y^2}$

   c $\dfrac{2x}{5} - \dfrac{x}{3}$

2 Solve these.

   a $\left(\dfrac{x-3}{4}\right)^2 = 9$

   b $\dfrac{32}{x-3} + 2 = 18$

   c $\dfrac{x-2}{2} - \dfrac{x+4}{3} = \dfrac{1}{3}$

3 Find the value of x in these.

   a   **b**   **c**

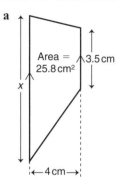

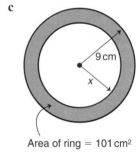

Perimeter = 28 cm   Area of ring = 101 cm²

4 List the integers that satisfy both these inequalities simultaneously.

$$-4 < x \leqslant 3 \qquad \text{and} \qquad 4 - (2 - x) \geqslant 3(x + 2)$$

5 Find the area of this rectangle
if the perimeter is 42 cm.

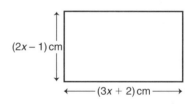

6 Factorise these completely and check your answer by expanding the brackets.

   a $3a^4b - 3a^2b^3$
        b $3x^2 + 3x - 18$
        c $8x + 2x^2 - x^3$

7 Simplify these.

   a $\dfrac{x^2 + x - 2}{x^2 - x}$

   b $a^{-3} + \dfrac{1}{a^2}$

   c $a^{-3} \div \dfrac{1}{a^2}$

8 The sum of the squares of two consecutive integers is 365. Find the integers.

9 At a concert, tickets cost either £10 or £15. Twice as many £10 tickets were sold as £15 tickets. The total takings were £8750. How many tickets were sold?

10 Prove that $(\sqrt{2} + 1)$, $(\sqrt{2} - 1)$ and $\sqrt{6}$ could be the sides of a right-angled triangle.

11 Make x the subject of these.

   a $c = \dfrac{a}{\cos d + x}$

   b $s = ut + \dfrac{1}{2}xt^2$

   c $b = \sqrt{ax^2 + bx^2}$

12 Solve $4x^2 + 10x - 3 = 0$, by completing the square.

13 For each of these, state whether it is an expression, equation or identity.

   a $4(2 - x) - 2 = 6 - 4x$ **b** $4(2 - x) = -2$ **c** $4(2 - x) - 2$

14 The triangles shown are similar in shape.

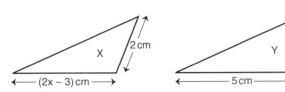

   a (i) Form an equation and show that it simplifies to $2x^2 - 3x - 10 = 0$.

       (ii) Use the quadratic formula to solve this equation for x.

   b If the area of triangle **Y** is $6\,\text{cm}^2$, find the area of triangle **X**.

15 The cube of y varies directly as the square of x. If $x = 12$, $y = 6$, find these.

   a the formula for y in terms of x

   b y when $x = 4$

   c x when $y = 4$

16 Find the shaded area in these.

   a

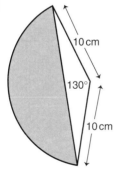

                                    b ABCDE is a regular pentagon of side 6 cm.

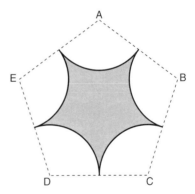

17 Find the coordinates of the points of intersection of $y = 2(x + 1)$ and $4 = x^2 + y^2$.

18 Newton reworked Kepler's third law and produced the formula shown, to calculate the mass, in kg, of a 'heavenly object' by using the orbit of its moon or planet.

$$\text{mass} = \frac{4\pi^2 d^3}{Gt^2}$$

Here d is the orbiting distance, in metres, t is the time of one orbit, in seconds, and $G = 6.67 \times 10^{-11}$, in appropriate units, is called the 'gravitational constant'.

   a The distance from the Earth to the Moon is 3.844×10^5 km. Taking t as 27.3 days, calculate the mass of the Earth.

   b The Sun has a mass of 1.99×10^{30} kg. Calculate its distance from Earth.

Straight line graphs

Graphs of the form $y = mx + c$

The equation of any straight line graph can always be written in the form $y = mx + c$, where m is the **gradient** and c is the **y-intercept**.

Line a has a gradient of $\frac{4}{2} = 2$ (so $m = 2$), and a y intercept of $+4$.

Therefore its equation is $y = 2x + 4$.

Line b has a gradient of $-\frac{2}{4} = -\frac{1}{2}$ $\left(\text{so } m = -\frac{1}{2}\right)$, and a y intercept of $+4$.

Therefore its equation is $y = -\frac{1}{2}x + 4$.

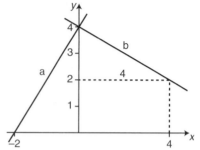

Graphs of the form $ax + by = c$

The graph of $3x + 4y = 12$ can be arranged to give $y = -\frac{3}{4}x + 3$, showing that it is a straight line with gradient $-\frac{3}{4}$ and y intercept at 3. To sketch the graph of $3x + 4y = 12$, substitute $x = 0$, to get the y intercept of 3, and substitute $y = 0$ to get the x intercept of 4.

Other graphs

These graphs are often used to model real-life situations.

Quadratic graphs $y = ax^2 + bx + c$
Parabolas

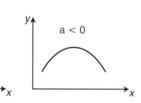

Solution of $0 = ax^2 + bx + c$

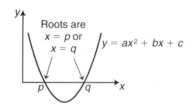

Cubic graphs $y = ax^3 + bx^2 + cx + d$

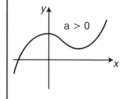
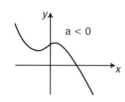

Reciprocal graphs $y = \dfrac{a}{x}$

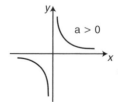
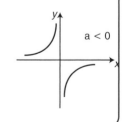

Distance–time graphs

Gradient of slope = speed

Velocity

Gradient OA $= \dfrac{10\,\text{m}}{2\,\text{s}} = 5\,\text{m/s}$

Gradient AB $= \dfrac{0\,\text{m}}{4\,\text{s}} = 0\,\text{m/s}$

Gradient BC $= \dfrac{-10\,\text{m}}{5\,\text{s}} = -2\,\text{m/s}$

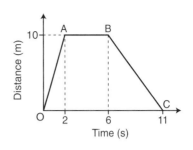

Speed–time graphs

Gradient of slope = acceleration
Area under graph = distance travelled

Acceleration

Gradient OA $= \dfrac{10\,\text{m/s}}{2\,\text{s}} = 5\,\text{m/s}^2$ (speeding up)

Gradient AB $= \dfrac{0\,\text{m}}{3\,\text{s}} = 0\,\text{m/s}^2$ (constant speed)

Gradient BC $= \dfrac{-10\,\text{m/s}}{4\,\text{s}} = -2.5\,\text{m/s}^2$ (slowing down)

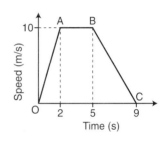

Average speed

Average speed $= \dfrac{\text{distance travelled}}{\text{time}} = \dfrac{\frac{1}{2} \times (3+9)\,\text{s} \times 10\,\text{m/s}}{9\,\text{s}} = 6\dfrac{2}{3}\,\text{m/s}$

To solve simultaneous equations graphically

◆ Draw the graphs for both equations on one set of axes.

◆ The solution is at the intersection points of the graphs.

◆ If the graphs don't intersect, there is no solution.

◆ If the graphs are the same, there are an infinite number of solutions.

Solve the simultaneous equations

$x + y = 6$, $2x - y = 0$

Solution is $x = 2$, $y = 4$.

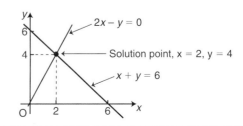

Simultaneous inequalities

Inequalities can be shown graphically by shading regions to identify solutions in unshaded regions.

Solve the inequalities $x \geqslant 0$, $y \geqslant 0$, $x + y \leqslant 3$ and $y < 2$ by drawing suitable lines (solid or broken) and shading *unwanted* regions.

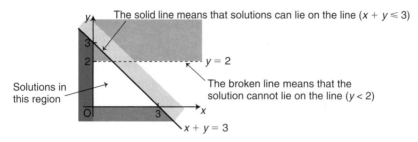

The solid line means that solutions can lie on the line $(x + y \leqslant 3)$

$y = 2$

Solutions in this region

The broken line means that the solution cannot lie on the line $(y < 2)$

$x + y = 3$

Sequences

To continue a sequence

Find the difference between each term.

Sequence	2		7		12		17		22	...
Differences		5		5		5		5		

The difference is 5 so the next term is 27.

To find the rule if the first row of differences is constant

If the differences are equal to a, the formula for the nth term will be $an \pm b$ where b is another constant.

Sequence	−5		− 2		1		4	...
Differences		+3		+ 3		+ 3		

Therefore the rule $= +3n + b$. When $n = 1$, the formula must give the first term as -5. Thus $3 \times 1 + b = -5$, giving $b = -8$. Therefore the rule for the nth term is $3n - 8$.

To find the rule if the second row of differences is constant

The formula contains an n^2 term. To find the rule, the second row of differences must be found. If this difference is $2a$, the formula will contain an^2.

Exercise 65 (Revision)

1 For the sequence 3, 9, 15, 21, ..., find
   a the next three terms
   b the 50th term
   c a formula for the nth term

2 a What name is given to the sequence 1, 4, 9, 16, ...?
   b Find the next three terms of this sequence.
   c Find the 20th term of this sequence.

3 a Use the difference method to find the next three terms of the sequence 1, 2, 4, 7, 11, ...
   b Find the terms a and b in the sequence ..., a, 2, 9, 16, 23, b, ...

4 a How many terms are in the sequence 7, 10, 13, 16, ..., 94?
   b The formula for the nth term of the sequence 4, 10, 18, 28, ... is $n^2 + an$.
      Find the value of a.

5 Here is a sequence of blue tiles surrounding white tiles.

   a Copy and complete this table.

Number of white tiles (w)	1	2	3	4	5
Number of blue tiles (b)	8				

   b Find a formula giving b in terms of w.
   c How many blue tiles are needed to surround the pattern with 25 white tiles?
   d A pattern has 126 blue tiles. How many white tiles are there?

6 The diagram shows four graphs
   a $y = 3$ b $x = 3$ c $y = \frac{1}{2} - 2x$ d $y = \frac{1}{2}x - 2$
   Which graph is which?

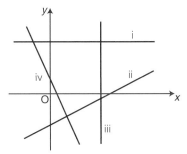

7 a Draw on one set of axes the two graphs $y = 2x - 1$ and $y = 2 - \frac{1}{2}x$ for $-1 \leqslant x \leqslant 3$.
   b Use your graph to solve the simultaneous equations $y = 2x - 1$ and $y = 2 - \frac{1}{2}x$.
   c By shading the *unwanted* regions, find the region satisfying $y \leqslant 2x - 1$ and $y \geqslant 2 - \frac{1}{2}x$.

8 A is $(1, 2)$ and B is $(7, 4)$.

    a Find the gradient of AB and the mid-point M of AB.

    b Find the equation of the straight line L through M perpendicular to AB.

    c What is the area of the triangle formed by L, the x-axis and the y-axis?

9 **a** Draw an accurate graph of $y = x^2 + x - 1$ for $-3 \leqslant x \leqslant 2$.

    b Use your graph to solve the equation $x^2 + x - 1 = 0$.

    c Use your graph to solve the equation $x^2 + x = 2$.

    d Use your graph to find the smallest value of $f(x)$ where $f(x) = x^2 + x - 1$.

10 If the graph of $y = x^2 + 2x - 1$ has been drawn, what is the equation of the line that should be drawn to solve these?

    a $x^2 + 2x = 2$ **b** $x^2 + x = 3$

11 This diagram shows the graphs of $y = x^2 - 3x + 1$ and $y = x - 1$.

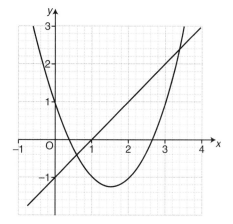

    a What equation in x is solved by the intersection points of these graphs?

    b Use the diagram to solve the equation in part **a**.

12 This diagram shows the graph of $f(x)$.

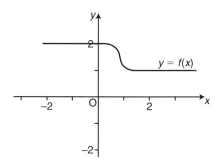

On a copy of the diagram, sketch these.

    a $f(-x)$ **b** $\frac{1}{2}f(x)$ **c** $f(x - 2)$

Exercise 65★ (Revision)

1 For the sequence 201, 197, 193, 189, ... , find

    a the next three terms

    b the 50th term

    c a formula for the nth term

2 **a** Use the difference method to find the next three terms of the sequence 7, 12, 20, 31, 45, ...

    b Find the terms a and b of the sequence ... a, 21, 39, 55, 69, 81, b, ...

3 **a** How many terms are in the sequence 100, 96, 92, 88, ... , 24?

    b The formula for the nth term of the sequence 3, 10, 21, 36, ... is $an^2 + bn$.
       Find the values of a and b.

4 The formula for the sum of n terms of a certain series is $5n^2 - 3n$.

    a What are the first and second terms of the series?

    b How many terms are needed to make a sum of 938?

5 Here is a sequence of triangles made from matches.

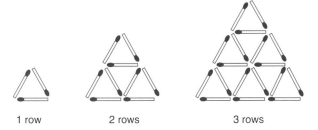

           1 row   2 rows   3 rows

    a Copy and complete this table.

Number of rows (r)	1	2	3	4	5
Number of small triangles (t)	1	4			
Number of matches (m)	3				

    b Find a formula giving t in terms of r.

    c A pattern has 225 triangles. How many rows has it?

    d By considering $\frac{1}{2}(r^2 + r)$, find a formula giving m in terms of r.

6 A is the point $(0, 5)$, B is the point $(4, 7)$ and C is the point $(8, 1)$.

    a Find the equations of the perpendicular bisectors of AB and BC.

    b Solve graphically the simultaneous equations found in part **a**.

    c Show, using compasses, that the intersection point found in part **b** is the centre of a circle
       passing through A, B and C. Calculate the radius of the circle.

7 This diagram shows four graphs:

   a $y = 4 - x^2$

   b $y = (x - 2)^2 - 1$

   c $3y = 6 - x$

   d $y = (x + 1)^3$

   Which graph is which?

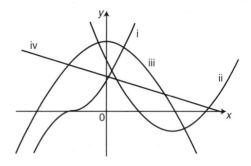

8 This diagram shows the graphs of
$y = x^3 - 3x^2 + 1$ and $y = x - 1$.

   a What equation in x is solved by the
intersection points of these graphs?

   b Use the diagram to solve the equation in
part **a**.

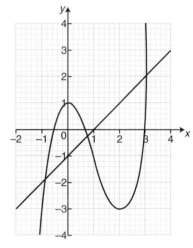

9 a Draw an accurate graph of $y = 4x - 1 - x^2$ for $-1 \leqslant x \leqslant 5$.

   b Use your graph to solve the equation $4x - x^2 = -1$.

   c Use your graph to solve the equation $5x - x^2 = 3$.

10 If the graph of $y = 4 + 2x - x^2$ has been drawn, what is the equation of the line that should
be drawn to solve these?

   a $1 + 2x - x^2 = 0$ **b** $x^2 - 4x - 2 = 0$

11 This diagram shows the graph of $f(x)$.
On a copy of the diagram, sketch these.

   a $-f(x)$

   b $f\left(\frac{1}{2}x\right)$

   c $f(x + 2)$

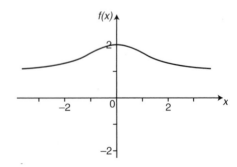

12 a Solve the simultaneous equations $x^2 + y^2 = 4$ and $2y = 3 - x$ graphically.

   b By shading the unwanted regions, find the region satisfying $x^2 + y^2 < 4$ and $2y \geqslant 3 - x$.

Shape and space 4 (Revision)

Sine, cosine and tangent ratios

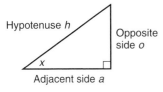

$$\blacklozenge \quad \sin x = \frac{o}{h}$$

$$\blacklozenge \quad \cos x = \frac{a}{h}$$

$$\blacklozenge \quad \tan x = \frac{o}{a}$$

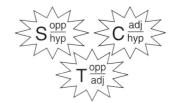

Similar triangles

The two triangles are similar because their corresponding angles are the same.
The corresponding sides are in the same ratio.

$$\frac{a}{x} = \frac{b}{y} = \frac{c}{z}$$

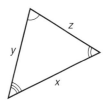

Bearings

Bearings are measured from North and clockwise.

Angles of elevation/depression

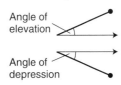

Solving problems using trigonometry

The top of a 30 m electric pylon is observed from a position X, 50 m away from the centre of its base. Find the angle of elevation of the top of the pylon from X.

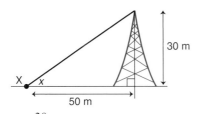

$$\tan x = \frac{30}{50}$$

$$x = 31.0° \text{ (to 3 s.f.)}$$

A ship travels on a bearing of $060°$ for 12 km. How far North is the ship from its starting point?

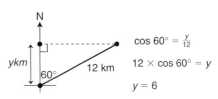

$$\cos 60° = \frac{y}{12}$$

$$12 \times \cos 60° = y$$

$$y = 6$$

So the ship is 6 km North of its starting point.

Transformations

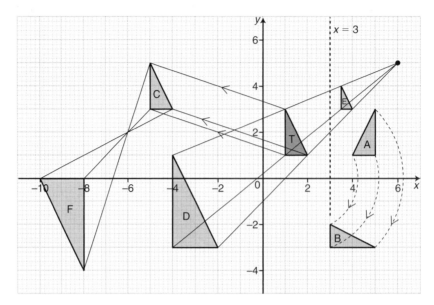

- ◆ △A is a **reflection** of △T in the line $x = 3$.
- ◆ △B is a **rotation** of △A 90° clockwise (−90°), centre (2, 0).
- ◆ △C is a **translation** of △T by the vector $\begin{pmatrix} -6 \\ +2 \end{pmatrix}$.
- ◆ △D is an **enlargement** of △T by a scale factor 2, centre (6, 5).
  The area of △D is four times the area of △T. ($4 = 2^2$)
- ◆ △E is an **enlargement** of △T by a scale factor $\frac{1}{2}$, centre (6, 5).
  The area of △E is one-quarter of the area of △T. $\left(\frac{1}{4} = \left(\frac{1}{2} \right)^2 \right)$
- ◆ △F is an **enlargement** of △C by a scale factor −2, centre (−6, 2).
  The area of △F is four times the area of △C. ($4 = (-2)^2$)

Locus

A locus is the position of a set of points that obey a particular rule.
It can be a line, surface or a region, depending on the rule.

- ◆ *Rule*: All points equidistant from a fixed point O.
  Locus is a circle with centre O.

- ◆ *Rule*: All points equidistant from fixed points A and B.
  Locus is the perpendicular bisector of AB.

Circle theorems

Angles between a tangent to the radius = 90°.

Angles subtended off the diameter in a semicircle = 90°.

Angles in same segment subtended off a chord are equal.

Angle at the centre is twice angle formed at the circumference in same segment subtended off a chord.

$a + c = 180°$
$b + d = 180°$

Opposite angles in a cyclic quadrilateral sum to 180°.

Triangle OAB is isosceles.

Compass constructions

60° angle (equilateral triangle)
Draw arc from A to intersect AB at P.

Keeping same radius, draw arc from P to intersect arc at Q.
$\angle$BAQ = 60°

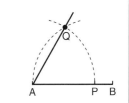

Bisecting an angle
Draw arc from A to intersect lines at P and Q.

Keeping the same radius, draw arcs from P and Q to intersect at R.

Draw AR.
$\angle$PAR = $\angle$QAR.

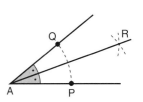

Perpendicular bisector of a line
Draw arc from A, with same radius, longer than $\frac{1}{2}$ AB, above and below line.

Keeping the same radius, draw arcs from B to intersect those from A above and below the line.

These points are P and Q.

Draw line PQ, the perpendicular bisector of AB.

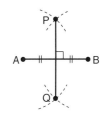

Exercise 66 (Revision)

1 Find lengths of sides p and q and sizes of angles r and s in these triangles.

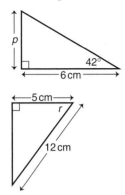

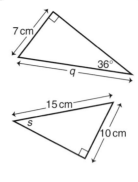

2 A school, S, is 10 km due North of the church, C. A village, V, is 5 km due west of C. Calculate these bearings.

a S from V   b V from S

3 Solve these trigonometric equations for $0° \leqslant x \leqslant 360°$.

a $\sin(x) = 0.5$ b $\cos(x) = \dfrac{\sqrt{3}}{2}$ c $\tan(x) = \sqrt{3}$

4 Calculate the value of the side x and angles y and z.

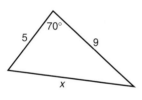

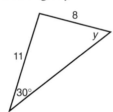

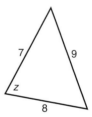

5 In this diagram, a boat is within 50 km of port A and within 40 km of port B.

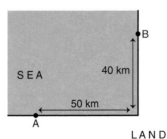

a Copy the diagram and show the region where the boat could be.

b If it is now known that the boat is equidistant from both ports, show where the boat could be on your diagram.

6 Find angles x and y, giving reasons for each step of your calculation.

a

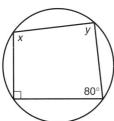

b

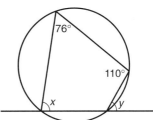

c

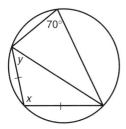

d

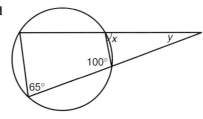

7 A point P has coordinates $(3, 5)$. State the new position of P after each of these.

  a Reflection in the x-axis

  b Rotation about O, $90°$ clockwise

  c Translation along $\begin{pmatrix} -4 \\ 4 \end{pmatrix}$

  d Reflection in the line $x = 5$

8 State whether the pairs of triangles are congruent. If they *are* congruent give reasons.

a

b

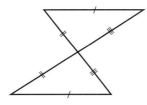

9 $\mathbf{u} = \begin{pmatrix} 2 \\ 3 \end{pmatrix}$ and $\mathbf{v} = \begin{pmatrix} -1 \\ 5 \end{pmatrix}$. Find $2\mathbf{v}$, $\mathbf{u} + \mathbf{v}$, $\mathbf{u} - \mathbf{v}$ and the length of $2\mathbf{u} - 3\mathbf{v}$.

10 In the diagram, M, N and O are the mid-points of AB, BC and CA respectively.

$\overrightarrow{OA} = \mathbf{x}$, $\overrightarrow{OB} = \mathbf{y}$.

Find, in terms of vectors $\mathbf{x}$ and $\mathbf{y}$, $\overrightarrow{AB}$, $\overrightarrow{OM}$, $\overrightarrow{ON}$ and $\overrightarrow{MN}$.

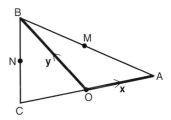

Exercise 66★ (Revision)

1 Find the angle x and length y in each of these triangles.

a

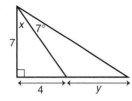

b

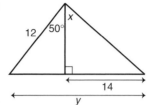

c

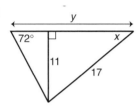

2 Solve these for x, where $0° \leqslant x \leqslant 360°$.

a $\sin(2x) = 0.5$

b $\cos(x + 60°) = \dfrac{\sqrt{3}}{2}$

c $\tan(x - 45°) = \dfrac{1}{\sqrt{3}}$.

3 A regular tetrahedron of side 10 cm is shown. P is directly below O on horizontal base ABC and Q is the mid-point of AB.

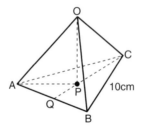

a Find the length of AP, PQ and OQ.

b What angle does OA make with ABC?

c What angle does OAB make with ABC?

4 A and B are two ski-huts on the same horizontal level at a distance of 2000 m apart. A mountain peak P can be seen from both huts. The bearings of B and P from A are 35° and 135° respectively, whilst the bearing of P from B is 150°. The angle of elevation of P from B is 15°.

a Draw a diagram of the plan view containing A, B and P.

b Use the sine rule to find the height of P above the horizontal level containing A and B.

c Use the sine rule to find the angle of elevation of P from A.

5 Positions on a flat field are given as coordinates relative to an origin O. Three youths place a large firework in the field at point P. They set light to the firework and then sprint away at equal speeds so that a few moments later their positions are given as A(4, 4), B(10, 10) and C(4, 20). Find the coordinates of P by construction.

6 If PA and PB are tangents, PA is parallel to BC and angle APB is 78°, calculate the angles x, y and z, being careful to state reasons for each step of your working.

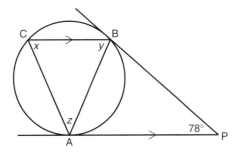

7 a Draw x and y axes from -4 to 8 and on these axes draw and label the triangle P with vertices (1, 1), (1, 3) and (2, 1). Four transformations are defined:

A   Reflection in $y = -1$

B   Reflection in $y + x = 0$

C   Enlargement, centre 0, scale factor 2

D   Translation along $\begin{pmatrix} -3 \\ -1 \end{pmatrix}$

b Draw on the same axes, triangles Q, R, S and T where:

(i) A(P) = Q   (ii) B(Q) = R   (iii) C(P) = S   (iv) D(S) = T

c Find the angle and centre of rotation that takes P onto R.

d Find the scale factor and centre of enlargement that takes P onto T.

8 You are given these vectors:

$$\mathbf{x} = \begin{pmatrix} 1 \\ 1 \end{pmatrix} \qquad \mathbf{y} = \begin{pmatrix} 2 \\ -3 \end{pmatrix} \qquad \mathbf{z} = \begin{pmatrix} -5 \\ 5 \end{pmatrix}$$

a If $\mathbf{x} + \mathbf{y} + \mathbf{z} = \mathbf{w}$, find the length of $\mathbf{w}$.

b If $p\mathbf{x} + q\mathbf{y} + \mathbf{z} = \mathbf{0}$, find values of p and q.

9 Find the sides x and y.

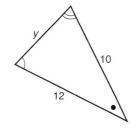

Data display

Discrete data is data that can be listed and counted, for example the number of peas in a pod, or the number of pages in a book. Continuous data is data that cannot be listed and counted, for example time, mass and length.

Displaying data

The number of coloured marbles in a bag, distributed as shown in the table, can be displayed in a pictogram, a pie chart, a bar chart or a frequency polygon.

Colour	Frequency
Red	1
Yellow	3
Blue	2
Green	4

Pictogram

Marble colour

Red	◐
Yellow	◐ ◐ ◐
Blue	◐ ◐
Green	◐ ◐ ◐ ◐

Pie chart

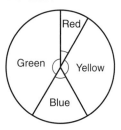

Bar chart

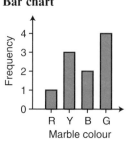

Frequency polygon

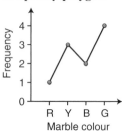

A **stem and leaf diagram** is just like a tally chart, except that only the last digit of each number is written down. For example, the numbers 34, 56, 47, 38, 49, 27, 33, 41 and 52 are shown in this stem and leaf diagram.

Group		Frequency
2–	7	1
3–	4, 8, 3	3
4–	7, 9, 1	3
5–	6, 2	2
		Total = 9

Scatter diagrams are used to illustrate whether two sets of data are related.

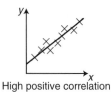

High positive correlation

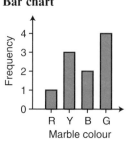

Line of best fit

High negative correlation

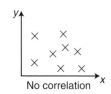

No correlation

A **box and whisker plot** is a simple diagram that displays the range and interquartile range. The 'box' displays the quartiles and the 'whisker' displays the range.

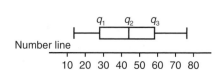

Number line

Averages

Example set of data; 23, 5, 7, 8, 10, 7

$$\textbf{mean} = \frac{\text{total of all values}}{\text{total number of values}} = \frac{23 + 5 + 7 + 8 + 10 + 7}{6} = 10$$

mode = value that occurs most often = 7

median = value in the middle when the data is arranged in ascending order = 7.5
(The median of 5, 7, 7, 8, 10, 23 is 7.5, because it is in the middle of 7 and 8.)

Grouped data

$$\textbf{Estimate of mean} = \frac{\Sigma fx}{\Sigma f}$$

$$= \frac{\text{sum of (frequency} \times \text{mid-point)}}{\text{sum of frequencies}}$$

Time (s)	Frequency f	fx
20–25	5	$5 \times 22.5 = 112.5$
25–35	15	$15 \times 30 = 450$
35–40	10	$10 \times 37.5 = 375$
	$\Sigma f = 30$	$\Sigma fx = 937.5$

The estimated mean is therefore $937.5 \div 30 = 31.25\,\text{s}$.

Cumulative frequency

Cumulative frequency is always plotted on the vertical axis against the **end-points** of each group. Points are joined by a smooth curve. This cumulative frequency curve can be used to *estimate* the quartiles.

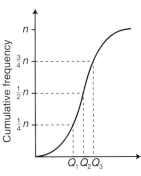

Quartiles	Cumulative frequency	Percentile (%)
Lower quartile Q_1	$\frac{1}{4}n$	25
Median m	$\frac{1}{2}n$	50
Upper quartile Q_3	$\frac{3}{4}n$	75

Measures of spread

Range = largest value − smallest value

Interquartile range = upper quartile − lower quartile = $Q_3 - Q_1$

Probability

The theoretical probability of an event E happening:

$$p(E) = \frac{\text{number of desired outcomes}}{\text{total number of possible outcomes}}$$

Impossible $0 \leqslant p(E) \leqslant 1$ certain

The probability of an event not happening is $p(\bar{E})$.

$$p(E) + p(\bar{E}) = 1$$

Experimental probability is measured by **relative frequency** $= \dfrac{\text{number of successes}}{\text{total number of trials}}$

Independent events

If two events have no effect on each other, they are said to be independent.

For example, the fact that it rains on Tuesday is not going to have an effect on whether the QE2 liner sails from Portsmouth on Friday.

Mutually exclusive events

A light cannot be both on and off. Such events are said to be mutually exclusive.

Single events

From an ordinary pack of 52 cards, one card is selected at random.

$p(\text{Selecting a queen}) = \frac{4}{52} = \frac{1}{13}$ $p(\textit{Not} \text{ selecting a queen}) = 1 - \frac{4}{52} = \frac{12}{13}$

Combined events

An ordinary dice is thrown twice.
Let event A be that a 6 is thrown. Then $\bar{A}$ is the event that a 6 is *not* thrown.

$$p(\text{Throwing only one 6}) = [p(A) \times p(\bar{A})] + [p(\bar{A}) \times p(A)]$$

Tree diagram

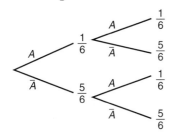

$p(\text{Throwing } \textit{only} \text{ one 6}) \quad = \left(\frac{1}{6} \times \frac{5}{6}\right) + \left(\frac{5}{6} \times \frac{1}{6}\right)$

$= \frac{10}{36} = \frac{5}{18}$

$p(\text{Throwing } \textit{at least} \text{ one 6}) = p(AA) + p(A\bar{A}) + p(\bar{A}A)$

$= 1 - p(\bar{A}\,\bar{A})$

$= 1 - \frac{5}{6} \times \frac{5}{6}$

$= 1 - \frac{25}{36} = \frac{11}{36}$

Exercise 67 (Revision)

1 Find the mean, median and mode of these scores from a class test.

9 7 6 5 8 7 6 7 4 5

2 **a** Construct a tally chart of the scores thrown by the dice in a game of ludo.

1	4	5	6	3	2	3	5	1	3	6	4	3	6	2
3	3	3	5	6	4	5	4	5	2	1	4	1	2	6

b Calculate the mean score.

3 College athletes were timed for a 200 m sprint as part of a fitness-testing programme. Their times are given in seconds.

a Construct an ordered stem and leaf diagram of the times.

b Find the median and quartiles.

c Draw a box and whisker diagram to display the statistics.

22.3	24.7	24.9	25.0	23.8
25.4	23.6	24.1	23.7	23.3
22.5	22.8	22.9	23.6	24.9
23.1	25.2	23.4	22.5	24.6
23.9	24.7	23.1	24.8	24.1

4 Two normal six-sided dice are thrown. X is the difference between the scores.

a Copy and fill in this table to show all the possible values of X.

b Calculate $p(X = 1)$

c Calculate $p(X > 2)$

X	1	2	3	4	5	6
1						
2						
3						
4						
5						
6						

5 Lesley and Nicky both have their driving test on the same day.

Their probabilities of passing are $\frac{3}{5}$ and $\frac{3}{4}$ respectively.

a Copy and complete this tree diagram.

Work out the probabilities of these events.

b Both pass their tests.

c At least one of them passes.

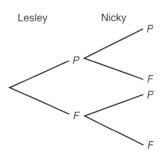

6 The probability that the penalty taker for Midchester Rovers scores at each penalty is 0.8. Ron has two penalties during the season. Calculate these probabilities.

    a Ron scores two goals.   **b** Ron scores only one goal.

7 Sketch a scatter diagram to show that there is a high degree of negative correlation between the number of hot drinks sold at an outdoor market and the air temperature.

8 A skating rink keeps daily records of the number of skaters requiring first-aid. This number is compared with the daily attendance over one week.

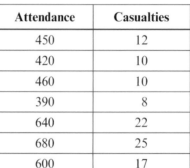

  a Plot the points onto a scattergram and draw in the line of best fit. Comment on the correlation.

  b Estimate the number of casualties if the attendance on one day is 500.

  c Estimate the attendance if there are 17 casualties on one day.

Attendance	Casualties
450	12
420	10
460	10
390	8
640	22
680	25
600	17

9 Explain the meaning of *random* in the term 'a random sample'.

10 A Headteacher is investigating the difficulties that the pupils have in getting to and from school. She plans to survey a sample of 30 pupils.

Construct a plan for a stratified sample according to the groups in the table.

Mode of travel	Number
Walk	85
Cycle	20
Car	95
Coach	200
Train	100

For Questions 11 and 12, refer to this frequency table which shows the distribution of heights of a batch of laurel shrubs grown at a garden centre.

Height (cm)	f
20–40	15
40–50	18
50–55	22
55–60	19
60–70	18
70–90	8

11 Use the garden centre data in the table for this question.

  a Calculate the frequency density for each group.

  b Draw a histogram of the data.

  c Calculate, to one decimal place, an estimate of the mean height of a shrub.

12 Use the garden centre data in the table for this question.

  a Calculate the cumulative frequencies.

  b Draw the cumulative frequency graph.

  c From your graph, work out the median, quartiles and interquartile range.

13 A garage recorded the mileage of a sample of 150 cars at their 12-month service. The results are displayed in this cumulative frequency diagram.

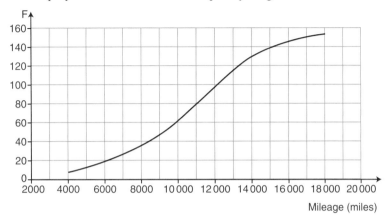

  a Write down the median, quartiles and interquartile range of the mileages.

  b Calculate the percentage of cars with less than 14 000 miles on the clock.

Exercise 67★ (Revision)

1 This bar chart shows the size of the emails in a phone-in mailbox.

  a Construct the frequency table.

  b Calculate the mean, median and mode of the size of emails.

  c Display the results in a pie chart.

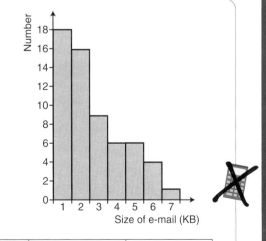

2 This stem and leaf table gives the ages of the employees at a small company.

  a Work out the frequencies.

  b Use the individual ages to calculate the mean age and median age.

Group		Frequency
2–	1 1 3 4 5 5 6 7 8 9 9 9	
3–	0 1 3 4 5 5 6 6 9	
4–	0 1 1 5 6 9	
5–	0 3 7	

3 When selecting a card from a normal pack of 52 cards, the events 'select a spade' and 'select a red card' are mutually exclusive'. Explain what *mutually exclusive* means.

4 There are two bags. The red bag contains seven black balls and three white balls, and the green bag contains four black balls and six white balls. A ball is chosen at random from each bag. Draw a tree diagram and calculate the probability of these events.

  a Selecting two white balls   **b** Selecting a ball of each colour

5 A packet of fruit gums contains two yellow, three red, four green and six black sweets placed randomly in the pack. If you take the top two sweets, what is the probability of these events?

  a They are both black ones.   **b** They are the same colour.

  c They are different colours.

6 Three pairs of socks are lying separately in a drawer. Amir grabs two socks without looking. Calculate the probability of these events.

  a He selects a matching pair   **b** He selects a pair of odd socks.

7 Two pupils from a class of 25 are to be chosen at random to escort a VIP guest around the school. The probability that two girls are chosen is 0.4.
Calculate the probability that two boys are chosen.

8 A group of netball players completed a shooting test at the end of a coaching course. Each took ten shots at the ring from a measured distance. This table shows the average score (y) from each distance (x).

x (m)	y
2	8.5
3	7.5
4	7.2
5	6.4
6	6.1
7	5.3

  a Plot the points onto a scattergram and draw in the line of best fit.
Comment on the correlation.

  b Working to 1 decimal place, calculate the equation of your line of best fit.

  c Use the equation of your line to estimate the score for shots taken from 9 m away.

9 Criticise the conclusion in this statement.
30 out of 120 cars involved in accidents on the Newtown by-pass had faulty brakes.
Therefore 25% of cars in this area have faulty brakes.

10 The manager of a cinema wishes to survey a stratified sample of 50 from an evening audience. The ticket office gives him the data in the table.

Calculate how many of these groups should be in the sample.

	Male	Female
Child	33	22
Adult	84	106
OAP	45	60

  a OAPs

  b Male adults

  c Female children

11 Researchers investigated a new health diet by setting a fitness test (scored out of 100) to 75 volunteers before and then after a three-week period on the diet. The cumulative frequency diagram displays the results.

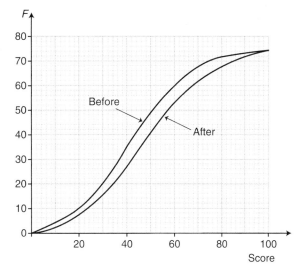

a Write down the median, quartiles and interquartile range for each set of results.

b Present each set of statistics in a box and whisker plot.

c Compare the results and comment on the effectiveness of the diet.

12 The mass of each potato from a 20 kg sack gave the distribution given in the frequency table.

a Calculate the mean mass of a potato.

b Draw the cumulative frequency curve for these data.

c Work out the median, quartiles and interquartile range from your diagram.

Mass (g)	f
60–80	15
80–100	31
100–120	53
120–140	40
140–160	24
160–180	9

13 This frequency table and the histogram show the match times of the 64 first-round games in the Ladies Singles at a tennis tournament.

Time (min)	Frequency
30–45	
45–60	
60–70	
70–80	12
80–90	10
90–120	6
120–150	3

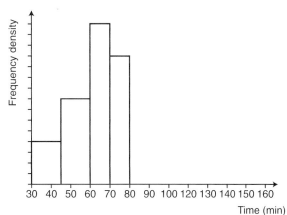

a Copy and complete the frequency table.

b Copy and complete the histogram and write in the scale on the frequency density axis.

c Extend the frequency table and thus calculate an estimate of the mean length of a game.

Numeracy practice 4

Skills practice

Number

Work out these.

1 67.3×45 **2** 78.9×76 **3** $18.96 \div 2.4$ **4** $13.72 \div 2.8$

5 $29.4 \div 7$ **6** $1157 \div 13$ **7** $(1.3)^2$ **8** $(1.7)^2$

9 $837 \div 3^3$ **10** $416 \div 4^3$ **11** $10^{-2} - 3$ **12** $10^{-2} - 2$

13 128×4^{-4} **14** 1625×5^{-2} **15** $(6.4 \times 10^5)^{\frac{1}{2}}$ **16** $(3.6 \times 10^3)^{\frac{1}{2}}$

17 $(7 \times 10^4) - (8 \times 10^3)$ **18** $(4 \times 10^4) - (5 \times 10^3)$

19 $\sqrt{3} \times 2\sqrt{3}$ **20** $\sqrt{5} \times 3\sqrt{5}$ **21** $1 - (3 \times 10^{-3})$ **22** $2 - (4 \times 10^{-2})$

Change these to a decimal.   Change these to a fraction.

23 $\frac{3}{8}$ **24** $\frac{5}{8}$ **25** $0.3\dot{8}$ **26** $0.4\dot{6}$

Estimate these.

27 $25.7^2 \div 13.7^2$ **28** $86^2 \div 44^2$ **29** 953×5^{-4}

30 6573×7^{-3} **31** $(6.31 \times 10^{-3})^{\frac{1}{2}}$ **32** $(2.48 \times 10^{-3})^{\frac{1}{2}}$

Algebra

Simplify these.

1 $\frac{3a}{b} \div 3a^2$ **2** $\frac{a}{b} \div 3a^2$ **3** $a \div (3a)$ **4** $2 \div (2b)$

5 $a^{-3} \times a^{-1}$ **6** $b^3 \times b^{-4}$ **7** $a^{-3} \div a^{-1}$ **8** $b^3 \div b^{-4}$

9 $\dfrac{a^2 + a^2 + a^2 + a^2}{a^2}$ **10** $\dfrac{2a^2 + 2a^2 + 2a^2 + 2a^2}{2a^2}$

Factorise these completely.

11 $2x^2 + 4x - 6$ **12** $2x^2 + 8x + 6$ **13** $4x^2 - y^2$ **14** $a^2 - 9b^2$

15 $ab^2 - a^3$ **16** $2a^2 - 8b^2$

Solve these for x.

17 $\dfrac{x}{2} + \dfrac{2x}{3} = 3\frac{1}{2}$ **18** $\dfrac{x}{2} - \dfrac{x}{4} = 3$ **19** $x^2 - 2x = 8$ **20** $x^2 + 4x = 21$

Solve these inequalities.

21 $3x + 4 < 6(x + 2)$ **22** $2x - 5 > 3x + 2$

Challenges

1 **a** The final medals table for the Sydney
Olympics 2000 and the countries'
populations are shown.
Compile another table ranking the
countries in millions of people per
point, where gold = 3 points,
silver = 2 points, bronze = 1 point.
Comment on your findings.

Sydney Olympics 2000

Country	Gold	Silver	Bronze	Population (millions)
United States	39	25	33	278.4
Russia	32	28	28	146.9
China	28	16	15	1277.6
Australia	16	25	17	18.9
Germany	14	17	26	82.2
France	13	14	11	59.1
Italy	13	8	13	57.3
Netherlands	12	9	4	15.8
Cuba	11	11	7	11.2
Great Britain	11	10	7	58.8
Romania	11	6	9	22.3
South Korea	8	9	11	46.8
Hungary	8	6	3	10.0
Poland	6	5	3	38.8
Japan	5	8	5	126.7
Bulgaria	5	6	2	8.2
Greece	4	6	3	10.6
Sweden	4	5	3	8.9
Norway	4	3	2	5.4
Ethiopia	4	1	3	65.3
Canada	3	3	8	31.1
Mexico	1	2	3	98.4
Brazil	0	6	6	170.3
South Africa	0	2	3	40.4
Ireland	0	1	0	3.7
India	0	0	1	1013.7

b From the data shown, draw a scatter graph to
compare the performance of these ten
countries between the Olympic Games in 2000
and in 1988.
Comment on your findings.

Seoul Olympics 1988

Country	Gold	Silver	Bronze
USSR (Russia)	55	31	46
Germany	48	49	45
United States	36	31	27
South Korea	12	10	11
Hungary	11	6	6
Bulgaria	10	12	13
Romania	7	11	6
France	6	4	6
Italy	6	4	4
China	5	11	12

2 Solve this equation for x using an algebraic method: $x^4 - 13x^2 + 36 = 0$

3 A fly crawls around a circle at a constant speed. How long does it take to crawl once around
a circle with a radius of r^2 at a speed equal to the reciprocal of the square of r cm/s? If the
journey takes 32π seconds, find the radius of the circle.

Fact finder: Recycling

Recycling is important because it conserves natural resources, saves energy and landfill space, and reduces air and water pollution.

Aluminium, a light metal with a density of **2.7 g/cm³**, is one of the major recycled materials in the UK. It can be recycled indefinitely, as reprocessing does not damage its structure.

The UK's latest used aluminium recycling plant produces **8 m** long aluminium ingots weighing **26 tonnes**, each of which makes **1.6 million** cans. If you were to drink one can per day, it would take you over **4000 years** to use up the cans produced by one ingot!

Production of aluminium from raw materials is costly, demanding large quantities of energy. Recycling **one** aluminium can takes about **5%** of the energy needed to produce the can from raw materials.

In 1998, about **4 × 10⁹ cans** were used in the UK. The average can has a height of **14.5 cm** and diameter of **6.5 cm**. Of these, **36%** were recycled and the rest went into landfills. If all the recycled cans were laid end to end, they would stretch from Land's End to John O'Groats **160 times**.

A bin liner holds about **200** loose cans, while **one tonne** of crushed cans takes up about **4 m³**. In October 2000, you would have received **£650 per tonne** for loose cans.

Glass is another of the major recycled materials, with the first bottle banks in the UK appearing in 1977.

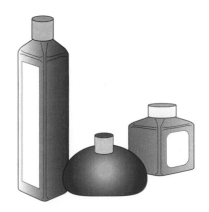

At the end of 1999 there were about **22 020** bottle banks in the UK, one for every **2700** people, and **499 000 tonnes** of glass were recycled. Bottle banks are about **1.5 m** high with a diameter of **1.25 m** and can hold up to **3000** bottles or jars before they need emptying.

On average, every household in the UK consumes around **500** glass bottles and jars per year.

The density of glass is the same as that of aluminium, and there are approximately **3000** glass bottles or jars to a **tonne**. The average bottle or jar has a height of **19 cm** and diameter of **7 cm** and contains **22%** recycled glass. The largest glass furnaces can produce about **400 tonnes** of glass every day.

Exercise

1 Estimate the mass of a glass bottle and an aluminium can in grams.

2 Find the density of aluminium in tonnes per m^3.

3 What is the cross-sectional area in m^2 of an aluminium ingot produced by the latest recycling plant?

4 It is claimed that if you were to drink one can per day, it would take over 4000 years to use one ingot. How many years would it actually take?

5 How many recycled cans can be made using the same energy as is needed to make a new can?

6 Estimate the population of the UK in 1999, giving your answer in standard form.

7 If all the glass that is recycled came from bottles, how many bottles were recycled in 1999?

8 What is the distance from Land's End to John O'Groats?

9 What would be a fair selling price for a bin liner of loose cans?

10 In 1998, if all the cans that went to landfill sites were crushed instead, what volume would they have taken up?

11 When aluminium cans are crushed, approximately what percentage is air?

12 Estimate how many times each bottle bank is emptied each year.

13 Show that a full bottle bank must contain some broken bottles.

14 If all the bottles recycled in 1999 were laid end to end, how many times would they go round the Earth's equator? (Assume the Earth is a sphere with radius 6400 km.)

15 Assume that all the recycled glass from 1999 together with new glass is used to make new bottles.

   a How many bottles can be made?

   b How many furnaces would be required?

   c What volume (in m^3) of glass is involved?

16 Estimate the average number of people in a family in the UK.

The Tower of Bramah

> In the great temple at Benares, beneath the dome that marks the centre of the world, rests a brass plate in which are fixed three diamond needles, each a cubit high and as thick as the body of a bee. On one of these needles, at the creation, God placed sixty-four discs of pure gold, the largest disc resting on the brass plate, and the others getting smaller and smaller up to the top one. This is the Tower of Bramah. Day and night unceasingly the priests transfer the discs from one diamond needle to another according to the fixed and immutable laws of Bramah, which require that the priest on duty must not move more than one disc at a time and that he must place this disc on a needle so that there is no smaller disc below it. When the sixty-four discs shall have been thus transferred from the needle on which at the creation God placed them to one of the other needles, tower, temple and priests alike will crumble into dust, and with a thunderclap the world will vanish.
>
> M. De Parville, *La Nature*, 1884

The Tower of Hanoi puzzle is just like the Tower of Bramah, but with fewer discs, and was invented in 1883 by the French mathematician Edouard Lucas.

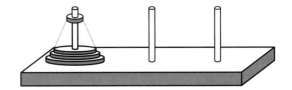

1 If there are only two discs, what is the smallest number of moves required to transfer the discs from one spike to another?

2 Show that a minimum of seven moves are needed when there are three discs.

3 Investigate the minimum number of moves needed to transfer *n* discs.

4 If the priests move one disc every second and never make a mistake, how long does the world last according to this legend?

5 **Investigate** what happens if there are more than three spikes, and find upper bounds on the number of moves required.

6 In the **bimetal Tower of Bramah**, the difference is that for every size of disc there are two discs, one gold and one silver. Initially, there are two towers of discs alternating between gold and silver. The discs must be moved using the same rules, with the aim of making two towers, one consisting of all the gold discs and the other consisting of all the silver discs. The biggest discs must swap positions. Investigate this version of the game.

7 **Investigate** what happens if you allow arbitrary initial and final states. For example, you could start by considering the initial state and final state shown.

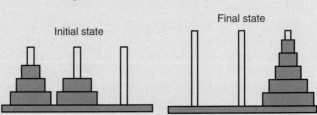

Examination practice 4

Paper 4A (Non-calculator)

1 Work out these.

a $7 \times \dfrac{3}{2.8}$ **b** $608.4 \div 13$

c 24.5×0.94 **d** $10^{-4} \div 10^{-5}$

2 This diagram shows the start line and the positions of two yachts A and B just before a race begins.

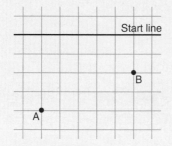

The skipper of yacht C wishes to position himself so that he is closer to A than B, but also closer to the start line than B.

a Copy the diagram and shade the locus of C's position.

b Within his restrictions, assume that C gets as close to B as he can. If A is becalmed, sketch the track of C as B moves directly to the start line.

3 Using a scale of 1 cm to 1 unit, draw rectangular axes, labelling both axes from −6 to 6. On your diagram, draw and label the triangle P with vertices $(2, 2)$, $(2, 4)$ and $(3, 4)$.

a Rotate P, −90° about the point $(-1, 2)$. Label the image A.

b Translate P through the vector $\begin{pmatrix} -6 \\ 1 \end{pmatrix}$. Label the image B.

c Describe fully the single transformation that maps A to B.

4 An exercise has 100 questions.

a A mathematics teacher asks one pupil to do each question numbered $5n - 2$ where n is an integer. How many questions does the pupil do?

b Another pupil is told to do questions 2, 6, 10, 14, ... Find a formula to generate this sequence. How many questions does this pupil do?

5 The pie chart displays the scores from a series of 40 games of Pontoon.

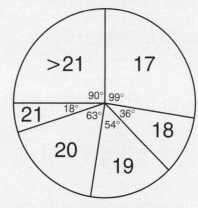

a Draw a bar chart of the scores.

b Find the median of all the scores.

c Calculate the mean of the scores of '21 or under'.

6 **a** Express 504 as a product of prime factors using indices where necessary.

b Find the LCM and the HCF of 30 and 21.

7 Find the sides x and y.

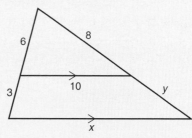

8 A pulley P is vertically above B and PB = 24 m. C is a point level with B and 18 m from it. A 50 m rope has one end pegged at C and the other end at Q, hanging over the pulley as shown.

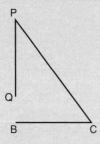

a Find the length CP.

b How far is Q above B?

c The peg C is moved to a new position 14 m further from B and still on the same level. By how much does Q rise?

9 Identify the flaws in these two statements.

a 90% of car-owners who returned their cars to the showroom for repair stated that they would never buy another of this model. Therefore the car company decides to discontinue this model.

b 75% of shoppers questioned one morning in a Shopping Mall stated that they would attend a Protest Meeting later in the day. As a result, 2000 protesters were expected by the organisers.

10 Fran has a box containing a *very large* number of stamps. Two-thirds are Cuban; the remainder are from Brazil. She randomly picks out two without replacement.

a Calculate an estimate of the probability that she has selected
  (i) two Cuban stamps
  (ii) a Cuban and a Brazilian stamp.

b A third stamp is randomly withdrawn from the box.
Calculate the probability that Fran has at least two Brazilian stamps from her three selections.

11 This frequency table gives the weights of a catch of cod landed from one boat at Aberdeen one morning.

Weight, w (kg)	Frequency, f
$0 \leqslant w < 1$	16
$1 \leqslant w < 1.5$	24
$1.5 \leqslant w < 1.75$	25
$1.75 \leqslant w < 2$	35
$2 \leqslant w < 2.5$	29
$2.5 \leqslant w < 4$	21

A histogram is drawn of this distribution and the tallest bar is 7 cm high. Work out the height of the bar for these groups.

a $1.5 \leqslant w < 1.75$

b $2 \leqslant w < 2.5$

c $0 \leqslant w < 1$

12 An adult has 5 litres of blood and 5 million red blood cells, each of a diameter of $8\,\mu m$ $(1\,\mu m = 10^{-6}\,m)$. Each cell contains 6.4×10^8 haemoglobin molecules.

  a Find the number of haemoglobin molecules in an adult

  b Find the number of red blood cells per mm^3

13 This figure shows three identical spherical billiard balls of diameter 6 cm inside an equilateral triangle.

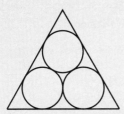

Work out the perimeter of the frame, leaving your answer in surd form.

14 a A parallelogram is a quadrilateral whose opposite sides are parallel.

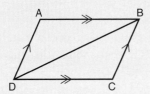

Copy and complete this proof, to prove that the opposite sides are also equal in length.

In triangles ABD and CDB

1 $\angle ABD = \ldots\ldots$
  $(\ldots\ldots\text{parallel}\ldots\ldots)$

2 $\angle ADB = \ldots\ldots$
  $(\ldots\ldots\text{parallel}\ldots\ldots)$

3 $\ldots\ldots$ is common

∴ $\triangle ABD$ and $\triangle CDB$ are $\ldots\ldots$
  $(\ldots\ldots)$

∴ $BC = \ldots\ldots$ and $AB = \ldots\ldots$

b The mid-point theorem states that 'the straight line joining the mid-points of two sides of a triangle is parallel to and one half of the third side'.

In this figure, XY is produced to Z, where CZ is parallel to BA.

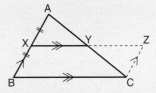

Use congruent triangles to prove the mid-point theorem.

15 $f(x) = \dfrac{2x+2}{2x+5}$

  a Find $f(2)$.

  b Find the value of x so that $f(x) = 0$.

  c If x is very large, what is the approximate value of $f(x)$?

  d Find the two values of x so that $f(x) = x$.

16 The x-axis is tangent to a circle at the point $A(2, 0)$. The circle passes through the point $B(6, 2)$.

  a Write down the x coordinate of the centre of the circle.

  b Find the gradient of AB and the mid-point M of AB.

  c Find the equation of the line perpendicular to AB passing through M.

  d Find the centre of the circle and write down the radius.

17 Write each of these expressions in the form a^x and hence solve the equation for a.

  a $\dfrac{a^2}{a^{-2}}$, $16 = \dfrac{a^2}{a^{-2}}$ **b** $\dfrac{1}{\sqrt[3]{a}}$, $a^{-\frac{1}{3}} = \dfrac{1}{2}$

  c $\dfrac{1}{a^2} + a^{-2}$, $32 = \dfrac{1}{a^2} + a^{-2}$

18 In the diagram O is the centre of the circle and the lines PT and QT are tangents to the circle.

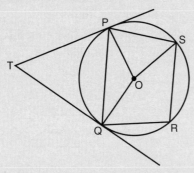

If angle PTQ = 48° and angle PSO = 42°, find the size of the following angles, giving brief reasons for your answers.

a angle QPO   **b** angle QPS

c angle QRS

MEI

19 Shane takes off from the top of a skateboard ramp. The ramp can be modelled by

$$y = 3 - \frac{1}{2}x$$

while Shane's path can be modelled by

$$y = 1 + 2x - \frac{1}{2}x^2$$

with units in metres.

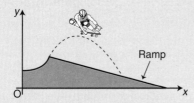

Find, by calculation, the coordinates of where Shane takes off and lands.

20 a Find the values of a and b such that
$$x^2 - 12x = (x + a)^2 + b$$

b Hence solve the equation
$$x^2 - 12x = 13.$$

c For what values of k will the equation $x^2 - 12x = k$ have no solutions?

Paper 4B (Calculator)

1 a According to a recent survey, one-third of boys exercise regularly by the age of 15 and a quarter of girls. Find, as a percentage, how many more boys exercise than girls.

b Hamial's normal temperature is 37 °C.
  (i) He catches an infection and his temperature rises by 4%. Find his high temperature.
  (ii) After taking antibiotics, his temperature drops by 4%. Find his final temperature, correct to 2 significant figures.

2 a Solve these inequalities.
  (i) $4 - 2(x + 4) < 10x$
  (ii) $\dfrac{22 + x}{4} \geqslant 3x$

b Write these inequalities,

$$2 > \frac{x}{2} + 1 \quad \text{and} \quad -7 < 2 + 3x$$

in the form $\ldots < x < \ldots$ and list the integers in the solution set.

3 A black dice and a red dice are thrown together and their scores are added. What is the probability that the sum is

a a multiple of 3?

b more than 9?

c a prime number?

4 Anne and Brian have some CDs. If Anne were to give Brian a CD, they would both have an equal number of CDs. If Brian were to give Anne a CD, then Anne would have twice as many CDs as Brian.

a Let x and y be the number of CDs Anne and Brian have respectively. Form a pair of simultaneous equations in x and y.

b Solve these equations to find how many CDs they each have.

5 **a** Pete thought of a number.
   He then added 3, multiplied the result
   by 5 and then subtracted 8.
   His answer was 42.
   What was the number he thought of?

b Subtract $1 + (x - y)$ from $y - (1 - x)$.

c Simplify $\left(\dfrac{x}{y} + \dfrac{y}{x}\right)^2 - \left(\dfrac{x}{y} - \dfrac{y}{x}\right)^2$.

6 A drugs company is to test a new
   dandruff treatment on a stratified sample
   of 50 volunteers. A survey of 2000
   customers who bought dandruff shampoo
   at a local supermarket gave these results.

	Male	Female
Brand A	342	480
Brand B	240	284
Brand C	498	156

a Calculate the number of females that
   should be included in the sample.

b Calculate the number of males who use
   Brand A drandruff shampoo that
   should be included in the sample.

7 Jupiter's diameter at its equator is
   $(89\,400 \pm 50)$ miles. The planet rotates
   once every 10 hours, correct to the nearest
   hour.

a Find the maximum speed of rotation at
   the equator in mph.

b Find the minimum speed of rotation at
   the equator in mph.

8 In the triangle OPQ, A and B are mid-
   points of the sides OP and OQ
   respectively, $\overrightarrow{OA} = \mathbf{a}$ and $\overrightarrow{OB} = \mathbf{b}$.

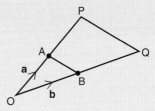

a Find in terms of $\mathbf{a}$ and $\mathbf{b}$: $\overrightarrow{OP}$, $\overrightarrow{OQ}$, $\overrightarrow{AB}$
   and $\overrightarrow{PQ}$.

b What can you conclude about AB and
   PQ?

9 In January 1999, by working out
   $2^{3021377} - 1$, a computer took 46 hours to
   find the largest prime number, and it
   contained 909 526 digits. Rebecca tries to
   write out this number at one digit per
   second with each 10 digits taking up 5 cm
   of space.

a Find the time it would take her.

b Find the length of the number, when
   written out, in kilometres.

10 Jamal runs a 100 m race in 14.2 s. This is
   the speed–time graph for Jamal's race.

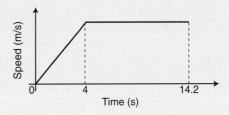

a Find his average speed for the race.

b What is the greatest speed reached by
   him in the race?

c Find his acceleration over the first four
   seconds.

d Sidd also runs in this race, accelerating
   constantly from the start for 5 s until he
   reaches a top speed of 8 m/s, which he
   maintains until the finish.
   Does Sidd beat Jamal?

11 An oil slick is trebling in area every day. When first discovered, it covered an area of $9\,m^2$.

a What is the area of the slick a week after it was discovered?

b When will the slick reach an area of $3^{12}\,m^2$?

c When the area is $3^{14}\,m^2$, the oil slick is sprayed with a chemical that dissolves two-thirds of the slick. What area is left?

12 Joyce is standing at point A in a field and observes a hare at B, running in a straight line towards a bush at C. The observation angle $x = 60°$ when the hare is first observed, and this changes at a rate of $6°$ per second as the hare runs towards the bush.

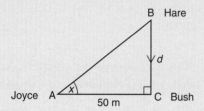

a If d is the distance of the hare from the bush, copy and complete this table.

t (s)	0	2	4	6	8	10
d (m)	86.6				10.6	

b Draw a graph of d(m) against time (s) and comment on it.

c Use the graph to *estimate* the gradient of the graph at $t = 6\,s$ and state what this represents.

13 A circular Big Wheel funfair ride of radius 20 m rotates in a clockwise direction. The lowest point is 10 m above the ground and the highest point on the wheel is P. The wheel rotates at $2°$ per second.

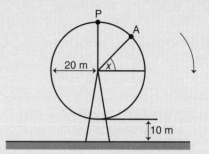

a Calculate the height of a chair at A above the ground if $x = 30°$.

b Find the height of the chair 20 s after reaching point A, above the ground.

c What is the height of the chart 130 s after reaching point A, below point P?

14 Mandy is investigating whether it is possible to have a right-angled triangle where the sides are three consecutive whole numbers. She lets x, $x + 1$ and $x + 2$ stand for the lengths of the sides.

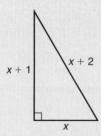

a Form and simplify an equation for x.

b Solve the equation and show that only one triangle is possible.

c Mick thinks it is possible to have a right-angled triangle where the sides are three consecutive odd whole numbers. Show that Mick is wrong.

15 5000 fourteen-year-old children completed a numeracy test as part of a government survey into educational standards. The results are given in this table.

Marks, x	Frequency, f
0–10	75
10–25	304
25–40	503
40–55	1105
55–70	1469
70–85	994
85–100	550

a Draw a cumulative frequency diagram for the results.

Use your diagram to estimate these.

b The median mark and the interquartile range

c The percentage who scored at least half-marks

16 This figure shows a frustrum with a circular base.

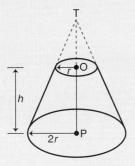

a Use similar triangles to show that OT = h.

b Show that the volume V of the frustrum is $V = \dfrac{7\pi r^2 h}{3}$

c Write the formula in part **b** in the form $V = kr^2 h$ where k is correct to 4 significant figures.

d The volume of another frustrum, where $r = h$, is $35\,\text{cm}^3$. Find the value of r.

17 Andy is investigating bees' honeycombs for his biology project. He wants to know the connection between the number of cells and the number of walls for different arrangements of the cells.

He first considers cells in a line.

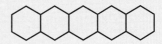

a Copy and complete this table, and find a formula for w in terms of c.

No. of cells (c)	No. of walls (w)
1	6
2	
3	
4	
5	26

He next considers cells arranged in triangles.

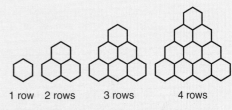

1 row   2 rows   3 rows   4 rows

b Copy and complete this table.

No. of rows (r)	1	2	3	4	5
No. of cells (c)	1				15
No. of walls (w)	6			42	
$r + c$	2				

c What formula connects w and $r + c$?

d Andy's teacher tells him that $c = \frac{1}{2}(r^2 + r)$. Use this and your answer to part **a** to find a formula connecting w and r.

e How many walls are in a triangular honeycomb with 10 rows?

18 SF and SJF represent routes on a ski slope. Two routes, one in a straight line from S to F and the other from S to F via J, are shown. Make a neat copy of this diagram.

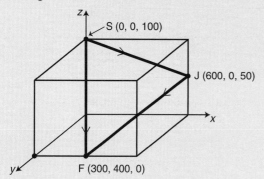

a Calculate the lengths SF, SJ and JF.

b Find the angle FSJ.

The velocity, v m/s, of the skier straight down the slope, from S to F, is given by

$$v = 30 \sin a$$

where a is the angle the path makes with the horizontal.

c Find the time it takes the skier to go from S to F.

19 Damon wants a stand for his drum. His drum is 40 cm in diameter and he wants the centre Q to be 50 cm above the floor. To avoid damage to the drum the supports AB and CD must be tangential to the drum as shown in the diagram. Using axes as shown with 1 cm = 1 unit the x coordinate of point A is 16.

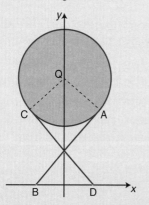

a Work out the y coordinate of A and the gradient of QA.

b Work out the gradient of AB and the equation of the line AB.

c Find the coordinates of B and hence the length of the support AB.

20 Kayleigh is designing a pendant. The outline of the pendant is given by $4x^2 + y^2 = 4$ with units in centimetres. She wants to divide up the pendant with two straight lines as shown in this diagram.

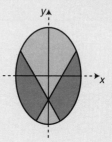

Kayleigh finds that the line $y = 2x - 1$ is suitable. The other line is a reflection of $y = 2x - 1$ in the y-axis.

a What is the equation of the other line?

b Kayleigh needs to find where the line $y = 2x - 1$ intersects the outline of the pendant. Solve the simultaneous equations $y = 2x - 1$ and $4x^2 + y^2 = 4$ to find these points.

c Where does the other line intersect the outline?

Paper 4C (Non-calculator)

1 Work out these.

  a $2\frac{1}{3} - 1\frac{3}{4}$

  b $2\frac{1}{3} \div 1\frac{3}{4}$

  c $4 + 2 \times 10$

  d $12^0 \div 12^{-1}$

2 To detect whether a star has a planetary system, astronomers measure the 'wobble' of the star. They can now detect a 'wobble' equivalent to a movement across the width of a human hair from a distance of 60 miles away.

Taking the width as 0.06 mm, copy and complete this statement.

This is equivalent to detecting a movement of .....cm on the Moon, which is 240 000 miles away.

3 A farmyard has horses and ducks in it. Altogether there are 17 heads and 58 legs in the farmyard.

  a Let x be the number of horses and y be the number of ducks. Form two equations involving x and y.

  b Solve the equations to find how many ducks there are.

4 a For a regular octagon, work out the size of the exterior angle.

  b Calculate the sum of the interior angles of a regular octagon.

  c Explain why regular octagons will *not* tesselate (meet around a point without any gaps or overlaps).

5 Use standard form to work out an estimate of these, giving your answers in standard form correct to 1 significant figure.

  a $(4.7 \times 10^6) \times (2.1 \times 10^{-4})$

  b $(4.6 \times 10^6) \div (2.1 \times 10^{-4})$

  c $(6.7 \times 10^{-5}) + (4.2 \times 10^{-6})$

  d $\sqrt{(3.8 \times 10^{-5})}$

6 Copy the diagram on graph paper.

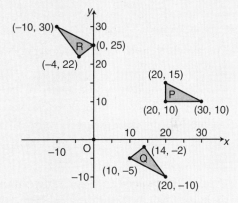

  a R is a reflection of P. Draw in the mirror line and find its equation.

  b Describe fully the transformation that maps R to Q.

  c Hence describe fully the transformation that maps P to Q.

7 $\mathbf{r} = \begin{pmatrix} 1 \\ 3 \end{pmatrix}$ and $\mathbf{s} = \begin{pmatrix} -2 \\ 5 \end{pmatrix}$.

  a Calculate $2\mathbf{r} - \mathbf{s}$.

  b Calculate $2(\mathbf{r} - \mathbf{s})$.

  c Calculate the length of vector $\mathbf{s}$ in surd form.

  d $v\mathbf{r} + w\mathbf{s} = \begin{pmatrix} -3 \\ 13 \end{pmatrix}$

What are the values of the constants v and w?

8 A miniature picture frame is supported by hooks at A and B. Draw the rectangle ABCD.

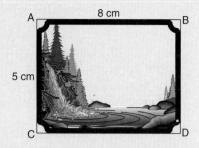

a Draw onto your diagram the locus of points A and D if the hook at A falls out.

The picture is to be hung with only one hook.

b Show on the diagram the locus of the single hook if it is to be closer to AB than CD.

9 The cradle used to raise the wreck of the 15th-century ship the Mary Rose, and the wreck itself weighed 15 times more out of the water than in. The ratio of the cradle's weight to the wreck's weight was 1:5. The cradle and wreck weighed 540 tonnes out of the water. What was the apparent weight of the wreck under the water, without the cradle?

10 PQR and PRS are right-angled triangles.

$\angle RPQ = 30°$.

$\angle PSR = 50°$.

$PR = 10\,m$.

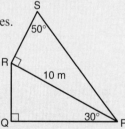

This table shows the trigonometry ratios correct to 3 significant figures.

Angle	sin	cos	tan
30°	0.500	0.866	0.577
50°	0.766	0.643	1.19

Calculate these to a suitable degree of accuracy.

a Length PQ

b Length QR

c Length RS

d Area PQRS

11 The three vertices of a triangle are A$(1, 1)$, B$(3, 2)$ and C$(-1, 5)$.

a Find the gradients of AB, BC and AC.

b Which of AB, BC and AC are perpendicular?

c Find the lengths of AB and BC, giving your answers as square roots.

d Hence find the exact area of the triangle.

12 The position of a pebble thrown from the top of a cliff, relative to the axes shown, is given by $y = 3x - 0.2x^2$, all units being in metres.

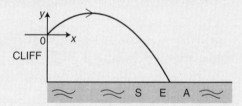

a Copy and complete this table and use the values to draw the graph for $0 \leqslant x \leqslant 20$.

x	0	4	8	12	16	20
y	0		11.2		-3.2	

b Use your graph to find the maximum height of the pebble above the sea, given the cliff is 20 m high.

c What is the horizontal distance from the cliff when the pebble is level with the cliff-top?

13 A cylindrical can of beans has a height of 15 cm and base radius of 4 cm. It is put into a cylindrical saucepan of radius 10 cm already fairly full with water, and as a result it is completely covered.

  a By how much does the water level rise?

  b If it was stood on its end, and the water was originally 7 cm deep, by how much would the water level rise now?

14 a When the same number, x, is added to both the top and bottom of the fraction $\frac{123}{456}$ the answer is $\frac{1}{2}$.

  Form an equation in x and solve it to find the number.

  b A rectangle has sides as shown in this diagram.

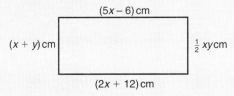

  Find x and y and the dimensions of each side.

15 A sector with an angle of $144°$ is cut out of a circle of radius 10 cm.
The remainder is turned into a cone by bringing two radii together.

  a Work out the circumference of the base of the cone in terms of π.

  b Find the base radius of the cone.

  c Calculate the height of the cone.

  d If the volume of the cone is the same as a sphere, find the radius of the sphere, leaving your answer as a cube root.

16

Share price: AFG plc	Five-point moving average
z	36.7
35.4	37.4
36.8	37.6
38.2	38.2
41.0	x
39.6	y
40.4	
38.8	

  a Calculate the next two moving averages, x and y.

  b Calculate the share price, z.

17 Cage X contains four hampsters, one white and three brown. Meanwhile cage Y has three hampsters, two white and one brown. One hampster is taken from cage X and placed in cage Y. Hampsters are then removed one by one from cage Y.

  a Copy and complete this tree diagram.

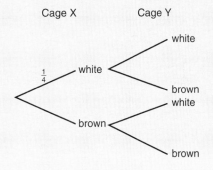

  b Use your tree diagram to find the probability that the first hampster removed from cage Y is

    (i) white   (ii) brown

  c What is the probability that, of the first two hampsters removed from Y, both are white?

18 Two circles C_1 and C_2 intersect at P and Q. The line AQT is a tangent to the circle C_1 at Q. XPB is a straight line.

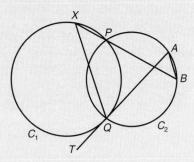

(i) Copy the diagram and join PQ. If the angle $TQX = 100°$, calculate the angles

  (a) XPQ (b) QAB

(ii) Make a second copy of the given diagram and prove that, whatever the size of angle TQX, XQ is parallel to AB.

MEI

19 An important formula in physics is

$$\frac{1}{u} + \frac{1}{v} = \frac{1}{f}$$

a Make u the subject.

b When $v > f$ and both v and f are positive, then $u > 0$. Investigate other similar conditions for v and f to give
(i) $u > 0$ (ii) $u \leqslant 0$

c Work out the value of u when $v = 4.8$ and $f = 2.4$.

20 Lemon Mobile Phones want to market a new phone card containing both peak units, costing 50p per unit, and off-peak units, costing 25p per unit. Let x be the number of peak units on a card and y the number of off-peak units on a card.

a There is to be a maximum of 30 units on a card. Express this as an inequality in x and y.

b The maximum cost of a card is to be £10. Form another inequality in x and y and show it simplifies to $2x + y \leqslant 40$.

c Using both x and y axes from 0 to 40, show both inequalities on one graph and shade the unwanted regions.

d If units are only available in multiples of 10, mark the possible combinations on your graph. Remember there must be some of each type of unit on the card. What combination of units would you recommend?

Paper 4D (Calculator)

1 Calculate the VAT for these purchases.

  a Six bottles of Chateau Le Plonque at
  £5.88 exclusive of 17.5% VAT.

  b 40 litres of petrol at 83.6p per litre
  inclusive of 17.5% VAT.

2 The Earth has a mass of 5.98×10^{24} kg.
Taking the Earth as a sphere of radius
6378 km, find its density in g/cm^3.

3 Jack needs to borrow £7500 to help buy
a new car. Calculate the interest charge
for a loan over four years from these
lenders.

  a A finance company, which charges 8%
  simple interest

  b A bank, which charges 7.2%
  compound interest

4 The Great Pyramid of Giza took
20 years to build with 2.4 million blocks
of stone each of an average weight of
2.5 tonnes.

  a Find the average number of blocks laid
  per day.

  b Find the average weight of blocks laid
  per day, correct to 2 significant figures.

  c How long would it have taken to build
  another pyramid, with 1.5 million
  blocks, with the same number of men?

5 The temperature of Kim's cup of coffee,
$t°$C, m minutes after it has been poured
into her mug, is given by the equation

$$t = \frac{425}{m} \quad \text{valid for } 5 \leqslant m \leqslant 10$$

  a Copy and complete this table and use it
  to draw the graph of t against m for
  $5 \leqslant m \leqslant 10$.

m	5	6	7	8	9	10
t	85			53.1		

  b Kim likes her coffee between the
  temperatures of 50°C and 70°C.
  Use your graph to find at what times
  Kim should drink her coffee.

6 The square-based cuboid shown has a
height 1m greater than the length x of the
side of the square. The volume is 40 m^3.

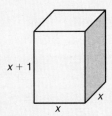

  a Find an equation for x.

  b Find, using trial and improvement, the
  value of x correct to 3 significant
  figures.

7 The total number of points scored in a
series of basketball matches is given in the
frequency table.

Points, x	Frequency, f
121–130	7
131–140	11
141–150	15
151–160	13
161–170	9
171–180	5

  a How many matches are included in the
  survey?

  b Calculate an estimate for the mean
  number of points scored per match.

  c Estimate the probability that the
  number of points scored in a match is
  between 125 and 155.

8 A triangle has two angles as shown in this diagram.

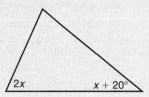

a Find the third angle in terms of x.

b There are three different isosceles triangles with these angles. Write down three equations giving these angles.

c Solve the equations to find the three different values of x which make the triangle isosceles.

9 The time, t minutes, left for recording on a video tape is given by $t = 11r^2 - 16$, where r cm is the radius of the unused tape.

a Mary wants to record an episode of 'Coastwatch' which lasts $\frac{3}{4}$ hour.
She finds a tape with 2.5 cm of unused tape on it. Is there enough blank tape?

b Frank wants to put marks on the casing of a tape to indicate 1 hour, 2 hours and 3 hours recording time left. Where should he put the marks?

10 Six shoppers gave these responses in a questionnaire at a supermarket.

No. of children, x	Weekly shopping bill, y
0	£44
1	£60
2	£75
3	£95
3	£80
6	£110

a Plot the data onto a scattergram and describe the correlation between the family size and the weekly shopping bill.

b Draw the line of best fit onto your diagram and find its equation.

c Estimate the weekly shopping bill for a family with four children.

11 At the end of the Ice Age, the water level in the Mediterranean rose by 120 metres in two years. 10 cubic miles of water cut through the Bosphorus into the Black Sea, flooding thousands of square miles.

a In the Mediterranean, what was the average increase in depth, in cm per day?

b Given that 1.609 km = 1 mile, change 10 cubic miles to cubic metres and write your answer in standard form.

c The area of the Isle of Wight is 38 000 hectares. (1 hectare = 10 000 m^2)
Find h.

Volume = 10 cubic miles

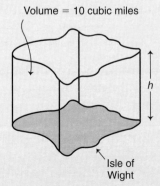

Isle of Wight

UNIT 4 ◆ Examination practice

12 a Solve the equation

$$\frac{x+5}{15} - \frac{x-5}{10} = 1 + \frac{2x}{15}$$

b The two rectangles shown in this diagram have the same area.

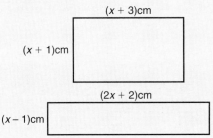

Find the value of x and the area of each rectangle.

13 A mechanical drawbridge 5 m above a river consists of two equal spans of length 15 m both rising up at the same rate of 5° per second.

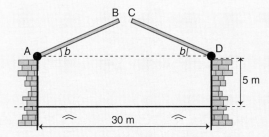

a When $b = 20°$, find distance BC and the height of B above the river.

b At the moment when $b = 20°$, a stuntman runs up the slope AB starting from A at a constant speed of 5 m/s attempting to jump across the gap. He can clear a horizontal distance of 5 m. Does he make the jump across the gap successfully?

14

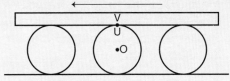

The diagram represents a heavy girder which is to be moved lengthwise across horizontal ground on three cylindrical rollers, each of radius 20 cm. The point O is the centre of a circular cross-section of one of the rollers, and U is its initial point of contact with the girder. V is the point *of the girder* initially in contact with the point U.

The rollers now carry the girder forward, without slipping, in the direction indicated until the point U is in contact with the ground.

a Through what angle have the rollers rotated?

b Calculate the distance through which the point O has moved.

c Through what total distance has the point V moved?

d If the centre of each roller is moving steadily at a speed of 0.4 m/s, at what speed is the girder moving?

MEI

15 A speed boat starts a race at S and travels on a bearing of 060°. After 5 minutes, it rounds buoy A and continues on a bearing of 160°. After 6 km, it rounds buoy B and heads back to the start on a bearing of 315°.

a Draw a neat diagram of the course and calculate the distances SA and BS.

b Assuming that the speed of the boat remains constant throughout, find the time, in minutes, it took to complete the course.

16 Mr Bingley is making a down-payment of £35 000 and taking out a mortgage loan of £60 000 over 20 years at 7% p.a. to buy a house for £95 000.

   a Use this formula to calculate his annual repayments:

$$A = \frac{PR^n(R-1)}{(R^n-1)}, \qquad R = 1 + \frac{r}{100}$$

   where r = interest rate p.a., £P = amount borrowed, n = number of years and £A = the annual repayment.

   b What is the total cost of his loan plus down-payment?

   c Calculate an estimate for the value of his house at the end of the mortgage term if house prices rise at the rate of 5% p.a.

17 A bag contains 16 marbles. Some are white; the remainder are black. Two marbles are taken out consecutively *without* replacement. The probability that two white marbles are picked is $\frac{1}{12}$.

   a How many white marbles are in the bag?

   b What is the probability that at least one of the two marbles will be white?

18 A ladder leaning against a vertical wall just reaches a window 5 m above the ground. Let x be the distance of the foot of the ladder from the wall and let l be the length of the ladder.

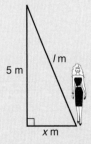

a Write an equation involving x and l.

b Chris thinks the ladder is unsafe. She pulls the base of the ladder out an extra 2 m. The ladder now only reaches 4 m up the wall. Write another equation involving x and l.

c Solve your two equations to find the length of the ladder.

19 To find the height h of a building, from a distance, two angles of elevation a and b are measured from Q and P respectively. The distance PQ is also measured.

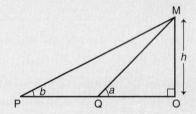

a Let PQ = y and QO = x. In triangle POM

$$\tan b = \frac{h}{x+y}$$

and in triangle QOM,

$$\tan a = \frac{h}{x}$$

Make x the subject in both equations and hence show that height h is given by

$$h = PQ \times \frac{\tan a \tan b}{\tan a - \tan b}$$

b If $a = (25 \pm 2)°$, $b = (20 \pm 2)°$ and PQ = 10 m, find the maximum and minimum height h.

20 The frame of a tubular steel chair is formed from part of the circle $x^2 + y^2 = 625$ and part of the parabola $y = -0.1x^2$ as shown in the diagram.

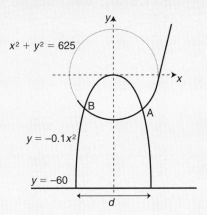

The floor is the line $y = -60$.
All dimensions are in centimetres.

a What is the radius of the circle?

b Find, by a graphical method, the distance d and the coordinates of the points A and B.

Paper 4E (Non-calculator)

1 Work out these.

a $2^{-3} \times 2^5 \div 2^{-2}$ **b** $(3^2)^{-\frac{1}{2}}$

c $(8)^{-\frac{2}{3}}$ **d** $1 \div 3^{-2}$

2 The annual total profits of Butterworth's Bazaar are always shared out as follows: 36 people get a fixed sum of £1000 each, and then the rest is split equally between 15 'shareholders'.

a In one year of trading, the shareholders got £800 each. What were the profits?

b In the following year, the shareholders got a 50% increase each. What was the percentage increase in profits?

3 The speed of a skier, v m/s, sliding down a mountain is proportional to the square root of the distance, d m, she has moved from her starting point.

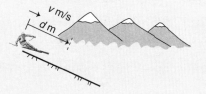

Given that $v = 20$ m/s when $d = 100$ m find

a a formula for v in terms of d

b the speed of the skier when she is 49 m from her starting point

c the distance travelled when the skier's speed is 10 m/s

4 AC is a tangent to the circle with centre at O. AB = 5 cm and BC = 12 cm.

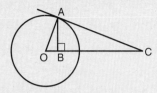

a Write down two triangles that are similar to △ABC.

b Calculate the length of OB.

c Calculate the length of AC.

5 A pupil is selected at random from the group shown.

Work out these probabilities.

a The chosen person wears glasses.

b He/she does not wear glasses.

c It is a male pupil.

6 Coventry is 150 km from London on a bearing of 315°. Felixstowe is 120 km from London on a bearing of 060°.

a Using a scale of 1 cm:10 km, construct, using ruler and compasses only, a triangle showing the positions of London, Coventry and Felixstowe.

b From your drawing, estimate the distance between Coventry and Felixstowe.

7 The figure shows a grid square, of width 4 cm, from a map of scale of 1:25 000. The grid reference of C is (287428).

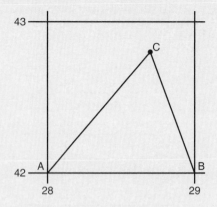

a Find the actual distance, in km, represented by AB.

b Find the actual area, in ha, represented by the triangle ABC. (1 ha = 10 000 m²)

8 Advertisements in the *Evening News* gave these prices and mileages for second-hand 'Valko' estate cars.

Price (£)	Mileage
18 995	5500
2950	65 000
16 000	12 000
10 000	40 000
12 999	20 000
3000	71 000

a Plot the data onto a scattergram and describe the correlation between price and mileage.

b Draw the line of best fit onto your diagram and estimate the price of a car with 50 000 miles on the clock.

c Estimate the mileage of a car costing £12 000.

9 This cumulative frequency diagram shows the distribution of adult female heights of two South American tribes.

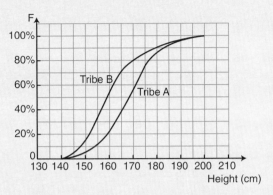

a Find the median and interquartile range of the height of each tribe.

b Referring to your statistics, comment briefly on the distribution of the heights of the two tribes.

10 A spherical drop of mercury splashes and breaks into equal spheres with radii one-quarter that of the original sphere.

a What is the ratio of the volume of one of the new spheres to that of the original sphere?

b How many new spheres are there?

c What is the ratio of the surface area of one of the new spheres to that of the original sphere?

d What is the ratio of the total surface area of all the new spheres to the surface area of the original sphere?

11 a Find the values of x, y and z.

b Find a triangle similar to △ABF.

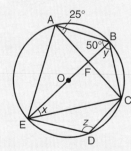

12 Three points A$(1, 6)$, B$(8, 7)$ and C$(9, 0)$ lie on a circle.

a Find the gradients of AB, BC and AC.

b Which of AB, BC and AC are perpendicular?

c Write down the centre of the circle.

d Work out the radius of the circle.

13 A Swing-Ball tennis game consists of a tennis ball attached to a 1m string, one end of which is fixed to a vertical pole of height h metres.

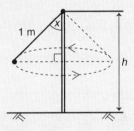

$\sin 30° = \cos 60° = \dfrac{1}{2}$

$\sin 60° = \cos 30° = \dfrac{\sqrt{3}}{2}$

a Given that, when angle $x = 60°$, the height of the ball above the ground is 1.5 m, find h.

b When $x = 60°$, the ball takes $\sqrt{3}$ seconds to perform one revolution of its circular path. Find the speed of the ball in terms of π.

c When $x = 30°$, the ball takes 2 seconds to perform one revolution of its circular path. Find the percentage change in the ball's speed from that at $x = 60°$.

14 a Express $2\sqrt{6}$ in the form $\sqrt{n}$.

b Simplify $\sqrt{20} + \sqrt{45}$.

c Simplify $4\sqrt{5} - 3\sqrt{5}$.

d Rationalise the denominator of $\dfrac{2}{\sqrt{2}}$.

15 a Change $0.3\dot{4}$ as a fraction.

b Change $\frac{3}{8}$ to a decimal.

c Find 2.8% of $40.

d What is the reciprocal of 0.5?

16 In the triangle shown, AC = CB and AD = AB.

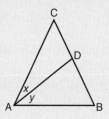

a Find an equation connecting x and y.

b If angle C = 40°, find another equation connecting x and y.

c Solve these equations to find x and y.

17 a The sum of any two sides of a triangle must be greater than the third side. Use this to form three inequalities involving x for this triangle.

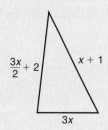

b Solve these inequalities to find the greatest and least values of x.

18 Rebecca and Sam are playing basketball. During the game, their position vectors on the court are defined relative to the axes on the diagram. At time t seconds after the whistle, their position vectors are given by **r** and **s** respectively:

$$\mathbf{r} = \begin{pmatrix} 2 \\ -1 \end{pmatrix} + t \begin{pmatrix} 1 \\ 2 \end{pmatrix}$$

$$\mathbf{s} = \begin{pmatrix} -3 \\ 4 \end{pmatrix} + t \begin{pmatrix} 3 \\ 1 \end{pmatrix}$$

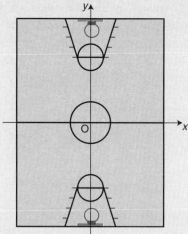

a Find the position vectors for Rebecca and Sam after:
(i) 1 s   (ii) 2 s

b Write down the vector from Rebecca to Sam after 2 s and use it to find how far apart they are at this moment. Leave your answer in surd form.

c Calculate the speeds of the two girls in surd form.

19 This diagram shows a hollow metal pipe.

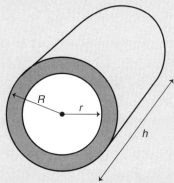

a Show that the volume V of metal is $V = \pi h(R - r)(R + r)$.

b Explain why the 'dimension' of the formula is 3.

c Find the volume of metal in a pipe where $R = 12.5$ cm, $r = 8.5$ cm and $h = 20$ cm. Take $\pi = 3\frac{1}{7}$.

d Another pipe has a cross-sectional area of 28 cm² and volume of 126 cm³. Find h.

20 Stacey is in charge of a computer-controlled cake icing machine. Stacey can input functions to produce a pattern or use some of the built-in functions, which she can then modify. The cakes are square with side 20 cm and the edges are already iced. The machine takes the origin at the centre of the cake, and automatically detects the edges to start and stop icing.

a What functions should Stacey input to produce this pattern?

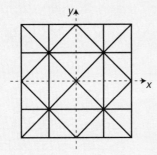

Two of the built-in functions $f(x)$ and $g(x)$ produce these patterns.

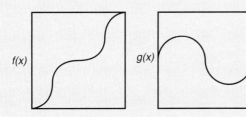

b Using $f(x)$, how can Stacey produce pattern A?

c Using $g(x)$, how can Stacey produce pattern B?

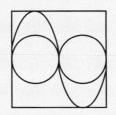

Pattern A   Pattern B

Paper 4F (Calculator)

1 Simplify these.

a $\dfrac{a}{4} + \dfrac{2a}{3}$

b $\dfrac{a}{4} \div \dfrac{2a}{3}$

c $\dfrac{a-b}{a} \times \dfrac{a}{b-a}$

d $\dfrac{x+2}{5} - \dfrac{x-3}{3}$

2 The world population in 2000 was 6 billion. By 2050, it is expected to have increased by an average of 0.9% per annum.

a Find the expected population in 2050.

b Find the average percentage increase per annum if, by 2050, the population were to have doubled.

3 The ages of the players at a football club are given in this table.

17	23	25	30	24	18
18	36	20	20	27	18
24	34	32	32	22	20
26	25	27	23	24	21
21	19	33	29	25	25

a Construct an ordered stem and leaf table of the data.

b Work out the median age of the players.

c Calculate the mean age of the players.

4 Zoë cycles at a constant speed from her house at 09:00, arriving at Greta's house, 10 km away, at 09:30. She stays there for one hour before cycling off further in exactly the same direction to visit Harry, who lives 14 km away from her home, arriving there at 11:00. She stays there for one hour also, before she returns home cycling at 10 km/h.

a Draw a distance–time graph representing Zoë's travels.

b Use your graph to find how fast Zoë cycles between visiting Greta and Harry.

c At what time does Zoë return home?

d What is her average speed while on the move?

5 Using a scale of 1 cm to 1 unit, draw rectangular axes, labelling both axes from -5 to 5.
On your diagram, draw and label the triangle P with vertices $(-2, 3)$, $(-2, 1)$, $(-1, 1)$.

a Triangle A is the image of P under reflection in the line $x = 1$.
Draw and label A.

b Triangle B is the image of P under a clockwise rotation of $90°$ about the point $(1, 1)$. Draw and label B.

c On your diagram, draw the line of reflection that maps A to B and write down its equation.

6 Mel is a bird-watcher who spots a crow flying directly towards her at a constant height of 25 m above her eye level.

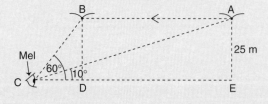

The bird is initially at A, at an angle of elevation of $10°$. Ten seconds later, it is at B, where the angle of elevation is $60°$.

a Calculate the distance CD

b Calculate the distance CE

c Calculate the crow's speed.

7 Garden trellis is made from strips of wood joined together with bolts. It comes in different sizes as shown in the diagrams. (Black dots represent the bolts.)

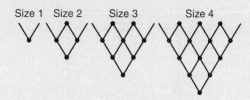

Size 1   Size 2   Size 3   Size 4

a Copy and complete this table.

Size	1	2	3	4	5	6
No. of bolts	1	4				

b Explain how the table could be extended.

c What size of trellis uses 89 bolts?

8 The graph of $y = x^3 - 5x^2 + ax + b$, where a and b are constants, passes through the points $P(0, 5)$ and $Q(1, 6)$.

a Show that the values of a and b are both 5 by making sensible substitutions using the coordinates of P and Q.

b Copy and complete this table for $-1 \leqslant x \leqslant 4$.

x	-1	0	1	2	3	4
y		5	6			9

c Draw the graph of $y = x^3 - 5x^2 + 5x + 5$.

d The curve represents a cross-section of a hill-side. The top of the curve (R) represents the top of a hill and the bottom of the curve (S) represents the bottom of a valley. State the coordinates of R and S.

9 A sample of 200 students is to be surveyed about student finance and accommodation at the University of the South of England. The sample is to be stratified according to 'status' and 'gender'. The total numbers of students are as shown. (UG = undergraduate; PG = postgraduate)

Status	Male students	Female students
1st-year UG	1258	1145
2nd-year UG	998	926
3rd-year UG	1004	900
4th-year UG	1088	913
PG	215	277

Calculate the number in each category. (You are advised to perform your calculation and to display your results in a table.)

10 Solve these for x in the range $-180° < x < 360°$. Give your answers correct to the nearest degree.

a $\sin x = -0.2$

b $\cos x = 0.7$

c $\tan x = 1.4$

11 Two towns are d miles apart. Ken travels between the two towns at an average speed of 30 mph.

a Write down an expression for the time in hours of Ken's journey.

b Ken's return journey is made at an average speed of 50 mph. Find an expression for the time it takes Ken to make both journeys and show that it simplifies to $8d/150$.

c Find Ken's overall average speed.

12 Motor-cycle despatch riders in London were sent questionnaires about their work. This histogram shows the age distribution of those who responded.

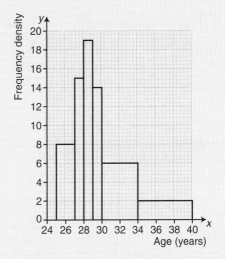

a Construct a frequency table.

b Use your frequency table to calculate the total number of responses.

c Estimate the mean age of the despatch riders who replied.

13 The Mayan people, who lived in South America between AD 300 and AD 800, calculated the average length of one year to be 365.2 days. The accurate figure has been calculated to be 365.2422 days.

a Find the percentage error in the Mayan figure.

b Write your answer to part **a** as 'Accurate to about one part in ..... thousand'.

14 y is inversely proportional to the square of x. Given that $y = 10$ when $x = 2$, find these.

   a The formula for y in terms of x

   b The value of y when $x = \frac{1}{4}$

   c The value of x when $y = \frac{1}{4}$

15 A particular type of cell divides into two every 20 minutes. Alex starts a biology experiment with one of these cells.

   a How many cells are there after 2 hours?

   b How long is it until there are 2^9 cells?

   c After 4 hours, the cells cover an area of $8 \, \text{mm}^2$. What area did they cover after 3 hours?

   d After 5 hours, the cells start dividing into two every hour. How many cells are there after 8 hours?
     (Give your answer as a power of 2.)

16 A music CD rotates at different rates in order to maintain a constant linear velocity (CLV) of $1.3 \, \text{m/s}$. Its playing time is 75 minutes and etched into its surface is a continuous spiral track containing 1500 million pits.

   a Find the total length of the spiral track in kilometres.

   b Find the mean number of pits
     (i)   per millimetre of spiral track
     (ii) detected by the CD player's laser pickup per second.

17 Two flights of stairs on the deck of a ship are as shown. The total height of the stairs is $14.43 \, \text{m}$ and $\tan x + \tan y = 2.31$.

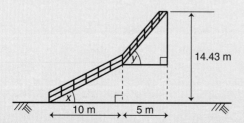

a Form two simultaneous equations involving $\tan x$ and $\tan y$.

b Solve these equations to find x and y.

18 The orbit of the Earth may be taken to be a circle around the Sun with radius 1 a.u. (1 a.u. is one astronomical unit and is the distance of the Earth to the Sun.)

   a What is the equation of the orbit of the Earth if the Sun is at the origin and the units are in a.u.?

   b The starship 'Centipede' cruises along the path given by $y = 4x^2 - 2$.
     Find, by a graphical method, where the path of the 'Centipede' intersects the orbit of the Earth.

19 In the figure, the perimeter is $4r$.

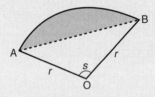

   a Find the arc length AB, in terms of r.

   b Show that the angle s is $114.6°$, correct to 4 significant figures.

   c Find, in terms of r, the shaded sector area.

20 Draw an accurate graph of $y = \tan x$ for $-180° \leqslant x \leqslant 360°$.

   a Solve for x in the equation $-1.5 = \tan x$ for $-180° \leqslant x \leqslant 360°$, correct to 3 significant figures.

   b On the same axes draw the graph of
$$y = \sin\left(\frac{x}{2}\right)$$
     and hence solve the equation
$$\sin\left(\frac{x}{2}\right) = \tan x$$
     for $-180° \leqslant x \leqslant 360°$.

Modelling 5

Mathematical models are used to describe situations that occur in everyday life. A mathematical model is not a physical model, but an equation or formula that can help to predict the value of an unknown quantity. Here are some typical examples met in more advanced studies.

♦ The position of a stone, y m below a cliff, t seconds after being dropped.

♦ The depth of water in a harbour, d m, t hours after midnight.

♦ The population of termites, P thousand, in a nest, t days after 1 June.

♦ The speed of a parachutist, v m/s, after falling y m from a plane.

♦ The deflection of a beam, y m, when W kg are placed on the end.

Using formulae to model such situations is quite simple. Finding them is much harder!

Using formulae to model real situations

Growth and decay of the type $y = a^x$

Patterns of growth and decay (for example, population changes or radioactive decay or the wealth of institutions) often closely resemble **exponential relationships**. These equations are of the type $y = a^x$, where x is called the **exponent**.

Example 1

Exponential growth

$y = a^x$ with $a > 1$

Draw $y = 2^x$ for $-3 \leqslant x \leqslant 3$.

x	-3	-2	-1	0	1	2	3
y	$\frac{1}{8}$	$\frac{1}{4}$	$\frac{1}{2}$	1	2	4	8

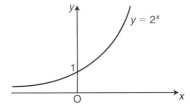

Example 2

Exponential decay

$y = a^x$ with $0 < a < 1$

Draw $y = \left(\frac{1}{2}\right)^x$ for $-3 \leqslant x \leqslant 3$.

x	-3	-2	-1	0	1	2	3
y	8	4	2	1	$\frac{1}{2}$	$\frac{1}{4}$	$\frac{1}{8}$

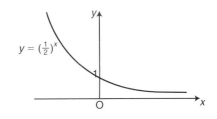

Exercise 68

For Questions 1–4, compile a suitable table in the given range, and then draw the graph.

1 $y = 3^x$ $\quad -3 \leqslant x \leqslant 3$ **2** $y = 5^x$ $\quad -2 \leqslant x \leqslant 3$

3 $y = \left(\frac{1}{3}\right)^x$ $\quad -3 \leqslant x \leqslant 3$ **4** $y = \left(\frac{1}{5}\right)^x$ $\quad -3 \leqslant x \leqslant 2$

5 The population of the UK in 2000 was about 60 million. The annual increase is 1%.

  a Find the projected population in 2001, 2002 and 2010.

  b Explain why the population in the UK, p million people, n years after 2000, is given by $p = 60 \times (1.01)^n$.

  c Draw the graph of p (millions) against n for $0 \leqslant n \leqslant 50$ by first compiling a suitable table in the given range.

  d Use your graph to find the population in 2025, and when the population in 2000 is increased by 25%.

6 A 500 g apple falls from a tree and gradually decays over a period of 30 days. The weight, W g, is reduced by 10% each day.

  a Find the weight after 1 day, 15 days and 30 days.

  b Explain why the weight of the apple, W g, t days after falling, is given by $W = 500 \times (0.90)^t$.

  c Draw the graph of W (g) against t (days) for $0 \leqslant t \leqslant 30$ by first compiling a suitable table.

  d Use your graph to find the time after which the apple is half its original weight, and the weight of the apple after two weeks.

Exercise 68★

For Questions 1 and 2, compile a suitable table in the given range, and then draw the graph

1 $y = 2^{x^2}$ $\quad 0 \leqslant x \leqslant 2$ **2** $y = 10^{\sin x}$ $\quad 0° \leqslant x \leqslant 30°$

3 Waterlilies are growing on a lake. The total area of the waterlilies doubles every ten years. The area presently covered is 100 m^2.

  a Copy and complete this table.

Time, t (years)	0	10	20	30	40	50
Area, $A (m^2)$	100			800		

  b Show that $A = 100 \times 2^{0.1t}$ and draw the graph of A against t for $0 \leqslant t \leqslant 50$.

  c Use your graph to find the area of the lake covered after 25 years, and after how many years the area covered is 1200 m^2.

4 A radioactive substance decays at a slow rate. Its half-life is defined as the time taken for the radioactivity of the material to decay to half of its initial value. Radioactive waste is often buried deep underground for safety reasons.

  a Some waste with an initial radioactivity of 1000 and an expected half-life of 25 years is buried. If its radioactivity A decays by 2% each year, show that, after t years, A is given by $A = 1000 \times (0.98)^t$.

  b Draw the graph of A against t for $0 \leqslant t \leqslant 50$ by first compiling a suitable table.

  c Use your graph to estimate if the expected half-life of the buried waste is correct.

5 A bowl of soup cools such that its temperature, $T\,°C$, decreases by 7% of its value after t minutes. In a restaurant, Beverly orders soup, which is poured into her bowl at a temperature of 90 °C. The waiter takes 14 minutes to serve Beverly her soup. She will complain to the manageress if her soup temperature is below 38 °C.

  a Explain why $T = 90 \times (0.93)^t$ and draw the graph of T against t for $0 \leqslant t \leqslant 20$.

  b Use your graph to find out if Beverly complains to the manageress.

6 Police discover a dead body in an unheated room of Mary and Jack's house at 3 a.m. and start a murder investigation. The detective assumes that the body cooled by losing 6% of its temperature every 5 minutes. The temperature of the body on discovery was 15 °C.

  a Find the equation of the body's temperature, $T\,°C$, in terms of the time, t minutes, after death if normal body temperature is 38 °C.

  b Draw a graph of T against t for $0 \leqslant t \leqslant 120$.

  c Mary was seen leaving the house at 1 a.m. and Jack says he left at 2 a.m. No one else was at home that night. Use your graph to estimate the time of death. Who do you think the police should consider the chief suspect?

Activity 43

In a small town of 3280 people, a rumour is spreading .... Mrs Tattle tells three people in the first day, each of whom tell three more people (none of whom have heard the rumour yet) the next day, and they in turn each tell three more new people the day after. This pattern continues.

♦ Copy and complete this table.

Day	1	2	3	4	5
Number of people who have heard the rumour	4	13			

♦ After how many days will the whole town have heard the rumour?

♦ Find an expression for the number of people, n, who have heard the rumour after d days.

A frog sitting on a lily-pad in a pond wishes to reach the edge of the pond 10 m away in successive hops. His route is fully covered by lily-pads and he takes a direct line. His first hop is 1m, but he is tired, so each successive hop is reduced by 10%.

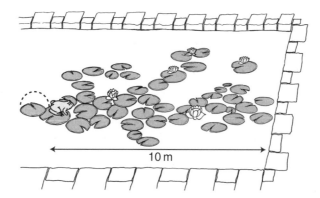

♦ Copy and complete the table.

Hop number	1	2	3	4	5	...
Distance hopped (m)	1	1×0.90				

♦ Find an expression for the length of hop h metres after n hops.

♦ Does the frog ever reach the edge of the pond?

Finding formulae to model real situations

One of the simplest graphs to understand is the straight line $y = mx + c$, where m is the gradient of the straight line and c is the intercept of the line on the y-axis.

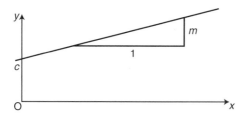

However, most relationships are not linear but curves. Sometimes, however, it is possible to use the straight-line relationship $y = mx + c$ to find the constants of a formula, even when the relationship is not linear.

Relationships of the type $y = ax^2 + b$

Example 3

A scientist gathers data in a particular experiment for variables x and y.

x	0	1	2	3	4
y	1	3	9	19	33

She suspects the relationship is $y = ax^2 + b$, for some unknown constants a and b.

a Draw a suitable graph to check this suspected linear connection between x^2 and y.

If y is plotted against x^2 rather than against x, and the suspected relationship is correct, a straight line is produced, and the following comparisons can be made:

$$y = ax^2 + b$$

$a = m$, the gradient of the line
$b = c$, the intercept of the line on the y-axis

$$y = mx + c$$

Here is the graph of y against x^2.

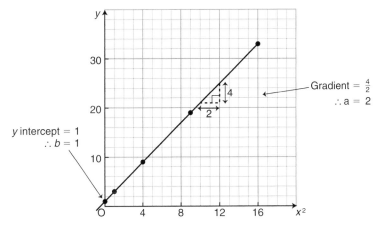

b Find the values of a and b using your graph.

The suspected formula is correct as the points lie on a straight line. The graph of y against x^2 shows that $a = 2$ and $b = 1$. Therefore $y = 2x^2 + 1$.

c Use this formula to find y when x is 1.5, and x when y is 25.

When $x = 1.5$, $\quad y = 2(1.5)^2 + 1 \qquad \therefore \quad y = 5.5$

When $y = 25$, $\quad 25 = 2x^2 + 1 \qquad \therefore \quad x = 2\sqrt{3} = 3.5\,(2\text{ s.f.})$

UNIT 5 ◆ Modelling

Relationships of the type $y = \dfrac{a}{x} + b$

Example 4

A chemistry experiment gives these results.

x	1	2	3	4	5
y	11	6	4.3	3.5	3

Helen suspects the relationship is

$$y = \frac{a}{x} + b$$

a Draw a suitable graph to check this suspected relationship between x and y.

If y is plotted against $\dfrac{1}{x}$ rather than against x, and the suspected relationship is correct, a straight line is produced, and comparisons can be made:

$$y = a\left(\frac{1}{x}\right) + b$$

$$y = mx \quad + c$$

$a = m$, the gradient of the line

$b = c$, the intercept of the line on the y-axis

Here is the graph of y against $\dfrac{1}{x}$.

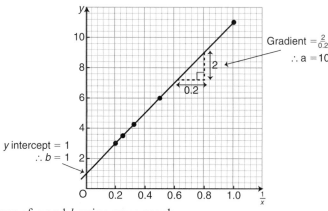

Gradient $= \frac{2}{0.2}$

$\therefore a = 10$

y intercept $= 1$

$\therefore b = 1$

b Find the values of a and b using your graph.

The suspected formula is correct as the points lie on a straight line. The graph of y against $\dfrac{1}{x}$ shows that $a = 10$ and $b = 1$. Therefore $y = \dfrac{10}{x} + 1$.

c Use this formula to find y when $x = 2.5$, and x when $y = 4$.

When $x = 2.5$, $\quad y = \dfrac{10}{2.5} + 1 \qquad \therefore \quad y = 5$

When $y = 4$, $\qquad 4 = \dfrac{10}{x} + 1 \qquad \therefore \quad x = 3.\dot{3}$

Activity 45

Examples 3 and 4 can be extended to solve other nonlinear relationships. Copy and complete this table.

Suspected relationship	Original shape	Plot to produce a straight line	Gradient	Vertical axis cut
$y = ax + b$	Straight line	y against x	a	b
$y = ax^2 + b$	Curve	y against x^2	a	b
$y = \dfrac{a}{x} + b$	Curve	y against $\dfrac{1}{x}$	a	b
$y = ax^3 + b$				
$y^2 = ax^2 + b$				
$\sqrt{y} = a\sqrt{x} + b$				
$y = ax^2 + bx$			a	b

Exercise 69

In Questions 1–4, the variables in the table are related by the equation shown. Draw a suitable graph to find an estimate for the constants a and b. Show your method clearly.

1 $y = ax^2 + b$

x	1	2	3	4	5
y	4	7	12	19	28

2 $y = \dfrac{a}{x} + b$

x	0.1	0.2	0.3	0.4	0.5
y	21	11	7.$\dot{6}$	6	5

3 $y = ax^2 + b$

x	1	2	3	4	5
y	-1	5	15	29	47

4 $y = \dfrac{a}{x} + b$

x	0.1	0.2	0.3	0.4	0.5
y	25	10	5	2.5	1

5 These readings from a physics experiment are approximately connected by the formula $y = ax^2 + b$.

x	0.2	0.4	0.6	0.8	1
y	2.1	2.5	3.1	4.0	5.0

a Draw a suitable graph to find the values of a and b.

b Use this formula to find the values of y when $x = 2$, and x when $y = 6$.

UNIT 5 ◆ Modelling

335

6 It is suspected that the results of an experiment are approximately connected by the formula

$$y = \frac{a}{x} + b$$

x	1	2	3	4	5
y	6.9	2.1	$0.\dot{3}$	-0.4	-1.1

   a Drawing a suitable graph, to find the values of a and b.

   b Use this formula to find the value of y when $x = 3.5$, and x when $y = 5$.

Exercise 69★

In Questions 1–3, the variables in the table are approximately related by the equation shown. Draw a suitable graph to find an estimate for the constants a and b. Show your method clearly.

1 $y = ax^3 + b$

x	0	1	2	3	4
y	-10	-9	-2	17	54

2 $y^2 = ax^2 + b$

x	0	1	2	3	4
y	2.2	2.6	3.6	4.8	6.1

3 $\sqrt{y} = a\sqrt{x} + b$

x	0	1	2	3	4
y	16.1	30.3	37.5	43.5	48.7

4 These readings are obtained by a scientist who believes they approximately obey the formula $y = ax^2 + bx$, where a and b are constants.

x	1	2	3	4	5
y	-1.1	1.9	9.1	19.1	34.7

   a By considering the graph of $\dfrac{y}{x}$ against x, show that the suspected formula is correct.

   b Use this graph to find the constants a and b.

   c Use this formula to find the value of y when $x = 4.5$, and x when $y = 4.5$.

5 Amanda hits a tennis ball vertically into the air such that its height above the ground, H metres, t seconds after contact, is approximately given by the formula

$$H = at^2 + bt$$

The ball is observed to be at these heights. One of the height readings is considerably inaccurate.

t	1	2	3	4	5
H	20.2	29.7	30.3	28.4	0.3

   a By drawing a suitable graph, state which point is inaccurate, and suggest a better value.

   b Find the values of constants a and b.

   c Use your formula to find the time at which the ball is 25 m above the ground.

6 A manufacturing plant makes cylindrical tanks of radius r m and volume $50\,\text{m}^3$. The total surface area (including base and top), $A\,\text{m}^2$, is believed to be related to r by the formula

$$A = pr^2 + \frac{q}{r}$$

r	1	2	3	4	5
A	106.3	75.1	89.9	125.5	177.1

where p and q are constants. The values of A and r shown in the table are found.

a Draw a suitable graph to find the value of the constants p and q, and use one of these to make an estimate for the value of π.

b Use your formula to find the total surface area for a tank of radius $6\,\text{m}$.

Activity 46

The naturalist Miriam Rothschild has spent her lifetime studying fleas, whose jumping ability is phenomenal.

These photographs,* taken at time intervals of 1/3800 second, show clearly that a flea takes off from its knees (the trochanters), because its feet are too fragile to withstand the force generated. The back legs are powered by an elastic protein (reselin), which releases energy more effectively than any known rubber.

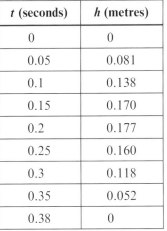

The data in this table were observed for a particular flea in a single jump. Its height (h metres) at t seconds are given.

t (seconds)	h (metres)
0	0
0.05	0.081
0.1	0.138
0.15	0.170
0.2	0.177
0.25	0.160
0.3	0.118
0.35	0.052
0.38	0

It is suspected that the relationship between h and t is of the form $h = at^2 + bt$ where a and b are constants.

◆ Plot a graph of h/t against t to verify the relationship.
  Use your graph to estimate for values of constants a and b.

◆ State the formula for h in terms of t.

◆ Use this formula to draw another graph to estimate the maximum height attained by this flea and when this occurs.

◆ Given that the flea is $\frac{1}{16}$ inch tall, how high would a six-foot person jump on this scale?

*Photographed by Miriam Rothschild with the assistance of Dr Kim Parker

Exercise 70 (Revision)

1 Draw the graph of $y = 4^x$ for $0 \leqslant x \leqslant 4$ by first compiling a suitable table, and then use your graph to find an estimate for the value of $4^{2.5}$.

2 A plant's height, y cm, doubles every month.

   a If the plant's height is initially 3 cm, explain why the plant's height after x months is given by
$$y = 3 \times (2)^x.$$

   b Draw a graph of y against x for $0 \leqslant x \leqslant 6$.

   c Use your graph to find the time after which the plant's height is 1 metre.

3 This table shows some of the points on the curve $y = a^x$.

x	0	1	2	3	4
y	1			125	

   a Find the value of a and copy and complete the table.
      Using these values, draw the graph of y against x for $0 \leqslant x \leqslant 4$.

   b Use your graph to estimate the value of $a^{3.5}$, and to find the solution to the equation $50 = a^x$.

4 In 2000, Martina buys a new sports car for £35 000, and it depreciates by 7% each year.

   a Explain why the car's value V (£1000s) after n years is given by
$$V = 35 \times (0.93)^n$$

   b Draw the graph of V against n for $0 \leqslant n \leqslant 10$ by first compiling a suitable table.

   c Use your graph to estimate the value of the car after 5 years, and the year in which the car's value falls below £20 000.

5 It is suspected that the results of an experiment obey the formula $y = ax^2 + b$.

x	1	2	3	4	5
y	-5	1	11	25	43

   a Draw a suitable graph to find the values of the constants a and b.
   b Hence find the value of x when $y = 15$.

Exercise 70★ (Revision)

1 a A naturalist researching great crested newts in a wetland area in East Anglia believes that their population will increase by 5% per year if their habitat is kept unspoilt. If there are 600 newts in the year 2000, find out how many there will be in 2001, 2002 and 2003.

b If there are N newts, t years after the year 2000, explain why $N = 600 \times (1.05)^t$.

c Draw the graph of N against t for $0 \leqslant t \leqslant 10$ by first completing this table.

t	0	2	4	6	8	10
N	600		729			

d Use your graph to find out the year in which the newt population has increased to 850.

2 The population of insects in a colony is always changing. The population, P, of insects in the colony, after t months have elapsed is given by $P = 4096 \times 2^t - 4096^{t/4}$.

a Calculate the value of P when $t = 1$.

P can be written in the form $P = 2^t(r - q)$ where r and q can be expressed as powers of 2.

b Calculate, as powers of 2:

(i) r (ii) q

c Copy and complete the table below and use it to draw the graph of P against t for $0 \leqslant t \leqslant 5$.

t	0	1	2	3	4	5
P	4095	8184	16 320			

d Use your graph to estimate the time after which the population reaches 50 000.

LONDON

3 The total stopping distance of a car, y metres, is related to the speed at which it is travelling, x mph, by the formula $y = ax^2 + bx$ where a and b are constants.

These are results of tests carried out on a car.

x	20	30	40	50	60	70	80
y	11.6	23.4	39.2	59	72.8	110.6	142.4

a Draw a graph of $\dfrac{y}{x}$ against x to find the values of the constants a and b, being careful to adjust for one of the readings for y, which was found to be unreliable.

b Use this formula to find the speed at which the stopping distance is 100 m.

4 The mass of bacteria, M, after t hours, is described by the curve $M = ab^t$, which passes through the points $(0, 100)$ and $(3, 800)$ on the graph of M against t.

a Finds the constants a and b.

b Use this formula to find the value of t when $M = 12\,800$.

Algebra 5

Expansions and factorising

When multiplying two brackets, each term in the second bracket must be multiplied by each term in the first bracket.

Example 1

Expand and simplify $(x - 3)(x^2 + 2x - 8)$.

Be systematic: multiply each term in the second bracket by x, and then multiply each term in the second bracket by -3. Then simplify.

$$(x - 3)(x^2 + 2x - 8) = x(x^2 + 2x - 8) - 3(x^2 + 2x - 8)$$
$$= x^3 + 2x^2 - 8x - 3x^2 - 6x + 24$$
$$= x^3 - x^2 - 14x + 24$$

Example 2

Expand and simplify $(x - 3)(x - 2)(x + 4)$.

Multiply the last two brackets together first: $(x - 2)(x + 4) = x^2 + 2x - 8$

Multiply $(x - 3)$ by $(x^2 + 2x - 8)$ as in Example 1. So

$$(x - 3)(x - 2)(x + 4) = (x - 3)(x^2 + 2x - 8)$$
$$= x^3 - x^2 - 14x + 24$$

Exercise 71

Expand and simplify these.

1 $(x - 1)(x^2 + 2x - 3)$ **2** $(x + 1)(x^2 - 3x + 2)$ **3** $(x + 3)(x^2 - 3x - 4)$

4 $(x - 2)(x^2 + x + 2)$ **5** $(2x - 3)(x^2 + 5x - 7)$ **6** $(3x + 2)(x^2 - 2x + 6)$

7 $(x + 1)(x + 2)(x + 4)$ **8** $(x + 1)(x + 3)(x + 5)$ **9** $(x - 1)(x + 5)(x - 2)$

10 $(x - 2)(x + 3)(x - 4)$ **11** $(3x + 1)(x - 5)(x + 7)$ **12** $(2x - 1)(x + 6)(x - 4)$

Exercise 71★

Expand and simplify these.

1 $(2x - 1)(x^2 + 3x + 1)$ **2** $(2x + 1)(x^2 - 4x + 3)$

3 $(x + 4)(3x^2 + 2x - 7)$ **4** $(x - 3)(4x^2 - x + 8)$

5 $(3x + 2)(2x^3 + x^2 - 3x - 5)$ **6** $(2x + 3)(3x^3 - x^2 + 2x + 4)$

7 $3(x-2)(2x+1)(x+3)$

8 $2(x+2)(3x-1)(x-3)$

9 $(2x+1)(3x+4)(x-7)$

10 $(4x+3)(2x-1)(x+9)$

11 $(x+1)(2x-3)(x+5)^2$

12 $(x-2)(3x+4)(x-6)^2$

Investigate

Pascal's triangle

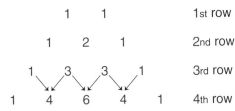

1 1		1st row
1 2 1		2nd row
1 3 3 1		3rd row
1 4 6 4 1		4th row

Each row starts and ends with 1, and then other terms are created from the row above.

The numbers in the fourth row, for example, are formed by adding together the two numbers above and either side in the third row (shown by the arrows).

Find the connection between the numbers in the nth row of Pascal's triangle and the expansion of $(x+y)^n$.

Finding the coefficient in an expansion

The coefficient of x^3 in $3x^4 - 7x^3 + 5x^2 - 2x + 4$ is -7; the coefficient of x^2 in $4x^2 - 3x + 1$ is 4. The coefficient of a power of x is the number in front of the power.

Example 3

Find the coefficient of x^2 in the expansion of $(x^2 + 2x - 1)(x^2 - 3x + 2)$.

There is no need to do the whole expansion. Systematically identify those terms which when multiplied together will give x^2 terms.

The x^2 terms are $2x^2 - 6x^2 - x^2 = -5x^2$

So the coefficient of x^2 is -5.

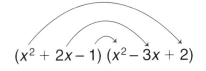

$$(x^2 + 2x - 1)(x^2 - 3x + 2)$$

Exercise 72

In Questions 1–10, find the coefficient of the power of x given in square brackets.

1 $(x+2)(x^2+3x+1)$ $[x^2]$

2 $(x+4)(x^2+2x+1)$ $[x^2]$

3 $(x+3)(x^2-3x+2)$ $[x^2]$

4 $(x+1)(x^2-5x+1)$ $[x^2]$

5 $(x-2)(x^3+x^2-4x-2)$ $[x^3]$

6 $(x+2)(x^3-3x^2+5x-1)$ $[x^3]$

7 $(x^2+2x-1)(x^2-2x+1)$ $[x^3]$

8 $(x^2-3x+2)(x^2+3x-2)$ $[x^3]$

9 $(x^2+3)(x^3+2x^2-3x+1)$ $[x^4]$

10 $(x^2-4)(x^3-4x^2-2x+3)$ $[x^4]$

Exercise 72★

In Questions 1–12, find the coefficient of the power of x given in square brackets.

1 $(x + 6)(2x^2 - 4x + 3)$ $\qquad [x^2]$ $\qquad$ **2** $(x + 5)(3x^2 - 2x + 4)$ $\qquad [x^2]$

3 $(3x + 2)(x^2 - 5x - 7)$ $\qquad [x^2]$ $\qquad$ **4** $(2x + 3)(x^2 - 7x - 6)$ $\qquad [x^2]$

5 $(4x - 1)(x^3 - 4x^2 + 2x + 3)$ $\quad [x^3]$ $\qquad$ **6** $(3x - 1)(x^3 - 5x^2 - x + 4)$ $\quad [x^3]$

7 $(2x^2 - 2x + 3)(x^2 + 5x - 3)$ $\quad [x^3]$ $\qquad$ **8** $(4x^2 - 3x + 2)(x^2 - 7x + 4)$ $\quad [x^3]$

9 $(2x^3 - 3x + 1)(5x^2 + 4)$ $\qquad [x^4]$ $\qquad$ **10** $(3x^2 - 4x - 1)(3x^3 - 2)$ $\qquad [x^4]$

11 $\left(x^2 + 1 - \dfrac{1}{x}\right)\left(x - \dfrac{1}{x}\right)$ $\qquad [x^2]$ $\qquad$ **12** $\left(1 - \dfrac{1}{x} + \dfrac{1}{x^2}\right)(x^2 - x + 1)$ $\qquad \left[\dfrac{1}{x}\right]$

13 The coefficient of x^2 in the expansion of $(x + 2)(x^2 + ax + 3)$ is 5. Find a.

14 The coefficient of x^3 in the expansion of $(x^2 - 3x + 4)(x^2 + bx + 3)$ is zero. Find b.

Division of polynomials

Example 4

Divide $x^3 - x^2 - 14x + 24$ by $x - 3$.

This is set out like ordinary long division:

① Divide x^3 by x to give x^2 and write it where shown.

② Multiply $x - 3$ by x^2 (the answer to ①) and write it where shown.

③ Subtract as shown.

④ Move the $-14x$ down.

⑤ Repeat the whole process.

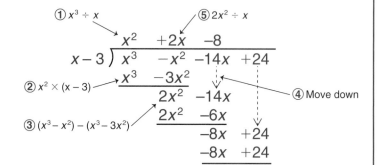

Exercise 73

Divide these.

1 $x^3 + 4x^2 + 7x + 6$ by $x + 2$ $\qquad$ **2** $x^3 + 5x^2 + 6x + 2$ by $x + 1$

3 $x^3 + 2x^2 - 13x - 6$ by $x - 3$ $\qquad$ **4** $x^3 + x^2 - 4x - 4$ by $x - 2$

5 $x^3 - x^2 - 13x - 3$ by $x + 3$ $\qquad$ **6** $x^3 + x^2 - 14x - 8$ by $x + 4$

7 $x^4 + x^3 - 5x^2 + 4x - 1$ by $x - 1$ $\qquad$ **8** $x^4 - 5x^3 + 8x^2 - 5x + 2$ by $x - 2$

9 $x^4 + 4x^3 + 2x^2 + 4x + 1$ by $x^2 + 1$ $\qquad$ **10** $x^4 + 2x^3 - 4x^2 - 2x + 3$ by $x^2 - 1$

Exercise 73★

Divide these.

1 $x^3 - x^2 - 13x + 4$ by $x - 4$

2 $x^3 - 2x^2 - 17x + 10$ by $x - 5$

3 $x^4 + 5x - 6$ by $x + 2$

4 $x^4 + 31x + 12$ by $x + 3$

5 $6x^3 + 13x^2 + x - 2$ by $2x + 1$

6 $6x^3 - 23x^2 + 16x - 3$ by $3x - 1$

7 $4x^5 - 5x^2 - 36x + 15$ by $x^2 - 3$

8 $3x^5 - 2x^4 + 6x^3 + 8$ by $x^2 + 2$

9 $x^5 - 2x^4 - 2x^3 + 13x^2 - 17x + 5$ by $x^2 + 2x - 1$

10 $x^5 - x^4 - 11x^3 + 23x^2 - 15x + 3$ by $x^2 - 3x + 1$

Using common factors

You should always look for any common factors when simplifying.

Example 5

Simplify $8(1 + x)^4 - 6(1 + x)^5$.

Here $2(1 + x)^4$ is a common factor, so

$$8(1 + x)^4 - 6(1 + x)^5 = 2(1 + x)^4[4 - 3(1 + x)]$$
$$= 2(1 + x)^4(4 - 3 - 3x)$$
$$= 2(1 + x)^4(1 - 3x) \qquad \text{(Leave your answer in factors)}$$

Example 6

Simplify $\frac{1}{6}(x + 1)(x + 2) - (x + 1)^2$.

Here $\frac{1}{6}(x + 1)$ is a common factor, so

$\frac{1}{6}(x + 1)(x + 2) - (x + 1)^2$

$= \frac{1}{6}(x + 1)(x + 2) - \frac{6}{6}(x + 1)^2 \qquad \left(\text{Use } \frac{6}{6} \text{ to make } \frac{1}{6} \text{ a common factor} \right)$

$= \frac{1}{6}(x + 1)[(x + 2) - 6(x + 1)]$

$= \frac{1}{6}(x + 1)(x + 2 - 6x - 6)$

$= \frac{1}{6}(x + 1)(-5x - 4)$

$= -\frac{1}{6}(x + 1)(5x + 4) \qquad \text{(Leave your answer in factors)}$

Example 7

Simplify $(x + 1)^2 + 5(x + 1) + 6$.

Substituting $a = (x + 1)$ gives

$a^2 + 5a + 6 = (a + 3)(a + 2)$

So $(x + 1)^2 + 5(x + 1) + 6 = [(x + 1) + 3][(x + 1) + 2]$

$= (x + 4)(x + 3) \qquad \text{(Leave your answer in factors)}$

Exercise 74

Simplify these.

1 $3(1+x)^2 + 2(1+x)^3$

2 $2(1-x)^3 + 3(1-x)^2$

3 $10(2-x)^3 - 2(2-x)^4$

4 $12(3+x)^2 - 3(3+x)^3$

5 $(x+1)^2(x-2) - (x+1)(x-2)^2$

6 $(x+3)(x-1)^2 - (x+3)^2(x-1)$

7 $(x+2)^2 + 2(x+2) + 1$

8 $(x-3)^2 + 4(x-3) + 4$

9 $\frac{1}{2}(x-1)(x+2) - (x+2)^2$

10 $\frac{1}{3}(x+1)^2 - (x+1)(x-4)$

Exercise 74★

Simplify these.

1 $2(4x-3)^2 - (4x-3)^3$

2 $(3x+5)^3 - 2(3x+5)^2$

3 $2(x-2)^3 + 6x(x-2)^2$

4 $5(x+1)^4 + 10x(x+1)^3$

5 $x(x+1)^2 + (x+1)(x^2-3)$

6 $(x+3)(x^2+1) + x(x+3)^2$

7 $(x+2)^2 - (x-3)^2$

8 $(x-4)^2 - (x+1)^2$

9 $35(x-1)^2 + (x-1) - 6$

10 $2(x+1)^2 + 7(x+1) - 4$

11 $\frac{1}{4}(x+1)^3(x+2) - (x+1)^4$

12 $\frac{1}{3}(x-3)^4 - (x-3)^3(x-1)$

13 $\frac{n}{6}(n-1)(n-2) + \frac{n}{2}(n-1)$

14 $\frac{1}{12}(x+1)(x+2)(x+3)(3x+4) - (x+1)^2(x+2)$

15 $(1-x)^3(x+2)^4 - (2x+4)^3(x-1)^4$

Algebraic fractions

To simplify algebraic fractions, factorise as much as possible and then cancel.

Example 8

Simplify $\dfrac{x^2 + x}{x + 1}$.

$$\frac{x^2 + x}{x + 1} = \frac{x(x + 1)}{x + 1} = x$$

Example 9

Simplify $\dfrac{2a^2 - 2b^2}{4a + 4b}$.

$$\frac{2a^2 - 2b^2}{4a + 4b} = \frac{2(a + b)(a - b)}{4(a + b)}$$

$$= \frac{a - b}{2}$$

Exercise 75

Simplify these.

1 $\dfrac{3x + 12}{2x + 8}$

2 $\dfrac{8u + 4v}{6u + 3v}$

3 $\dfrac{r + r^2}{s + rs}$

4 $\dfrac{xy + y^2}{x^2 + xy}$

5 $\dfrac{t^2 - t - 6}{t - 3}$

6 $\dfrac{p + 2}{p^2 + 4p + 4}$

7 $\dfrac{a^2 - b^2}{(a - b)^2}$

8 $\dfrac{(y + x)^2}{x^2 - y^2}$

9 $\dfrac{x^2 - x - 2}{x^2 - 5x + 6}$

10 $\dfrac{x^2 + 2x - 3}{x^2 + 4x + 3}$

Exercise 75★

Simplify these.

1 $\dfrac{6a + 9b}{10a + 15b}$

2 $\dfrac{14p + 35q}{6p + 15q}$

3 $\dfrac{x^2y + xy^2}{x^2y + x^3}$

4 $\dfrac{x^3y + xy}{xy^2 + x^3y^2}$

5 $\dfrac{3r^2 + 6r - 45}{3r^2 + 18r + 15}$

6 $\dfrac{2t^2 + 10t - 28}{2t^2 + 18t + 28}$

7 $\dfrac{a^3 - ab^2}{a^3 + 2a^2b + ab^2}$

8 $\dfrac{2ab - a^2 - b^2}{a^2b - b^3}$

9 $\dfrac{2x^2 + 12x - 32}{xy - 2y}$

10 $\dfrac{3x^3 - 3x^2 - 18x}{x^2y - 3xy}$

11 $\dfrac{a - b}{\sqrt{a} - \sqrt{b}}$

12 $\dfrac{x + 1 - \frac{2}{x}}{x^2 + x - 2}$

Multiplication and division

Again factorise as much as possible, and then simplify. If dividing, 'turn the second fraction upside down and multiply' in exactly the same way as number fractions are manipulated.

Example 10

$$\frac{x^2 - 2x}{x + 3} \times \frac{3x + 9}{x - 2}$$

$$= \frac{x(x - 2)}{x + 3} \times \frac{3(x + 3)}{x - 2} = 3x$$

Example 11

$$\frac{x^2 - 3x}{2x^2 + 7x + 3} \div \frac{x^2 - 5x + 6}{2x^2 - 3x - 2}$$

$$= \frac{x(x - 3)}{(2x + 1)(x + 3)} \times \frac{(2x + 1)(x - 2)}{(x - 3)(x - 2)}$$

$$= \frac{x}{x + 3}$$

Exercise 76

Simplify these.

1 $\dfrac{4x + 4}{x - 3} \times \dfrac{x^2 - 3x}{2x + 2}$

2 $\dfrac{x^2 + 2x}{x^2 - x} \times \dfrac{6x - 6}{x + 2}$

3 $\dfrac{x - y}{x^2 - xy} \times \dfrac{xy + y^2}{x + y}$

4 $\dfrac{2a + 4b}{ab + 2b^2} \times \dfrac{2a^2 - ab}{2a - b}$

5 $\dfrac{p^2 + p - 2}{p^2 - p - 6} \times \dfrac{p - 3}{p - 2}$

6 $\dfrac{r^2 - r - 2}{r^2 - 3r + 2} \times \dfrac{r + 2}{r + 1}$

7 $\dfrac{x + 2}{x + 4} \div \dfrac{x^2 - 2x - 8}{x^2 + 2x - 8}$

8 $\dfrac{x + 3}{x + 5} \div \dfrac{x^2 - 2x - 15}{x^2 + 2x - 15}$

9 $\dfrac{x^2 - 9}{x^2 - 6x + 9} \div \dfrac{x + 4}{x - 3}$

10 $\dfrac{x^2 + 5x + 6}{x^2 - 25} \div \dfrac{x + 3}{x - 5}$

Exercise 76★

Simplify these.

1 $\dfrac{4x + 28}{x^2 + 2x} \times \dfrac{x^2 - 3x}{2x + 14}$

2 $\dfrac{3x^2 - 12x}{3x + 18} \times \dfrac{2x + 12}{x^2 - 3x}$

3 $\dfrac{x^2 + 9x + 20}{x^2 - 16} \times \dfrac{x - 4}{x^2 + 6x + 5}$

4 $\dfrac{x^2 - x - 6}{x^2 - 9} \times \dfrac{x^2 + 4x + 3}{x + 1}$

5 $\dfrac{x^2 + x - 2}{x^2 + 3x - 4} \times \dfrac{x^2 + x - 12}{x^2 - 5x + 6}$

6 $\dfrac{x^2 - x - 2}{x^2 + x - 6} \times \dfrac{x^2 - x - 12}{x^2 + 3x + 2}$

7 $\dfrac{p^2 + 7p + 12}{p^2 - 7p + 10} \div \dfrac{p + 3}{p - 2}$

8 $\dfrac{q^2 - 5q - 14}{q^2 + 3q - 18} \div \dfrac{q - 7}{q - 3}$

UNIT 5 ◆ Algebra

9 $\dfrac{x^2 + xy - 2y^2}{x^2 - 4y^2} \div \dfrac{x^2 + 2xy - 3y^2}{xy - 2y^2}$

10 $\dfrac{x^2 - 2xy + y^2}{x^2 - y^2} \div \dfrac{x^2 + xy}{x^2 + 2xy + y^2}$

11 $\dfrac{x^2 + 2x - 8}{5 - x} \times \dfrac{x^2 - 8x + 15}{1 - x} \times \dfrac{x^2 + 2x - 3}{2 - x}$

12 $\dfrac{b^2 + 3bc + 2c^2}{b^3 - 3b^2c} \times \dfrac{b^3 + b^2c}{b^2 + 5bc + 6c^2} \div \dfrac{b^2 + bc}{3c - b}$

Addition and subtraction

As with number fractions, factorise the denominator first so that the lowest common denominator (LCD) can be found. Otherwise the working can become very complicated. Do not multiply out brackets; the answer is best left factorised.

Example 12

Express $\dfrac{1}{x} + \dfrac{1}{x+1}$ as a single fraction.

$$\dfrac{1}{x} + \dfrac{1}{x+1} = \dfrac{(x+1)+x}{x(x+1)} = \dfrac{2x+1}{x(x+1)}$$

Example 13

Express $\dfrac{x-6}{x^2-4} - \dfrac{x}{x^2+3x+2}$ as a single fraction.

$$\dfrac{x-6}{x^2-4} - \dfrac{x}{x^2+3x+2} = \dfrac{x-6}{(x+2)(x-2)} - \dfrac{x}{(x+2)(x+1)}$$

$$= \dfrac{(x-6)(x+1) - x(x-2)}{(x+2)(x-2)(x+1)} \qquad \text{(Note the use of the common denominator)}$$

$$= \dfrac{x^2 - 5x - 6 - x^2 + 2x}{(x+2)(x-2)(x+1)}$$

$$= \dfrac{-3(x+2)}{(x+2)(x-2)(x+1)}$$

$$= \dfrac{-3}{(x-2)(x+1)}$$

Exercise 77

Express these as single fractions.

1 $\dfrac{2}{x} + \dfrac{3}{y}$

2 $\dfrac{3}{p} - \dfrac{5}{q}$

3 $\dfrac{1}{2x} - \dfrac{3}{4x}$

4 $\dfrac{2}{3x} + \dfrac{1}{6x}$

5 $\dfrac{1}{x+1} + \dfrac{1}{x-1}$

6 $\dfrac{1}{x-1} - \dfrac{1}{x+2}$

7 $\dfrac{1}{x} - \dfrac{1}{x(x+1)}$

8 $\dfrac{1}{x(x+1)} + \dfrac{1}{x+1}$

9 $\dfrac{1}{x} + \dfrac{1}{3x} - \dfrac{1}{5x}$

10 $\dfrac{1}{2x} - \dfrac{1}{4x} + \dfrac{1}{6x}$

11 $\dfrac{1}{x^2+3x+2} + \dfrac{1}{x+2}$

12 $\dfrac{4}{x^2+2x-3} + \dfrac{1}{x+3}$

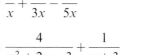

Exercise 77★

Express these as single fractions.

1 $\dfrac{4}{x+3} - \dfrac{3}{x+2}$

2 $\dfrac{5}{x+1} - \dfrac{2}{x+4}$

3 $\dfrac{1}{1+x} + x$

4 $1 - \dfrac{1}{x+1}$

5 $\dfrac{1}{x^2+2x+1} + \dfrac{1}{x+1}$

6 $\dfrac{1}{x^2+2x-3} + \dfrac{1}{x+3}$

7 $\dfrac{x+2}{x+1} - \dfrac{x+1}{x+2}$

8 $\dfrac{x+3}{x+2} - \dfrac{x-3}{x-2}$

9 $\dfrac{x+1}{x^2-4x+3} - \dfrac{x-3}{x^2-1}$

10 $\dfrac{x-2}{x^2-3x-4} - \dfrac{x-4}{x^2-6x+8}$

Equations with fractions

Clear any fractions by multiplying both sides of the equation by the LCD.

Example 14

To solve:
$$\dfrac{2x}{x-2} - \dfrac{4}{x+1} = 5 \qquad \text{(LCD is } (x-2)(x+1))$$

$$\dfrac{2x(x-2)(x+1)}{x-2} - \dfrac{4(x-2)(x+1)}{x+1} = 5(x-2)(x+1)$$

$$2x(x+1) - 4(x-2) = 5(x-2)(x+1)$$

$$2x^2 + 2x - 4x + 8 = 5x^2 - 5x - 10$$

$$3x^2 - 3x - 18 = 0$$

$$x^2 - x - 6 = 0$$

$$(x-3)(x+2) = 0$$

$$x = 3 \text{ or } x = -2$$

Exercise 78

Solve these equations.

1 $\dfrac{1}{2} - \dfrac{1}{x-2} = \dfrac{1}{4}$

2 $\dfrac{1}{x+4} - \dfrac{1}{3} = -\dfrac{1}{6}$

3 $\dfrac{x}{x+2} - \dfrac{1}{x} = 1$

4 $\dfrac{1}{x} + \dfrac{x}{x-3} = 1$

5 $\dfrac{6}{x-2} - \dfrac{6}{x+1} = 1$

6 $\dfrac{4}{x-1} - \dfrac{2}{x+2} = 1$

7 $\dfrac{x}{x-1} + \dfrac{8}{x+4} = 2$

8 $\dfrac{2x}{x-3} - \dfrac{4}{x+1} = 3$

9 $\dfrac{x-2}{x-1} = \dfrac{x+4}{2x+4}$

10 $\dfrac{2x-3}{x+1} = \dfrac{x+3}{x+5}$

Exercise 78★

Solve these equations.

1 $\dfrac{7}{9} - \dfrac{x}{x+5} = \dfrac{1}{3}$

2 $\dfrac{1}{2} + \dfrac{x}{x+7} = \dfrac{4}{5}$

3 $\dfrac{7}{x-1} - \dfrac{4}{x+4} = 1$

4 $\dfrac{7}{x-3} - \dfrac{6}{x+1} = 1$

5 $\dfrac{6x}{x+1} - \dfrac{5}{x+3} = 3$

6 $\dfrac{4x}{x+1} - \dfrac{8}{x+5} = 2$

7 $\dfrac{2x-1}{x+2} = \dfrac{4x+1}{5x+2}$

8 $\dfrac{2x+2}{x+8} = \dfrac{4x-1}{5x-2}$

9 $\dfrac{3x+2}{x+1} + \dfrac{x+2}{2x-5} = 4$

10 $\dfrac{4x-5}{x+2} + \dfrac{2x-4}{3x-8} = 3$

11 $\dfrac{3}{x+2} + \dfrac{4}{x+3} = \dfrac{7}{x+6}$

12 $\dfrac{4}{x-3} + \dfrac{3x-3}{x^2-x-6} = \dfrac{2-20x}{2x+4}$

13 $y - 1 = \dfrac{y^2+3}{y-1} + \dfrac{y-2}{y-6}$

UNIT 5 ◆ Algebra

Arithmetic sequences and series

In an **arithmetic sequence**, the *difference* between successive terms is constant.

Activity 47

Here is an example of an **arithmetic sequence**.

Rule: Starting with 2, keep adding 3 to create each new term:

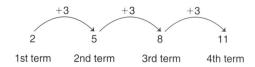

♦ Starting with 2, how many times do you add 3 to reach the fifth term?

♦ Starting with 2, how many times do you add 3 to reach the tenth term?
  What is the tenth term?

♦ Starting with 2, how many times do you add 3 to reach the 100th term?
  What is the 100th term?

♦ What is the nth term?

Example 15

Which of these are arithmetic sequences?

a 2, 7, 12, 17, 22, ... is an arithmetic sequence; the difference between terms is always 5.

b 2, 7, 13, 20, 28, ... is *not* an arithmetic sequence; the difference between terms changes.

c 7, 4, 1, -2, -5, ... is an arithmetic sequence; the difference between terms is always -3.

A sum where all the terms are from an arithmetic sequence, is called an **arithmetic series**.

Example 16

Find the sum, S, of the arithmetic series $1 + 2 + 3 + \cdots + 10$.

Write out the sum, and then write it out again backwards below the terms already written:

$$S = 1 + 2 + 3 + 4 + 5 + 6 + 7 + 8 + 9 + 10$$
$$S = 10 + 9 + 8 + 7 + 6 + 5 + 4 + 3 + 2 + 1$$

Add together $2S = 11 + 11 + 11 + 11 + 11 + 11 + 11 + 11 + 11 + 11 = 10 \times 11$

$$S = \frac{10 \times 11}{2} = 55$$

Activity 48

Extend the idea of Example 16 to find the sum of $1 + 2 + 3 + \cdots + 1\,000\,000$.

The sum of an arithmetic series

Suppose an arithmetic series has a as the first term, d as the difference between terms, and n as the number of terms.

Term number	1	2	3	4	$\ldots$	n
Term	a	$a + d$	$a + 2d$	$a + 3d$	$\ldots$	$a + (n - 1)\,d$

The nth term is $a + (n - 1)d$ because d is added on $(n - 1)$ times going from the first term to the nth term (see Activity 47). So

$$S = a + (a + d) + (a + 2d) + (a + 3d) + \cdots + (a + (n - 1)\,d)$$

Activity 49

Extend Example 16 to show that, for an arithmetic series, $S = \dfrac{n}{2}[2a + (n - 1)\,d]$

Key Points

♦ In an **arithmetic sequence**, the **difference** between successive terms is constant.

♦ The nth term of an arithmetic sequence is $a + (n - 1)\,d$.

♦ The sum of an arithmetic series is $S = \dfrac{n}{2}(2a + (n - 1)\,d)$.

Example 17

Find the sum of the arithmetic series $6 + 8 + 10 + \cdots + 100$.

$a = 6$ and $d = 2$.

The nth term is 100, so

$$100 = 6 + (n - 1)2$$
$$\Rightarrow \quad n - 1 = 47$$
$$\Rightarrow \quad n = 48$$

Substituting these values into the formula for the sum gives

$$S = 24(12 + 47 \times 2) = 2544$$

Exercise 79

For Questions 1–8, identify which are arithmetic sequences.

1 3, 5, 7, 9, ...

2 1, 5, 9, 13, ...

3 1, 3, 6, 10, ...

4 6, 4, 2, 0, ...

5 10, 7, 4, 1, ...

6 2, 3, 4, 6, ...

7 1.1, 1.2, 1.3, 1.4, ...

8 0.8, 0.6, 0.4, 0.2, ...

For Questions 9–16, each sequence is arithmetic.

9 The first term is 5 and the difference is 4. Find the 100th term.

10 The first term is 8 and the difference is 3. Find the 200th term.

11 The first term is 4 and the difference is 2.5. Find the sum of the first 21 terms.

12 The first term is 5 and the difference is 1.5. Find the sum of the first 17 terms.

13 The third term is 7 and the fifth term is 13. Find the sum of the first 101 terms.

14 The fourth term is 17 and the seventh term is 32. Find the sum of the first 51 terms.

15 The first term is 3 and the 20th term is 117. Find the sum of the first 40 terms.

16 The first term is 1 and the 15th term is 71. Find the sum of the first 50 terms.

17 Jenny starts a job at £17 000 per year increasing at £2000 per year.

   a What will her salary be at the start of the ninth year?

   b What will her total earnings be at the end of the 12th year?

18 Jim is cladding the gable end of a house with lengths of timber. The lengths of timber form an arithmetic sequence with first term 25 cm and difference 25 cm. The width of the timber is 20 cm and the gable is 4 m high.

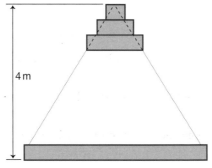

   a How many rows of timber are needed?

   b What is the total length of timber needed?

Exercise 79★

For Questions 1–10, each sequence is arithmetic.

1 The first term is 60. The difference is −6. Find the 100th term.

2 The first term is −20. The difference is 3. Find the 90th term.

3 The first term is −40. The difference is 5. Find the sum of the first 28 terms.

4 The first term is 15. The difference is −4. Find the sum of the first 36 terms.

5 The third term is 14. The 20th term is 65. Find the sum of the first 80 terms.

6 The fourth term is 44. The 12th term is 28. Find the sum of the first 100 terms.

7 The first term is 5. The difference is 4. The sum is 1325. Find the number of terms.

8 The first term is 80. The difference is −3. The sum is 920. Find the number of terms.

9 1, $2x$ and $5x$ are three successive terms. Find x.

10 $6x$, $4x$ and 3 are three successive terms. Find x.

11 Find the sum of the integers between 1 and 100 inclusive that are not divisible by 3.

12 Find the sum of the integers between 1 and 100 that are divisible by 2 or 3.

Geometric sequences and series

In a **geometric sequence**, the *ratio* between successive terms is constant.

Activity 50

Here is an example of a geometric sequence. *Rule*: Starting with 1, keep multiplying by 2 to create each new term:

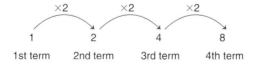

- Starting with 1, how many times do you multiply by 2 to reach the fifth term? What is the fifth term?
- Starting with 1, how many times do you multiply by 2 to reach the tenth term? What is the tenth term?
- Starting with 1, how many times do you multiply by 2 to reach the 100th term? What is the 100th term?
- What is the nth term?

Activity 51

A legend tells that the inventor of chess received a prize of 1 grain of rice on the first square of his chess board, 2 grains on the second square, 4 grains on the third square, 8 grains on the fourth square, and so on.

♦ How many grains of rice were on the last square?

♦ A grain of rice is about 5 mm long. If all the grains on the last square were placed end to end in a straight line, how long would the line be?

♦ How many times would this line stretch to the Sun? (The distance to the Sun is about 1.5×10^8 km.)

Example 18

Which of these are geometric sequences?

a 8, 12, 18, 27, . . . is a geometric sequence; the ratio between terms is 1.5.

b 4, 2, 1, $\frac{1}{2}$, . . . is a geometric sequence; the ratio between terms is $\frac{1}{2}$.

c 2, −4, 8, −16, . . . is a geometric sequence; the ratio between terms is −2.

A sum where all the terms are from a geometric sequence, is called a **geometric series**.

Example 19

Find the sum, S, of the geometric series $1 + 2 + 4 + 8 + \cdots + 128$.

The ratio of this geometric series is 2. Write out the sum, and then write out the sum multiplied by the ratio, 2, with terms 'moved' one place to the right:

$$S = 1 + 2 + 4 + 8 + 16 + 32 + 64 + 128$$
$$2S = \quad\ \ 2 + 4 + 8 + 16 + 32 + 64 + 128 + 256$$

Subtract S from $2S$

$$S = -1 \qquad\qquad\qquad\qquad\qquad + 256 = 255$$

Extend the idea of Example 19 to find the sum of $1 + 2 + 4 + 8 + \cdots + 4096$.

The sum of a geometric series

Suppose a geometric series has a as the first term, r as the ratio between terms, and n as the number of terms.

Term number	1	2	3	4	...	n
Term	a	ar	ar^2	ar^3	...	ar^{n-1}

The nth term is ar^{n-1} because a is multiplied by r only $(n-1)$ times going from the first term to the nth term (see Activity 50). So

$$S = a + ar + ar^2 + ar^3 + \cdots + ar^{n-1}$$

Activity 53

Extend the idea of Example 19 to show that, for a geometric series $S = \dfrac{a(r^n - 1)}{r - 1}$

Activity 54

- Use the formula from Activity 53 to find the total amount of rice on the chess board in Activity 51.

- If a rice grain is a cuboid measuring 5 mm by 1 mm by 1 mm, what is the volume of rice in km^3?

Multiplying top and bottom of $S = \dfrac{a(r^n - 1)}{r - 1}$ by -1 gives $S = \dfrac{a(1 - r^n)}{1 - r}$

This is easier to use when $|r| < 1$.

Key Points

- In a **geometric sequence**, the *ratio* between successive terms is constant.

- The nth term of a geometric sequence is ar^{n-1}.

- The sum of a geometric series is $S = \dfrac{a(r^n - 1)}{r - 1}$ or $S = \dfrac{a(1 - r^n)}{1 - r}$.

Exercise 80

For Questions 1–8, identify which are geometric sequences.

1 3, 6, 12, 24, ...

2 2, 6, 18, 54, ...

3 1, $1\frac{1}{2}$, 2, $2\frac{1}{2}$, ...

4 8, 2, 0.5, 0.125, ...

5 6.75, 4.5, 3, 2, ...

6 3, 2.75, 2.5, 2.25, ...

7 1, $-\frac{1}{2}$, $\frac{1}{4}$, $-\frac{1}{8}$, ...

8 4, −6, 9, −13.5

9 Find the 10th term of the geometric sequence with first term 1.5 and ratio 3.

10 Find the 12th term of the geometric sequence with first term 6 and ratio 2.

11 Find the sum of the first 15 terms of the geometric series with first term 4 and ratio 1.5.

12 Find the sum of the first 10 terms of the geometric series with first term 6 and ratio 2.5.

For Questions 13–16, each sequence is geometric.

13 The first term is 5. The third term is 180. Find the ratio of the sequence.

14 The first term is 3. The fourth term is 375. Find the ratio of the sequence.

15 The third term is 16. The sixth term is 1024. Find the ratio and the first term.

16 The fourth term is 54 and the sixth term is 486. Find the ratio and the first term.

Exercise 80★

1 Find the 16th term of the geometric sequence with first term 4 and ratio 1.2.

2 Find the 20th term of the geometric sequence with first term 5 and ratio 1.5.

3 Find the sum of the first 8 terms of the geometric series with first term 3 and ratio 4.

4 Find the sum of the first 10 terms of the geometric series with first term 2 and ratio 3.

5 The fifth term of a geometric sequence is 12 and the eighth term is 768.
Find the ratio and the 10th term.

6 The fourth term of a geometric sequence is 5 and the eighth term is 405.
Find the ratio and the 12th term.

7 1, $2x$ and $5x$ are successive terms of a geometric sequence. Find x.

8 $12x$, $4x$ and 2 are successive terms of a geometric sequence. Find x.

9 In the geometric sequence 1, 2, 4, 8, 16, 32, ..., 16 384 every third term is crossed out to give the sequence 1, 2, 8, 16, 64, ... Find the sum of the resulting series.

10 In the geometric sequence 1, 3, 9, 27, ..., 19 683 every other term is crossed out to give the sequence 1, 9, ... Find the sum of the resulting sequence.

11 On the island of Kaynine dog owners have to pay for an annual dog licence. The fee increases by 10% each year and was £50 in 2000.

    a Show that the fees paid each year form a geometric sequence.

    b What will the fee be in 2020?

    c What total amount would a dog owner pay in fees between 2000 and 2020?

12 Cliff is negotiating his fee for a forthcoming 30-day music tour. He has the choice of two schemes.
Scheme 1: 1p for the first day, 2p for the second, 4p for the third and so on, the amount doubling each day.
Scheme 2: £10 000 for the first day, £20 000 for the second day, £30 000 for the third day and so on, the amount increasing by £10 000 each day. Which scheme should he choose and why?

Infinite sequences and series

Sequences or series that go on and on for ever are called **infinite sequences** or **infinite series**.

Consider the series $10 + 1 + \frac{1}{10} + \frac{1}{100} + \cdots$

It 'seems obvious' that if you go on and on adding positive numbers, however small, then the sum of the series will get bigger and bigger.

Consider a paradox put forward by the Greek, Zeno of Elea, in the fifth century BC.

The paradox of Achilles and the tortoise

Achilles and a tortoise have a race. The tortoise has a head start of 100 m and travels at 1 m/s (quite a fast tortoise!) while Achilles runs at 10 m/s. Zeno argued as follows:

Achilles travels the first 100 m in 10 seconds. In the meantime the tortoise has travelled 10 m. It takes Achilles 1 second to travel that distance, while the tortoise advances another metre. Achilles covers that distance in $\frac{1}{10}$ second, and the tortoise is still $\frac{1}{10}$ m ahead.
And so on . . . .
The total number of seconds taken for Achilles to catch up with the tortoise is the infinite sum

    $10 + 1 + \frac{1}{10} + \frac{1}{100} + \cdots$

If this sum gets bigger and bigger the more terms you take, then Achilles will *never* catch the tortoise!'

We know that Achilles *does* catch the tortoise, so the sum $10 + 1 + \frac{1}{10} + \frac{1}{100} + \cdots$ cannot get bigger and bigger.

Copy and complete this table by using the formula for the sum of a geometric series.

Number of terms	5	10	50	100	1000
Sum of $1 + \frac{1}{2} + \frac{1}{4} + \frac{1}{8} + \frac{1}{16} + \cdots$	1.9375				
Sum of $1 + 2 + 4 + 8 + 16 + \cdots$	31				

It appears that the sum of a series can grow without limit (**diverge**) *or* tend towards some limiting value (**converge**). Consider this argument: Imagine a doorway 2 m tall, and you are going to make a pile of paper in this doorway using this rule:

Measure the gap between the top of the pile and the top of the door, then add a pile of paper equal to half this measurement. Repeat for ever.

At any stage there is a gap, which is only half-filled, thus leaving a gap for the next stage. This means that the pile will *never* fill the doorway. Yet the height of the pile is the sum of the series

$$1 + \frac{1}{2} + \frac{1}{4} + \frac{1}{8} + \frac{1}{16} + \frac{1}{32} + \cdots$$

If $|r| < 1$ then the term r^n in the formula $S = \dfrac{a(1 - r^n)}{1 - r}$

becomes smaller and smaller as n gets larger and larger. We say $r^n \to 0$ as $n \to \infty$.

The formula for the sum then becomes $S = \dfrac{a}{1 - r}$

Key Point

If $|r| < 1$ then the sum of a geometric series converges to the limit $S = \dfrac{a}{1 - r}$.

Exercise 81

For Questions 1 and 2, find the sum of the geometric series

1 $1 + 0.2 + 0.04 + 0.008 + \cdots$

2 $1 + 0.9 + 0.81 + 0.729 + \cdots$

For Questions 3 and 4, find the ratio.

3 The first term is 2 and the sum is 4.

4 The first term is 3 and the sum is 5.

5 A ball is dropped from a height of 3 m and bounces back to a height of 2.7 m, and then to 2.43 m and so on, all the heights forming a geometric sequence. Find the total distance the ball travels before coming to rest.

Exercise 81★

For Questions 1 and 2, find the sum of the geometric series.

1 $27 + 9 + 3 + 1 + \cdots$

2 $36 + 30 + 25 + 20\frac{5}{6} + \cdots$

For Questions 3 and 4, find the two possible values of the ratio.

3 The second term is 8 and the sum is 50.

4 The second term is 2 and the sum is $10\frac{2}{3}$.

5 A traveller in a desert is walking towards an oasis that is 110 km away. He walks 20 km on the first day, but because he is getting weaker on each successive day he only manages to walk 80% of the distance he walked on the previous day. Will he reach the oasis?

Paradoxes with infinite series

These two paradoxes show that you cannot apply the 'normal' rules of arithmetic to infinite series.

Paradox 1

Consider this series

$$S = 1 - 1 + 1 - 1 + 1 - \cdots$$

Grouping the terms one way gives

$$S = (1 - 1) + (1 - 1) + \cdots$$
$$= 0 + 0 + \cdots = 0$$

Grouping them another way gives

$$S = 1 - (1 - 1) - (1 - 1) - \cdots$$
$$= 1 + 0 + 0 + \cdots = 1$$

A third grouping gives

$$S = 1 - (1 - 1 + 1 - 1 + \cdots)$$

or $S = 1 - S$

implying that $2S = 1$ and $S = \frac{1}{2}$.

So this is an infinite series whose limit is apparently either 0, 1 or $\frac{1}{2}$.

Paradox 2

Consider these series

$$a = 1 + \frac{1}{3} + \frac{1}{5} + \frac{1}{7} + \cdots$$

and

$$b = \frac{1}{2} + \frac{1}{4} + \frac{1}{6} + \frac{1}{8} + \cdots$$

Every term in a is bigger than the corresponding term in b, so $a > b$.

But

$$2b = 1 + \frac{1}{2} + \frac{1}{3} + \frac{1}{4} + \cdots$$

In this series, we have all the terms for a and all the terms for b, so

$$2b = a + b$$

and $a = b$

But we have already shown that $a > b$.

Exercise 82 (Revision)

1 Expand and simplify $(x+2)(x^2-4x-3)$.

2 Divide $x^3+4x^2-16x+8$ by $x-2$.

Simplify

3 $(x+4)^3(x+6)-(x+4)^4$

4 $\dfrac{x^2-x-6}{2x-6}$

5 $\dfrac{x+3}{x-2} \div \dfrac{x^2+2x-3}{x^2-3x+2}$

6 Express as a single fraction $\dfrac{1}{x-2}-\dfrac{1}{x+3}$.

7 Solve $\dfrac{x}{x+3}+\dfrac{8}{3x-1}=2$.

8 Sum the series $5+7+9+11+\cdots+99$.

9 Find the sum of the first 12 terms of the series $3+6+12+24+\cdots$

10 Find the sum of the series $1+\frac{1}{4}+\frac{1}{16}+\frac{1}{64}+\cdots$

Exercise 82★ (Revision)

1 Expand and simplify $2(3x-1)(x^2-x+1)$.

2 Divide $x^4-5x^3+6x^2-9x+4$ by $x-4$.

Simplify

3 $(x+2)^3(x-1)^2-(x+2)^2(x-1)^3$

4 $\dfrac{2x^2+6x-8}{x^2-x}$

5 $\dfrac{x^2-3x-10}{x^2-x-6} \div \dfrac{x^2-4x-5}{x^2-2x-3}$

6 Express as a single fraction $\dfrac{x}{x^2-3x-4}-\dfrac{1}{x-4}$.

7 Solve $\dfrac{9x+1}{3x-2}-\dfrac{2x+1}{x+4}=3$.

8 Sum the series $30+27+24+21+\ldots-39$.

9 The sum of the first two terms of a geometric series is 8, and the sum of the first three terms is 26. If the ratio is positive, find the sum of the first 10 terms.

10 Two geometric series have the same first term, but the ratio of one series is twice the ratio of the other. The sum of one series is 12 and the sum of the other is 15. Find the possible values of the ratio.

Graphs 5

Areas under graphs

The area under a graph often represents a physical quantity (distance, speed, money, area, ...). The mathematician Leibniz was aware of this and introduced *calculus summatorius* in which he added up the areas of strips whose sum gave the total area under a curve. The mathematical sign for this process (integration), ∫, can be found throughout A-level texts.

Suppose speed is plotted against time. If the units on the axes are multiplied, the resultant quantity is distance.

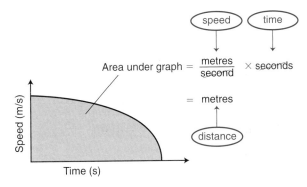

Area under graph = $\dfrac{\text{metres}}{\text{second}}$ × seconds

= metres

Remember

> The area under a speed–time graph represents the distance travelled.

Example 1

A farmer plots the cost/month spent on fertiliser against time. What quantity does the area under the graph represent?

The area under the graph represents the total cost spent by the farmer on fertiliser.

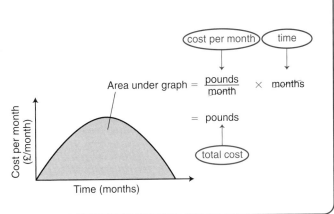

Area under graph = $\dfrac{\text{pounds}}{\text{month}}$ × months

= pounds

Key Point

♦ In a graph of *A* against *B*, the quantity represented by the area under the graph is given by (units of *A*) × (units of *B*).

Copy and complete this table to show, in a graph of *A* against *B*, what quantity is found by the area under the graph.

Quantity *A*	Quantity *B*	Area under graph represents...
Speed (m/s)	Time (s)	Distance (m)
Water flow (litres/hour)	Time (hours)	
Cost per day (£/day)	Time (days)	
Height (m)	Width (m)	
Frequency (vibrations per second)	Time(s)	
Mass per hour (kg/h)	Time (h)	

Summation of trapeziums

The area under a curve can be *estimated* by counting squares. Here an alternative method is introduced: splitting the area into trapeziums and summing them.

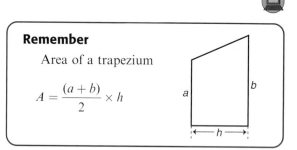

Remember

Area of a trapezium

$$A = \frac{(a+b)}{2} \times h$$

When trapeziums are used to approximate the area, some strips will be underestimates; others will be overestimates.

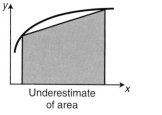

Underestimate of area

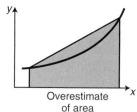

Overestimate of area

Example 2

A civil engineer has to make a cutting into some land for a new motorway. The cross-section of the cutting is constant and its length is 100 m. The cross-section is modelled by the graph of $y = 10 - 0.01x - 0.01x^2$ (for $0 \leqslant x \leqslant 20$) where all units are in metres.
Estimate the volume of earth to be moved, down to $y = 0$, as shown in the diagram.

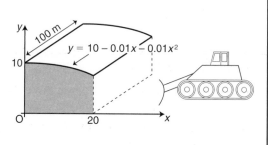

$y = 10 - 0.01x - 0.01x^2$

Example 2 continued

To estimate this volume, he needs to find the cross-sectional area of the cutting. He divides up the area into trapeziums and sums them.

The length of each ordinate (y-value) is calculated from the equation and tabulated so that the trapeziums can be sketched.

x	0	5	10	15	20
y	10	9.7	8.9	7.6	5.8

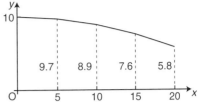

Volume of earth moved, V = cross-sectional area × 100.

Cross-sectional area, $A \simeq$ area of the four trapeziums.

$A \simeq \frac{1}{2}(10 + 9.7) \times 5 + \frac{1}{2}(9.7 + 8.9) \times 5 + \frac{1}{2}(8.9 + 7.6) \times 5 + \frac{1}{2}(7.6 + 5.8) \times 5$

$\simeq 170.5 \, \text{m}^2$

$V \simeq 170.5 \times 100 \simeq 17\,050 \, \text{m}^3$ (This is an underestimate for V.)

Exercise 83

1 Estimate the shaded areas under these curves by addition of trapeziums.

a

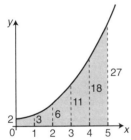

b

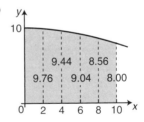

c

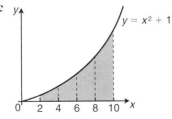

d

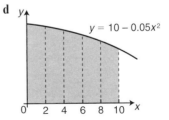

2 The speed of a rocket, V m/s, after t seconds, is given by $V = 100 - 0.1t^2$ (for $0 \leqslant t \leqslant 20$).

   a Divide the area under the curve into five trapeziums and estimate this area.

   b Use your answer to part **a** to estimate the mean speed of the rocket.

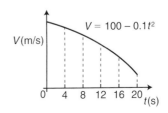

UNIT 5 ◆ Graphs

363

3 A 1 km long tunnel of constant cross-section has a curved ceiling above a straight 3 m high side wall. The shape of the ceiling has been modelled by the curve $y = 8 - 0.05x^2$ (for $-10 \leqslant x \leqslant 10$) relative to the set of axes shown, where all units are in metres.

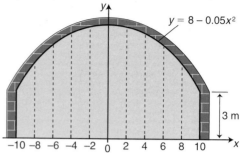

a Divide the cross-sectional area under the curved ceiling into trapeziums of width 2 m, and estimate the total area of the cross-section.

b Health Inspectors decide that the air in the tunnel should be changed every hour. Calculate an estimate for the rate at which the air must be changed in m^3/s.

4 A river has a constant cross-section whose profile is given by $y = 0.5x^2 - 5x$ (for $0 \leqslant x \leqslant 10$) relative to the set of axes shown, where all units are in metres.

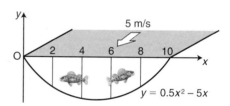

a Divide the cross-sectional area over the curve into trapeziums of width 2 m, and estimate the cross-sectional area of the river.

b If the river's speed is constant at 5 m/s, estimate the rate of flow in m^3/day in standard form correct to 2 significant figures.

Trapezium rule

Consider the area under the curve shown for $a \leqslant x \leqslant b$. It is divided up into four trapezium strips of equal width h with five ordinates as shown (y_1, y_2, y_3, y_4 and y_5).

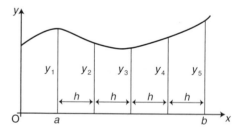

If A is the exact area under the curve for $a \leqslant x \leqslant b$, then

$$A \simeq \frac{(y_1 + y_2)}{2} \times h + \frac{(y_2 + y_3)}{2} \times h + \frac{(y_3 + y_4)}{2} \times h + \frac{(y_4 + y_5)}{2} \times h$$

$$A \simeq \frac{h}{2}(y_1 + y_5 + 2y_2 + 2y_3 + 2y_4)$$

This is the rule for five ordinates; it can of course be extended to n ordinates

Key Point

The area under a curve, A units^2, which is divided up into trapeziums of equal width h and n ordinates, is given by the **trapezium rule**:

$$A \simeq \frac{h}{2}[y_1 + y_n + 2(y_2 + y_3 + y_4 + \cdots + y_{n-1})]$$

Example 3

Calculate an approximation for the area under the curve $y = x^2 + 1$, valid for $0 \leqslant x \leqslant 10$, using the trapezium rule with five strips.

There are five strips, so the width of each strip, h, is given by

$$h = \frac{\text{interval width}}{\text{number of strips}}$$

$$= \frac{10 - 0}{5} = 2$$

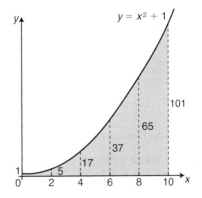

The length of each ordinate is calculated from $y = x^2 + 1$. A table is used so that errors can be spotted easily and to tidy up the calculation.

x	y	Multiplier, m	my
0	1	1	1
2	5	2	10
4	17	2	34
6	37	2	74
8	65	2	130
10	101	1	101
			$\Sigma my = 350$

If A is the area under the curve, the trapezium rule gives

$$A \simeq \frac{2}{2} \times 350$$

$$A \simeq 350 \text{ units}^2$$

Exercise 83★

1 Use the trapezium rule to make an estimate for the shaded area under these curves with the given number of strips.

a
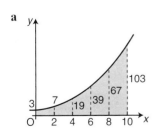

b
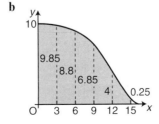

c
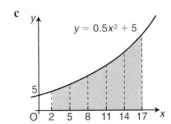

2 The velocity of a car, V m/s, t seconds before coming to rest, is given by the formula
$V = \sqrt{(1000 - t^3)}$, valid for $0 \leqslant t \leqslant 10$.

    a Use the trapezium rule with 10 strips to estimate the total distance travelled after 10 seconds.

    b What is the mean speed of the car over this period?

3 The power, P joules/second, produced by a small micro-light aircraft engine after t seconds is given by $P = 250 + t + t^2$, valid for $0 \leqslant t \leqslant 100$.

    a Use the trapezium rule with 10 strips to estimate the area under the graph of P against t for $0 \leqslant t \leqslant 100$.

    b Energy is measured in joules. State the energy produced by the engine in this period, and use this figure to estimate the mean power of the engine over this time period.

4 The volcano Mount Summo has sprung to life and its lava flow slides down a straight channel of constant cross-section of profile modelled by $y = 0.3x^2 - 3x$, valid for $0 \leqslant x \leqslant 10$, relative to the set of axes shown. All units are in metres.

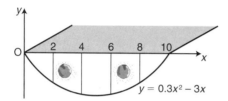 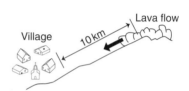

The exact cross-sectional area of the lava flow is A m^2. Given that the lava flows at a constant rate of 5 m^3/s, estimate A and hence estimate how many hours the local residents have to evacuate their village.

Activity 57

♦ Consider the curve $y = x^2 - 3x + 10$ for $0 \leqslant x \leqslant 10$. Estimate the area under this curve using the trapezium rule with 1 strip, 2 strips and 10 strips.

♦ Use a suitable computer program to estimate this area using 20 strips, 50 strips and 100 strips.

♦ What do you notice?

Exercise 84 (Revision)

1 The area under the curve $y = 50 - x - x^2$ is shown. Use the trapezium rule to estimate the area under this curve for $0 \leqslant x \leqslant 6$.

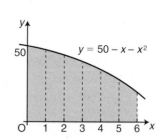

2 Use the trapezium rule to estimate the shaded areas under these curves with the given number of strips.

a

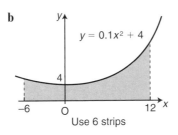

b

c

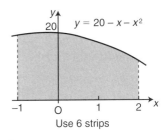

3 a Calculate an approximation for the area under the curve $y = x^2 + x + 1$ for $0 \leqslant x \leqslant 2$ using the trapezium rule with 4 strips, and then 8 strips.

   b The exact area is $6\frac{2}{3}$ units^2. Find the percentage errors to your two answers to part **a**. Comment.

4 Estimate the area under the curve $y = 2^x$ for $0 \leqslant x \leqslant 5$ using the trapezium rule with 10 strips.

Exercise 84★ (Revision)

For Questions 1 and 2, calculate an approximation for the area under the curve using the trapezium rule with 10 strips.

1 $y = \cos x$ for $0° \leqslant x \leqslant 90°$ **2** $y = \sin 2x$ for $0° \leqslant x \leqslant 90°$

3 A machine part vibrates with a frequency, f (hundreds of vibrations per second), after t seconds given by $f = 0.01(t^3 - t^2 - t)$, valid for $0 \leqslant t \leqslant 10$.

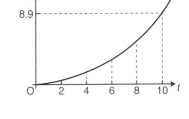

   a What physical quantity is represented by the area under the curve?

   b Use the trapezium rule with 10 strips to estimate this area for $0 \leqslant x \leqslant 10$.

   c Estimate the machine part's mean number of vibrations per second in this interval.

4 An aircraft hanger of constant cross-sectional area has a roof modelled on the curve $y = 20 - 0.01x^2$, valid for $-25 \leqslant x \leqslant 25$, relative to the set of axes shown. All units are in metres and the building is 50 m in length.

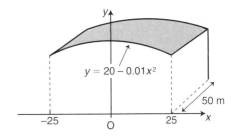

Use the trapezium rule with 10 strips to estimate the volume of the building, correct to 3 significant figures.

Rates of change 5

Tangents to curves

The gradient of a straight line at a given point on a graph often provides useful information.

Graph	Gradient
Distance (m) – time (s)	Speed (m/s)
Velocity (m/s) – time (s)	Acceleration (m/s^2)
Temperature (°C) – time (min)	Rate of change of temperature (°C/min)
Population (ants) – time (weeks)	Rate of change of ants (ants/week)
Financial profit (£) – time (year)	Rate of change of profit (£/year)

Most graphs in nature are curves rather than straight lines, but it is still possible to extract information on rates of change by drawing a tangent to the curve and estimating the gradient of the curve at that point.

> ### Remember
>
> The gradient of a curve at point A is equal to the gradient of the tangent to the curve at this point.
>
>
>
> Note that the angle the tangent makes with the curve is the same on either side of point A.

This diagram shows lots of gradients to the ellipse $\dfrac{x^2}{4} + \dfrac{y^2}{9} = 1$.

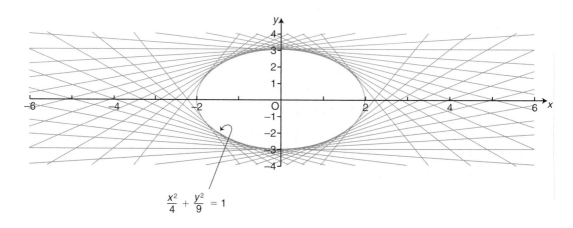

$$\frac{x^2}{4} + \frac{y^2}{9} = 1$$

Example 1

By drawing suitable tangents to the curve, estimate the gradient of the curve $y = x(4 - x)$ at the points where $x = 1$, $x = 2$ and $x = 3$.

Reading the graph below:

♦ Gradient of tangent at $x = 1$ is $+2$.

♦ Gradient of tangent at $x = 2$ is 0.

♦ Gradient of tangent at $x = 3$ is -2.

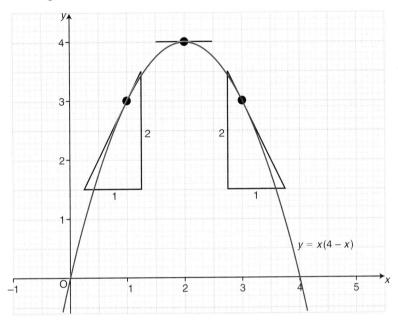

Exercise 85

1 **a** Plot the graph of $y = x(6 - x)$ for $0 \leqslant x \leqslant 6$. Use your graph together with suitable tangents to estimate the gradient of the curve at $x = 0$, $x = 2$ and $x = 5$.

   b Where on the curve is the gradient equal to zero?

2 **a** Plot the graph of $y = x(x - 4)$ for $-2 \leqslant x \leqslant 6$. Use your graph together with suitable tangents to estimate the gradient of the curve at $x = 0$, $x = 2$ and $x = 5$.

   b Where on the curve is the gradient equal to 4?

3 **a** Plot the graph of $y = 2^x$ for $0 \leqslant x \leqslant 5$. Use your graph together with suitable tangents to estimate the gradient of the curve at $x = 1$ and $x = 3$.

   b Where on the curve is the gradient equal to 12?

4 **a** Plot the graph of $y = x^2(x - 4)$ for $-2 \leqslant x \leqslant 4$. Use your graph together with suitable tangents to estimate the gradient of the curve at $x = -1$ and $x = 3$.

  b Where on the curve is the gradient equal to zero?

5 At the point $x = a$ the gradient of the curve $f(x) = \sin x$ is equal to b.
  What is the gradient at $x = a$ of these curves?

  a $f(x) + a$ **b** $f(x) - a$ **c** $-f(x)$ **d** $2f(x)$

Example 2

Part of a distance–time graph describing the motion of a Border Collie running parallel to a straight fence is shown. Initially, the shepherd is 10 m away from the dog.

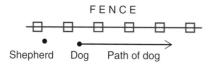

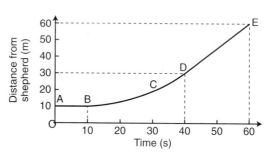

a Describe how the dog's speed varies.

A to B: The dog is stationary for the first 10 s, 10 m away from the shepherd.

B to D: The dog moves off gradually with an increasing speed over 30 s.

D to E: The dog moves at a constant speed of 1.5 m/s; the gradient is $\frac{30}{20}$.

b Find the dog's speed after 30 seconds.

Imagine the graph at C magnified 100 times. It would look like a straight line and its gradient is the speed after 30 s.

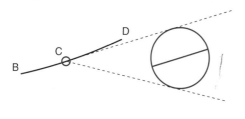

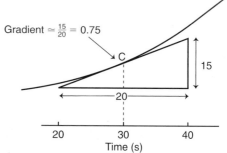

Gradient $\approx \frac{15}{20} = 0.75$

The gradient of 0.75 indicates a speed of 0.75 m/s.

Example 3

The area of weed covering part of a field doubles every 10 years. The area now covered is 100 m².

a Given that the area of weed, A m², after n years, is given by $A = 100 \times 2^{0.1n}$, draw the graph of A against n for $0 \leqslant n \leqslant 40$.

n (years)	0	10	20	30	40
A (m²)	100	200	400	800	1600

This is the graph of area of weed against time.

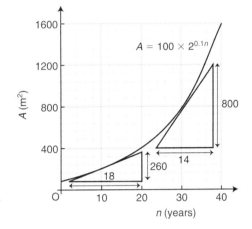

b By drawing suitable tangents, find the rate of growth of the weed in m² per year after 10 years and after 30 years.

Rate of growth at 10 years $\simeq \dfrac{260 \text{ m}^2}{18 \text{ years}} \simeq 14 \text{ m}^2/\text{year}$.

Rate of growth at 30 years $\simeq \dfrac{800 \text{ m}^2}{14 \text{ years}} \simeq 57 \text{ m}^2/\text{year}$.

The rate of growth is clearly increasing with time.

Exercise 85★

1 The temperature of a cup of coffee ($T°C$) after t minutes is given in this table.

t (min)	0	1	2	3	4	5	6
T (°C)	80	71	62	55	49	43	38

a Draw the temperature–time graph of this information.

b Estimate the rate of change of the temperature in °C/min when $t = 0$ and when $t = 6$. Comment.

2 The depth, d mm, of fluid poured into a conical beaker at a constant rate, after t seconds, is shown in this table.

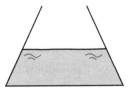

t (s)	0	4	8	12	16	20
d (mm)	1	2.5	6.3	15.8	39.8	100

a Draw the graph of depth against time from this table.

b Estimate the rate of change of the depth in mm/s when $t = 10$ s and when $t = 15$ s. Comment.

3 The depth of water, y metres, at Brigstock Port, t hours after 6 a.m., is given by this formula:

$$y = 5 + 3\sin(45t)°$$

a Copy and complete this table and use it to plot the graph of y against t for $0 \le t \le 12$.

t (hours)	0	2	4	6	8	10	12
y (m)	5			2			5

b A boat requires a depth of 4 m for it to leave the port.
If it is docked at 6 a.m., what is the latest time for the boat to be able to leave?

c By drawing suitable tangents to the curve, estimate the rate of change of the depth in cm per minute at 7 a.m., 9 a.m., and at 1 p.m.

4 A party balloon of volume 2000 cm³ loses 15% of its air every 10 min.

a Find the formula for the volume V cm³ after t minutes and then copy and complete this table.

t (min)	0	10	20	30	40	50	60	70	80	90
V (cm³)	2000		1445							

b Draw the graph of V against t for $0 \le t \le 90$ min and use it to estimate when the balloon's volume is half its initial value.

c Calculate the rate of change of the balloon's volume in cm³ per minute after 10 min and 80 min. Comment.

5 A catapult fires a stone vertically upwards. The height, h metres, of the stone, t seconds after firing, is given by the formula $h = 40t - 5t^2$.

a Draw the graph of h against t for $0 \le t \le 8$ s.

b Draw tangents to this curve and measure their gradients. Then copy and complete this table

t (s)	0	1	2	3	4	5	6	7	8
Velocity (m/s)	40		20			−10			−40

c Draw the velocity–time graph for the stone for $0 \le t \le 8$ s.

d What can you say about the stone's acceleration?

Basic calculus

The technique of drawing tangents to curves to estimate rates of change is cumbersome and often inaccurate. The mathematicians Leibniz and Newton first thought of a process called differentiation in which the rates of change could be calculated by a simple process. They called this branch of mathematics *fluxions*; nowadays, it is called *calculus*.

Calculus involves considering very small increments in x and y: δx and δy. δx is pronounced 'delta x' and is shorthand meaning an increment (small distance) along the x-axis. It does *not* mean δ multiplied by x. The gradient at a point is estimated by the slope of a chord $\delta y / \delta x$ and then δx is made as small as possible, i.e. $\delta x \to 0$. The gradient is then the limit of $\dfrac{\delta y}{\delta x}$ as $\delta x \to 0$.
This is written as $\lim\limits_{\delta x \to 0} \dfrac{\delta y}{\delta x}$.

Example 4

Consider the graph $y = x^2$.

The gradient of the curve at point A is equal to the tangent to the curve at this point.

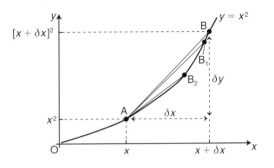

A good 'first attempt' in finding this gradient is to consider a point B up the curve from A. The gradient of chord AB will be close to the required gradient if the steps along the x and y axes (δx and δy respectively) are small.

Let the *exact* gradient of $y = x^2$ at A be m. An estimate of m is found from:

$$\frac{\delta y}{\delta x} = \frac{[x + \delta x]^2 - x^2}{\delta x} \qquad \text{[Expand } (x + \delta x)^2\text{]}$$

$$= \frac{[x^2 + 2x\delta x + (\delta x)^2] - x^2}{\delta x}$$

$$= \frac{2x\delta x + (\delta x)^2}{\delta x}$$

$$= \frac{\delta x(2x + \delta x)}{\delta x} = 2x + \delta x$$

So the estimate of m is $\dfrac{\delta y}{\delta x} = 2x + \delta x$

This estimate of m improves as point B slides down the curve to B_1, B_2, etc., closer and closer to A, resulting in δx and δy becoming smaller and smaller until, *at* point A, $\delta x = 0$.

What happens to $\dfrac{\delta y}{\delta x}$ as δx approaches zero?

So we can write the exact gradient as $m = \lim\limits_{\delta x \to 0} (2x + \delta x)$

Clearly, as δx gets smaller, $2x + \delta x$ approaches $2x$, and eventually, *at* A, $m = 2x$.

This is a beautifully simple result implying that the gradient of the curve $y = x^2$ at *any* point x is given by $2x$. So, at $x = 10$, the gradient of $y = x^2$ is 20, and so on.

♦ Using a similar process to that used in Example 4, show that the rule which gives the gradient m at any point on the curve $y = x^3$ is given by $m = 3x^2$.

Start your proof like this:

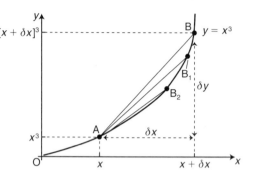

$$\frac{\delta y}{\delta x} = \frac{[x + \delta x]^3 - x^3}{\delta x} \qquad \text{[Expand } (x + \delta x)^3]$$

$$= \frac{[x^3 + 3x^2 \delta x + 3x(\delta x)^2 + (\delta x)^3] - x^3}{\delta x}$$

$$= \ldots$$

State the gradient of $y = x^3$ at $x = 0$, $x = 2$ and $x = -2$.

♦ Using the same method, copy and complete this table.

Graph of	General formula for gradient, m	Gradient of the curve at the stated value of x	
$y = 2x$	$m = 2$	$x = 3$	$m = 2$
$y = x^2$	$m = 2x$	$x = 3$	$m = 6$
$y = x^3$	$m = 3x^2$	$x = 3$	$m = 27$
$y = 2x^2$		$x = 3$	
$y = 2x^2 + 2x$		$x = 3$	
$y = \dfrac{1}{x}$		$x = 3$	
$y = \sqrt{x}$		$x = 3$	
$y = ax^n$		$x = b$	

This method is very tedious to use *every* time you want to find the gradient of a curve. Luckily a simple rule exists to speed up the process.

Key Point

♦ The gradient, m, to the curve $y = ax^n$ is given by the formula $m = nax^{n-1}$

♦ To find the gradient at the point where $x = b$, substitute to give $m = nab^{n-1}$

Example 5

Find the gradients of the tangents to these curves at the points given in square brackets.

Let the gradient functions of the curves be m.

a $y = 3x^2$ [at $x = 1$]   For $y = 3x^2$, $m = 6x$. At $x = 1$, $m = 6$.

b $y = 4x^3$ [at $x = 2$]   For $y = 4x^3$, $m = 12x^2$. At $x = 2$, $m = 48$.

c $y = x^2 + 3x$ [at $x = 3$]   For $y = x^2 + 3x$, $m = 2x + 3$. At $x = 3$, $m = 9$.

d $y = 3x^2 - 1$ [at $x = 4$]   For $y = 3x^2 - 1$, $m = 6x$. At $x = 4$, $m = 24$.

Example 6

Find the equation of the tangent to the curve $y = 2x^2 + 1$ at the point where $x = 1$.

The gradient function, $m = 4x$, so at $x = 1$, $m = 4$.

The straight line has the equation

$$y = mx + c$$

so $y = 4x + c$

When $x = 1$, $y = 3$

$$3 = 4(1) + c$$

$$c = -1$$

Therefore the equation of the line is

$$y = 4x - 1$$

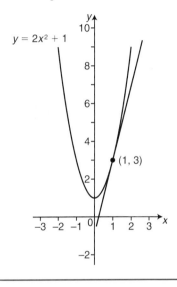

$y = 2x^2 + 1$

$(1, 3)$

Exercise 86 (Revision)

1 **a** Draw the curve $y = x(x - 5)$ for $0 \leqslant x \leqslant 6$.

   b By drawing suitable tangents, find the gradient of the curve at the points $x = 1$, $x = 2.5$ and $x = 5$.

2 The height of a walnut tree, y cm after t months, is given in the table.

t (months)	0	6	12	18	24	30	36
y (cm)	1	2.5	6.3	15.8	39.8	100	251

   a Draw the graph of y against t.

   b By drawing suitable tangents to the curve, estimate the rate of growth of the walnut tree in cm *per year* when $t = 15$ and when $t = 30$. Comment.

3 Steve performs a 'bungee-jump' from a platform above a river. His height above the river (h metres) t seconds after the jump is plotted on the graph. The tangents are also shown at various points.

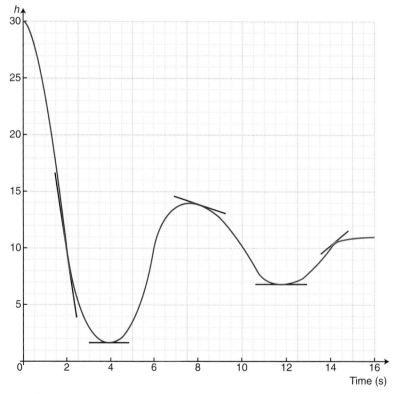

   a Use the graph to copy and complete the table of Steve's speed (v m/s) after t seconds.

t (s)	0	2	4	6	8	10	12	14	16
v (m/s)	0			5		−2.1			

   b Plot the graph of v against t and state Steve's maximum speed.

   c What quantity would be found by taking the gradient of the graph of v against t?

Exercise 86★ (Revision)

1 Find the equation that gives the gradient at any point to these curves and find the gradient of the curves at the stated value of x.

   a $y = 5x^2$ [at $x = 2$]   **b** $y = 5x^3$ [at $x = 3$]

   c $y = x(x - 1)$ [at $x = 2$]   **d** $y = x^2(x - 1)$ [at $x = 3$]

2 The point A(1, 3) is on the graph of $y = x(4 - x)$ as shown.

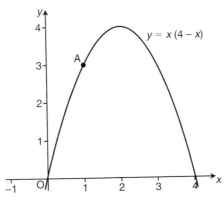

   a Find the equation of the gradient of the curve at any point.

   b Find the gradient of the curve at point A.

   c What is the equation of the tangent to the curve at A?

3 **a** Where on $y = x^3 - 12x + 2$ is the gradient zero?

   b Find the equation of the tangent to the curve at point A where $x = 1$.

   c Find the equation of the line perpendicular to the tangent to the curve passing through point A. (This is called the *normal*.)

Measures of spread 5

The **range** and the **interquartile range** are useful statistics for measuring the 'spread' of a data set. They are simple to work out using cumulative frequency.

However, only two values are required for the range, and the interquartile range uses only the middle half of the data, so they can misrepresent a non-typical distribution. They are most commonly used to compare two or more similar data sets.

Example 1

$$5 \quad 8 \quad 12 \quad 13 \quad 14 \quad 15 \quad 16 \quad 18 \quad 20 \quad 24 \quad 30$$

Range $= 30 - 5 = 25$

IQR $= 20 - 12 = 8$

The standard deviation

The standard deviation is another statistic that measures 'spread'. It is derived from *all* the data and gives equal weight to all results in a data set; and so, as a statistic, it is much more reliable than the range and interquartile range.

One important thing to note about the standard deviation is that for most 'normal' sets of data, 95% of the results lie within two standard deviations of the mean.

Example 2

The average height of a large sample of Year 10 pupils is 170 cm. The standard deviation is 3.8 cm. Estimate the range of heights of the 'middle' 95% of the pupils.

$2 \times$ standard deviation $= 2 \times 3.8$ cm $= 7.6$ cm

mean $- (2 \times$ standard deviation$) = 170$ cm $- 7.6$ cm $= 162.4$ cm

mean $+ (2 \times$ standard deviation$) = 170$ cm $+ 7.6$ cm $= 177.6$ cm

$\therefore$ 95% of the heights lie within the range 162.4–177.6 cm.

A small number (5%) of very short, or extremely tall, pupils are outside this range!

Calculating standard deviation

The **standard deviation** (s.d.) is defined as the square root of the **variance**, σ^2 by these equations:

$$\sigma^2 = \frac{\Sigma(x - \bar{x})^2}{n} \qquad \text{s.d.} = \sigma = \sqrt{\frac{\Sigma(x - \bar{x})^2}{n}}$$

The calculation is best done, step-by-step, in a calculation table, as illustrated in Example 3.

Example 3

The Test Match against the West Indies, at Leeds, in August 2000 was the first international cricket match since 1945 to be completed in two days. The ages of the players in that England cricket team were

| 30 | 30 | 24 | 31 | 37 | 25 | 34 | 30 | 29 | 31 | 29 |

a Calculate the mean and standard deviation of the ages.

Construct a table, and fill it in as you go through the calculation.

x	$x - 30$	$(x - 30)^2$
30	0	0
30	0	0
24	-6	36
31	1	1
37	7	49
25	-5	25
34	4	16
30	0	0
29	-1	1
31	1	1
29	-1	1
$\Sigma x = 330$	$\Sigma(x - \bar{x}) = 0$	$\Sigma(x - \bar{x})^2 = 130$

Mean, $\bar{x} = \dfrac{\Sigma x}{n}$

$\quad = \dfrac{330}{11}$

$\quad = 30$

Variance, $\sigma^2 = \dfrac{\Sigma(x - \bar{x})^2}{n}$

$\quad = \dfrac{130}{11}$

$\quad = 11.82$

s.d. $= \sigma$

$\quad = \sqrt{11.82}$

$\quad = 3.44$

b Work out the median, range and interquartile range of the ages.

Median, $m = 30$. $q_1 = 29$. $q_3 = 31$.

IQR $= 31 - 29 = 2$. Range $= 37 - 24 = 13$.

c Comment on the statistics.

The mean and median both indicate that the average age of the team is 30.

s.d. uses *all* the ages and therefore is representative of the whole team.

The IQR does not indicate that the team includes one old (and experienced) player and two new young players.

The range does not indicate that the bulk of the team are aged about 30.

Rearranging the standard deviation formula

The calculation in Example 3 could have been much more difficult. Imagine if the mean had been $\frac{328}{11} = 29\frac{9}{11}$! Luckily, the formula for the variance, and hence the standard deviation can be rearranged into a different form, which is easier to calculate when the mean is not a whole number:

$$\sigma^2 = \frac{1}{n}\Sigma x^2 - (\bar{x})^2$$

Example 4

Use the alternative formula to calculate the standard deviation of the cricketers' ages in Example 3:

$$\sigma^2 = \frac{1}{n}\Sigma x^2 - (\bar{x})^2$$

$$= \frac{10\,030}{11} - 30^2$$

$$= 911.82 - 900$$

$$= 11.82$$

$$\therefore \quad \sigma = \sqrt{11.82} = 3.44$$

x	x^2
30	900
30	900
24	576
31	961
37	1369
25	625
34	1156
30	900
29	841
31	961
29	841
$\Sigma x = 330$	$\Sigma x^2 = 10\,030$

Key Points

♦ Standard deviation $\sigma = \sqrt{\text{variance}}$

♦ Variance $\sigma^2 = \dfrac{\Sigma(x - \bar{x})^2}{n}$ (Best when $\bar{x}$ is a whole number)

$\sigma^2 = \dfrac{1}{n}\Sigma x^2 - (\bar{x})^2$ (Best when $\bar{x}$ is an awkward number)

Exercise 87

1 100 Dundee cakes were weighed at the end of a production line at a bakery.
The mean was 2100 g and the standard deviation was 45 g.
Estimate the range of the weight of the middle 95% of the cakes.

2 A large sample of 'supalite' trainers were weighed and the following statistics calculated.
Mean = 290 g. Standard deviation = 15 g.
Estimate the range of the weight of the middle 95% of the trainers.

3 95% of Norfolk Terriers are between 31 and 38 cm tall.
Estimate the mean and standard deviation of the height of this breed of dog.

4 95% of 'Violet Viv' tulips grow to a height between 26 and 31 cm.
Estimate the mean and standard deviation of the height of this type of tulip.

For Questions 5–8, construct a calculation table to work out Σx, Σx^2, $\Sigma(x - \bar{x})$ and $\Sigma(x - \bar{x})^2$, and then find the mean and standard deviation of the data, checking that both formulae for σ^2 give the same result.

5 The points scored by each of the eight players in a basketball team:

    0   16   14   12   4   6   10   10

6 The number of typing errors per page of a document:

    3   4   5   6   8   2   4   5   1   2

7 The ages of the cars, in years, on a garage forecourt:

    2   3   4   4   5   6   6   8   10   12

8 The rainfall, in mm, for the first seven days of the year, recorded at a weather station:

    15   8   5   10   9   1   8

For Questions 9–12, calculate the mean and then, selecting the best formula, calculate the standard deviation of the data.

9 The numbers of pages per essay received by a history teacher from a sixth-form class:

    2   4   5   5   5   6   6   8   9   10   10

10 The number of hours of sunshine per day was recorded for the peak holiday week at an east coast resort:

    6 h   4 h   14 h   13 h   3 h   10 h   8 h

11 The weights of a sample of chocolate bars:

    75.3 g 75.4 g 75.8 g 76.2 g 75.7 g 75.6 g 76 g 75.9 g 75.8 g 75.3 g

12 In July 2000, the cost of a litre of unleaded petrol was surveyed at a sample of ten garages in Cornwall:

    80.4p 81.2p 79.1p 80.4p 80.4p 79.2p 80.7p 81.8p 79.9p 79.9p

13 Two darts players recorded these series of results in a match.

Player 1	60	65	81	85	55	60	46
Player 2	120	75	100	26	60	45	36

  a Calculate the mean and standard deviation of their scores.

  b Comment on the level and consistency of each player. Who is the better player?

14 A sixth-form class achieved the following marks in two modules at the end of the lower sixth.

Pure maths	83	64	100	107	97	65	58	82
Mechanics	95	60	105	118	109	87	41	98

a Calculate the mean and standard deviation of each set of marks.

b Work out the median and interquartile range of each set.

c Use the statistics to comment on the performances in the two subjects.

Standard deviation of frequency distributions

In most practical situations, a large data set is collected. Continuous data are 'grouped' and both discrete and continuous data are presented as frequency distributions. The distribution may be presented in a diagram and statistics are calculated for analysis.

Example 5

A survey revealed these results for the time spent on homework for a Friday night by a group of 60 school children. Calculate the mean and standard deviation.

Prepare a calculation table. (Calculate the mean first before deciding which form of the formula to use.)

Time t (min)	No. of children, f	Mid-point x	fx	fx^2
0–30	6	15	$6 \times 15 = 90$	$6 \times 15^2 = 1350$
30–60	12	45	540	24 300
60–80	18	70	1260	88 200
80–100	12	90	1080	97 200
100–120	9	110	990	108 900
120–180	3	150	450	67 500
	$\Sigma f = 60$ ①		$\Sigma fx = 4410$ ②	$\Sigma fx^2 = 387450$ ③

① $\Sigma f = 60 \Rightarrow n = 60$

② $\Sigma fx = 4410 \Rightarrow$ mean $\bar{x} = \dfrac{4410}{60} = 73.5$

③ $\therefore$ variance $\sigma^2 = \dfrac{\Sigma fx^2}{n} - \bar{x}^2$

$\qquad = \dfrac{387\,450}{60} - 73.5^2$

$\qquad = 1055.25$

♦ $\therefore$ Standard deviation $\sigma = \sqrt{1055.25} = 32.5$

$\qquad$ Mean time = 73.5 min $\qquad$ Standard deviation = 32.5 min

Statistical calculators

For large data sets, the formula

$$\sigma^2 = \frac{1}{n}\Sigma x^2 - (\bar{x})^2$$

is more often used because the statistical function on a calculator enables data to be entered in frequency form, and has functions that produce Σx, Σx^2, n, $\bar{x}$ and σ, but not the function $\Sigma(x - \bar{x})^2$.

Read the instruction booklet for your calculator so that you can enter data and produce these statistics, and then check the working in Example 5 using the statistical functions on your calculator.

Exercise 87★

For Questions 1–4, calculate the mean and standard deviation of each data set.

1   The first eight customers at a petrol station one morning bought these amounts of petrol.

   £50   £50   £40   £30   £20   £20   £20   £10

2   An apartment block has eight studio flats with these floor areas.

   900 m²   600 m²   400 m²   400 m²   300 m²   300 m²   200 m²   100 m²

3   A woman advertising her car for sale received these offers.

   £3900   £3700   £4400   £3600   £3800   £4000

4   Eight ticket touts offered seats for a popular West End show at these prices.
   £70   £80   £80   £80   £90   £90   £100   £130

5   The sizes of each family living in a block of flats are recorded in this table.

Calculate the mean and standard deviation of the number of children per family.

Number of children, x	Frequency, f
0	11
1	14
2	16
3	7
4	2

6   A traffic survey recorded the number of people in cars photographed at a busy junction during the morning rush-hour.

Calculate the mean and standard deviation of the number of occupants per car.

Occupants of car, x	Frequency, f
1	36
2	23
3	9
4	9
5	3

7 A class mathematics test produced these results. Calculate the mean and standard deviation of the marks.

Mark, x	f
0–3	0
4	3
5	3
6	4
7	7
8	8
9	4
10	1

8 A sample of 100 matchboxes was chosen to test the claim on the box: 'Average contents 40 matches'.

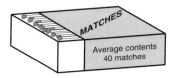

Calculate the mean and standard deviation of these results.

No. of matches, x	f
36	2
37	4
38	15
39	18
40	19
41	22
42	14
43	6

For Questions 9 and 10, Calculate the values of a and b.

9 The mean and standard deviation of this set of numbers are 6 and 2 respectively.

| 6 | 8 | 5 | 3 | 8 | 5 | a | b |

10 The mean and variance of this set of numbers are 8 and 9 respectively.

| a | b | 7 | 9 | 10 | 12 | 11 |

11 The data give the distribution of the age of conception for births recorded in the UK in 1997.

a Calculate the total number of conceptions.

b Calculate estimates for the mean and standard deviation of this age (use 15 and 42 as the mid-points of the first and last groups).

Age in years, x	Frequency, f (1000s)
under 16	10
16–18	40
18–20	100
20–25	170
25–30	240
30–35	200
35–40	80
over 40	10

12 The data give the distribution of ages for all male deaths recorded in England and Wales in 1998.

a Calculate the total number of deaths.

b Calculate estimates for the mean and standard deviation of the age of death (use 90 as the mid-point of the last group).

Age in years, x	Frequency, f (1000s)
0−5	2.48
5−25	2.48
25−35	4.01
35−45	5.9
45−55	13.6
55−65	29.1
65−75	66.1
75−85	90.5
85+	50.4

Shapes of distributions

Most naturally occurring sets of data will produce a bar chart or histogram with shape similar to one of these three examples.

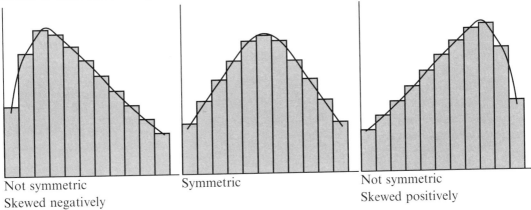

Not symmetric
Skewed negatively

Symmetric

Not symmetric
Skewed positively

Investigate

For this investigation you may use primary or secondary data.

♦ Collect samples of about 50 readings from your data source. Construct a frequency table and display the results in a bar chart or histogram. Try to produce at least one diagram that is similar to each of the three shapes.

  ▶ For each sample, comment briefly on the shape of your diagram.

  ▶ Without calculating the two types of average, which is the larger: the mean or the median?

  ▶ Which would be the better average: the mean or the median?

  ▶ Comment generally on when to use the mean or the median as the best average.

♦ Calculate the mean and standard deviation of each sample and mark the points $(\bar{x} - 2\sigma)$, $\bar{x}$ and $(\bar{x} + 2\sigma)$ onto your diagram. Comment on the percentage of the sample that does not lie between $(\bar{x} - 2\sigma)$ and $(\bar{x} + 2\sigma)$.

Exercise 88 (Revision)

1 It took eight students the following number of attempts to pass their driving tests:

   3   5   5   1   2   2   2   4

   a Construct a calculation table and work out the mean and standard deviation.

   b Give the mean and standard deviation of the number of *failures* for each student.

2 The following statistics have been calculated:

$$n = 11, \qquad \Sigma x = 84, \qquad \Sigma(x - \bar{x})^2 = 388\tfrac{6}{11}$$

   where x = the goals scored in a season by each player in a hockey team. Calculate these.

   a the mean   **b** the standard deviation   **c** Σx^2

3 95% of a large sample of cooking apples weigh between 200 and 250 g. Calculate estimates for the mean and standard deviation of the weight of this type of apple.

Exercise 88★ (Revision)

1 For each set of figures, construct a calculation table to work out the mean and standard deviation. Selecting the best formula, calculate σ.

   a   8   13   12   9   9   8   11   10

   b   5   5   6   7   8   8   8

2 The mean and variance of this set of numbers are 9 and 12 respectively. Calculate the values of x and y.

   x y 13   5   5   11   10   6   9   6

3 The scores from the first 30 throws of a die in a game are listed below

   1   4   6   5   3   2   1   1   2   5
   4   3   3   2   6   6   4   3   5   5
   2   1   1   3   4   6   2   2   1   4

   a Construct a frequency table of the scores.

   b Calculate the mean and standard deviation of the scores.

UNIT 5 ♦ Measures of spread

386

SELECTED ANSWERS

UNIT 1

Number 1

EXERCISE 1 (page 2)

1 **a** 4 days **b** 2 days **c** $2\frac{2}{3}$ days

3 **a** 8 men **b** 16 men **c** 32 men

5 **a** 60 years **b** 15 years **c** 1200 years

7 **a** 12 hours **b** 72 km/hour

EXERCISE 1★ (page 3)

1 **a**

Number of light bulbs (N)	Power of each bulb (P)
6	**500**
5	600
2	**1500**
30	100
N	P

b $3000 = NP$

3 **a** $12\ \mathrm{g/cm^3}$ **b** $1.5\ \mathrm{cm^3}$

5

Number of men	Number of tunnels	Time in years
100 000	4	**4**
100 000	**2**	2
20 000	8	**40**
400 000	2	0.5

7 **a** 5 **b** 1000 **c** 2.26×10^8 tonnes

EXERCISE 2 (page 5)

1 0.375 3 0.08 5 0.28125

7 $0.\dot{2}$ 9 $0.1\dot{8}$ 11 $0.2\dot{6}$

13 $0.3\dot{8}$ 15 $\frac{9}{16}$ 17 $\frac{3}{20}, \frac{5}{64}$

19 $\frac{1}{3}$ 21 $\frac{5}{9}$ 23 $\frac{7}{9}$

25 $\frac{7}{90}$ 27 $\frac{1}{30}$ 29 $\frac{1}{18}$

EXERCISE 2★ (page 6)

1 $0.4\dot{6}$ 3 $0.04\dot{6}$ 5 $2.\dot{3}\dot{0}$

7 $0.3\dot{0}\dot{1}$ 9 $\frac{11}{16}, \frac{7}{40}, \frac{3}{15}$ 11 $\frac{19}{20}, \frac{3}{25}, \frac{5}{64}$

13 $\frac{24}{99}$ 15 $\frac{10}{33}$ 17 $9\frac{19}{990}$

19 $\frac{3}{110}$ 21 $\frac{412}{999}$ 23 $\frac{128}{333}$

Algebra 1

EXERCISE 4 (page 10)

1 **a** $y = 5x$ **b** 30 **c** 5

3 **a** $y = 2x$ **b** 10 cm **c** 7.5 kg

5 1950 sales

EXERCISE 4★ (page 10)

1 **a** $v = 9.8t$ **b** 49 m/s **c** 2.5 s

3 **a** $d = 150m$ **b** 1500 km **c** 266.7 g

5 **a** $h = 3y/2$ **b** 0.75 m **c** 4 months

EXERCISE 5 (page 13)

1 **a** $y = 4x^2$ **b** 144 **c** 4

3 **a** $v = 2w^3$ **b** 54 **c** 4

5 **a** $y = 5t^2$ **b** 45 m **c** $\sqrt{20}\,\mathrm{s} \simeq 4.47\,\mathrm{s}$

EXERCISE 5★ (page 14)

1

g	2	4	6
f	12	**48**	108

3 **a** $R = \left(\frac{5}{256}\right)s^2$ **b** 113 km/hour

EXERCISE 6 (page 16)

1 **a** $y = \dfrac{12}{x}$ **b** $y = 6$ **c** $x = 4$

3 **a** $m = \dfrac{36}{n^2}$ **b** $m = 9$ **c** $n = 6$

5 **a** $I = 4 \times \dfrac{10^5}{d^2}$ **b** 0.1 candle-power

EXERCISE 6★ (page 17)

1

b	2	5	10
a	50	**8**	2

3 **a** $R = \dfrac{2}{r^2}$ **b** $\frac{2}{9}$ ohm

5 **a**

Day	N	t
Mon	400	25
Tues	**447**	20
Wed	500	**16**

b 407 approx.

Graphs 1

EXERCISE 8 (page 22)

1 $-\frac{1}{2}$ 3 $\frac{1}{3}$ 5 3

7 $-\frac{2}{3}$ 9 $\frac{1}{2}, -2$ 11 $-3, \frac{1}{3}$

13 Neither

15 Parallel

17 Perpendicular

19 $y = \frac{x}{2} + 1$

21 a 2
   b $-\frac{1}{2}$
   c Product is -1 so yes
   d Centres miss, but balls touch

EXERCISE 8★ (page 24)

1 $-\frac{1}{4}$ 3 5   5 $-\frac{3}{2}$

7 $\frac{1}{6}$ 9 $\frac{3}{8}, -\frac{8}{3}$ 11 $\frac{5}{4}, -\frac{4}{5}$

13 $y = -\frac{x}{8} + 8.4$

15 $y = 3 - 3x$

17 a 7 m   b $-\frac{5}{4}$ c 8.2 m

EXERCISE 9 (page 26)

1 $x = 5$ 3 $x = 4$ 5 $x = 2$

7

x	1	2	3	4	5
y	2	4	8	16	32

9 3 people

11 a

Day number (d)	Number of bacteria (b)
1	3
2	9
3	27
4	81
5	243
6	729

b $b = 3^d$ c 13 days

EXERCISE 9★ (page 27)

1 $x = 9$ 3 $x = 2$ 5 $x = 3$

7

x	1	2	3	4	5
y	10	20	40	80	160

9 a 16, 64 grains
   b $2^{63} \simeq 9 \times 10^{18}$ grains
   c About 46 km^3

Shape and space 1

EXERCISE 11 (page 33)

1 Yes, SAS

3 No

5 Yes, RHS

7 AB = XY, BC = YZ, ∠CAB = ∠ZXY

9 1 BE = DE (Given)
   2 AE = CE (**Given**)
   3 ∠AEB = ∠CED (**Vert. opp**)
   ∴ △ABE ≡ △CDE (**SAS**)
    ∴ ∠EDC = ∠**EBA**
     ∠ECD = ∠**EAB**
    and AB = **DC**

EXERCISE 11★ (page 35)

1 1 WX = YZ (**Opp. sides of parallelogram**)
   2 WZ = YX (**Opp. sides of parallelogram**)
   3 WY is common
    ∴ △WXY ≡ △YZW (**SSS**)
     ∴ ∠WXY = ∠**YZW**
      ∠XWY = ∠**ZYW**
    and ∠XYW = ∠**ZWY**

3 △ADE ≡ △BCE (SAS)
   ∴ AD = BC

5 △APY ≡ △BPZ (RHS)
   ∴ ∠AYP = ∠BZP
   ∴ △XYZ is isosceles
    ∴ XY = XZ

7 △BMO ≡ △BNO (SSS)
   ∴ ∠MBO = ∠NBO

9 △s EBF, FCG, GDH, HAE are congruent (SAS)
   ∴ EFGH is a square.

11 △POX ≡ △POY (RHS)
   ∴ PX = PY

EXERCISE 12 (page 41)

1 100°   3 45°   5 280°   7 60°   9 60°

11 ∠ADB and ∠BCA are angles in the same segment

13 LKMN is an isosceles trapezium

EXERCISE 12★ (page 42)

1 140°   3 115°   5 54°   7 119°   9 $3x$

11 ∠ADB = $x°$ (△ABD is isosceles),
   ∠BDC = $(180 - 4x)°$ (△BCD is isosceles)
   ∴ ∠ADC = $(180 - 3x)°$
   ∴ ∠ADC + ∠ABC = 180° so quadrilateral is concyclic

13 ∠BEC = ∠CDB (angles in the same segment)
   ∴ ∠CEA = ∠BDA

EXERCISE 13 (page 44)

1 70°   **3** 30°   **5** 50°   **7** 100°
9 a 90°   **b** 60°   **c** 60°   **d** 60°
11 a ∠NTM = ∠**NPT** (Alternate segment)
   b ∠PLT = ∠**NTM** (Corresponding angles)
13 a ∠ATC = ∠**ABT** (Alternate segment)
   b ∠ABT = ∠BTD (**AB parallel to CD**)

EXERCISE 13★ (page 47)

1 65°   **3** 140°
5 ∠ATE = 55° (alternate segment),
   ∠TBC = 125° (angles on straight line),
   ∠BTC = 35° (angle sum of triangle),
   ∠ATB = 90° (angles on straight line)
   ∴ AB is a diameter
7 a 56°   **b** 68°
9 a 55°   **b** 35°
   c ∠ADE = 70° (angle sum of triangle),
   ∠ACD = 35° (angle sum of triangle),
   ∴ △ACD is isosceles
11 20°
13 a Triangles ACG and ABF are right angled.
   b Angles ACG and ABF are equal and in the
   same segment of the chord FG.

Handling data 1

EXERCISE 15 (page 54)

1 Not enough evidence, could just be a
   'naturally occurring freak' result!
3 Sample is too small, unreliable conclusion.
   Collect more data!
5 40% of the *drivers who had accidents*! Only a
   small percentage of *all drivers*.
7 Only passengers with 'an axe to grind' bother
   to reply.

EXERCISE 16 (page 57)

1 a 3, 37   **b** 2.25 → 2, 27.75 → 28
3 a Bus A = 3, Bus B = 4   **b** 5 boys, 2 girls
5 Services 25.72 → 26, Manufacturing 6.44 → 6,
   Government 4.2 → 4, Energy and Agriculture
   0.84 → 1, Unemployed 2.8 → 3

7

France		75
Irish Republic		15
Netherlands		5
Belgium	1.67	2
Spain and Portugal	1.67	1*
Germany, Baltic and Scandinavia	1.67	2

*One needs to be rounded down.

EXERCISE 16★ (page 59)

1 a 12   **b** 16.87 → 17
3 a 13, 14, 16, 7   **b** 28, 22
   c

7	6
8	6
9	7
4	3

5 27 656–28 562
7 a 99   **b** 6

Numeracy practice 1

NUMBER (page 64)

1 67   **3** 58   **5** 38.06
7 −1.6   **9** 46.13   **11** 0.49
13 3   **15** 216   **17** 10^{-1}
19 13   **21** $5\frac{13}{21}$ **23** $\frac{36}{49}$
25 2.7×10^5 **27** 0.0469   **29** $\frac{1}{6}$
31 $\frac{1}{5}$ **33** $\frac{6}{7}$

ALGEBRA (page 64)

1 $6x^2$ **3** $8x^4$
5 $2a$ **7** $x^3 - 3x$
9 $2ab(2b - 3a)$ **11** $(x - 2)(x + 1)$
13 $x = 23$ **15** $x = 0.9$
17 $x = 3.25$ **19** $x = \pm2$
21 12   **23** $-3\frac{1}{4}$
25 25

UNIT 2

Number 2

EXERCISE 18 (page 75)

1 $\frac{1}{9}$ **3** 9   **5** $\frac{1}{64}$
7 3   **9** 2   **11** $\frac{1}{16}$
13 $\frac{1}{9}$ **15** $\frac{1}{16}$ **17** $\frac{1}{2}$
19 16   **21** 625   **23** 2.84
25 0.167   **27** 0.0123   **29** 46 700
31 0.0370   **33** 0.111   **35** 64
37 a **39** c^{-3} **41** e
43 a^{-2} **45** b^{-5} **47** c^2

EXERCISE 18★ (page 75)

1 $\frac{1}{64}$ **3** 5   **5** 1

7 512 **9** 12.5 **11** 4

13 10 **15** 8 **17** $\dfrac{1}{2}$

19 $\dfrac{1}{36}$ **21** 0.364 **23** 1.92

25 0.001 37 **27** a^2 **29** $2c^{-4}$

31 $3a^{-2}$ **33** $12a^{-1}$ **35** a

37 c^{-1} **39** 2 **41** 2

43 -3

EXERCISE 19 (page 77)

1 $\dfrac{1}{5}$ **3** $\dfrac{1}{5}$ **5** 8 **7** $\dfrac{1}{8}$

9 0.408 **11** 0.316 **13** 11.2 **15** 0.192

17 a^2 **19** c^3 **21** e^2

EXERCISE 19★ (page 77)

1 $\dfrac{1}{6}$ **3** 6 **5** 16

7 $\dfrac{1}{16}$ **9** 1.29 **11** 0.894

13 2.85 **15** 0.351 **17** a^{-2}

19 c^{-2} **21** e **23** 9

EXERCISE 20 (page 78)

1 3 **3** 27 **5** $\dfrac{2}{3}$ **7** $2\sqrt{2}$

9 $3\sqrt{5}$ **11** $2\sqrt{7}$ **13** $\sqrt{50}$ **15** $\sqrt{24}$

17 $\sqrt{28}$ **19** $7\sqrt{3}$ **21** 12 **23** $\sqrt{\dfrac{5}{2}}$

EXERCISE 20★ (page 79)

1 $2\sqrt{11}$ **3** $10\sqrt{10}$ **5** $\sqrt{125}$

7 $\sqrt{\dfrac{1}{2}}$ **9** $8\sqrt{2}$ **11** 60

13 $\dfrac{1}{2}$ **15** $7\sqrt{2}$ **17** 0

19 $5-\sqrt{3}$ **21** $9+4\sqrt{5}$ **23** $\dfrac{\sqrt{2}}{2}$

25 $2\sqrt{2}$ **27** $3\sqrt{2}$ **29** $\dfrac{\sqrt{3}}{3}$

EXERCISE 21 (page 81)

1 R, $\dfrac{57}{10}$ **3** R, $\dfrac{2}{1}$ **5** I

7 R, $\dfrac{7}{1}$ **9** I **11** I

13 e.g. 2 **15** e.g. $\sqrt{50}$

EXERCISE 21★ (page 82)

1 I **3** I **5** R, $\dfrac{2}{5}$

7 R, $\dfrac{9}{10}$ **9** R, 2 **11** R, $\dfrac{2}{1}$

13 e.g. $\sqrt{2}$ **15** e.g. $\sqrt{7}$

17 a e.g. 3, 4, 5 **b** e.g. $\sqrt{6}$, $\sqrt{30}$, 6

 c e.g. 2, 3, $\sqrt{13}$ **d** e.g. 2, $\sqrt{32}$, 6

Algebra 2

EXERCISE 23 (page 85)

1 a 7.07 cm² **b** $\dfrac{\pi x^2}{4}$

3 a 12.5 cm² **b** $x^2\left(4+\dfrac{\pi}{2}\right)$

5 a 25.7 cm **b** $x(2+\pi)$

7 a 48 cm² **b** $12x^2$

EXERCISE 23★ (page 86)

1 a 37.3 cm² **b** $x^2(1+\pi)$

3 a 14.8 cm **b** $x(2.5\pi+2)$

5 a 236 cm² **b** $3\pi x^2$

EXERCISE 24 (page 91)

1 a 9.77 cm **b** 67.0 cm

3 a 15.7 cm² **b** 314 cm²

5 a 44.0 cm² **b** 286 cm²

EXERCISE 24★ (page 92)

1 $r=19.5$ cm **3** $r=13.3$ cm

5 $r=33.1$ cm **7** 57.0 m

9 36.7 cm **11** 3.37 cm²

EXERCISE 25 (page 97)

1 a 56.5 m³ **b** 56.5 m²

3 a 6.37 cm **b** $h=49.6$ cm **c** 2110 cm³

5 17.5 cm

7 4.92 cm

EXERCISE 25★ (page 98)

1 12.7 cm **3** 6.20 cm **5** 8 cm

7 $h=r$ **9** 729 cm² **11** 0.796 cm

13 a 170 cm³

 b 195 cm²

15 a 6.16 cm

 b 626 cm²

EXERCISE 26 (page 103)

1 72 cm² **3** 135 cm³ **5** £160 **7** £40

EXERCISE 26★ (page 104)

1 31.25 cm³

3 a 25 cm **b** 48 g

5 $x=54$

7 $h=4.76$

9 75 cm²

Graphs 2

EXERCISE 28 (page 112)

1 $x^2 + y^2 = 16$
3 $x^2 + y^2 = 0.25$
5 $(0, 0); 9$
7 $x^2 + y^2 = 9$
9 $x^2 + y^2 = 52$
11 $x^2 + y^2 = 29$

EXERCISE 28★ (page 113)

1 $(x + 2)^2 + (y - 6)^2 = 64$
3 $(x - 3)^2 + (y + 9)^2 = 49$
5 $(-4, 7); 10$
7 $(x - 1)^2 + y^2 = 16$
9 $(x - 1)^2 + (y - 2)^2 = 25$
11 $(x + 4)^2 + (y + 4)^2 = 16$;
$(x + 4)^2 + (y - 4)^2 = 16$;
$(x - 4)^2 + (y - 4)^2 = 16$;
$(x - 4)^2 + (y + 4)^2 = 16$

EXERCISE 29 (page 115)

1 $x = -2.2$ or $x = 2.2$
3 $x = -1$ or $x = 2$
5 $x = -3.8$ or $x = 1.8$
7 $x = 0.6$ or $x = 3.4$
9 $x = -2.9$ or $x = 3.4$
11 No solutions

EXERCISE 29★ (page 116)

1 $x = -1.3$ or $x = 2.3$
3 $x = -2.6$ or $x = -0.4$
5 $x = 2$
7 $x = -2.7$ or $x = 2.2$
9 $x = -2.8$ or $x = 3.2$
11 No solutions

EXERCISE 30 (page 118)

1 a $x = 0$ or $x = 3$
  b $x = -0.56$ or $x = 3.56$
  c $x = 0.38$ or $x = 2.62$
  d $x = -0.24$ or $x = 4.24$
  e $x = -0.79$ or $x = 3.79$
  f $x = 0.21$ or $x = 4.79$
3 a $x = 1$ or $x = 3$
  b $x = -0.65$ or $x = 4.65$
  c $x = 0.70$ or $x = 4.30$
  d $x = -0.56$ or $x = 3.56$
5 a $2x^2 + 2x - 1 = 0$ b $x^2 + 5x - 5 = 0$
7 a $y = 2x + 2$ b $y = x$
  c $y = -3x - 3$
9 $(2.71, 3.5)$, no

EXERCISE 30★ (page 119)

1 a $x = 5$ or $x = 0$
  b $x = 4.30$ or $x = 0.70$
  c $x = 3.73$ or $x = 0.27$
  d $x = 0.76$ or $x = 5.24$
3 a $x = -1.78$ or $x = 0.28$
  b $x = -2.35$ or $x = 0.85$
  c $x = -2.28$ or $x = -0.22$
5 a $6x^2 - 7x - 2 = 0$ b $5x^2 - 7x - 4 = 0$
7 a $y = x + 2$ b $y = -2x - 1$

EXERCISE 31 (page 121)

1 a $x = -1.73$, $x = 0$ or $x = 1.73$
  b $x = -1.53$, $x = -0.35$ or $x = 1.9$
  c $x = -1.62$, $x = 0.62$ or $x = 1$
3 a $x = -0.53$, $x = 0.65$ or $x = 2.88$
  b $x = -1$ or $x = 2$
  c $x = -1.11$, $x = 1.25$ or $x = 2.86$
5 $x = -1$ or $x = 3$

EXERCISE 31★ (page 121)

1 a $x = 1.78$
  b $x = -3.30$, $x = -1.05$, $x = 1.05$ or $x = 3.30$
  c $x = -2.84$, $x = -1.46$ or $x = 0.96$
3 $y = 3x + 8$
5 $x = -1.25$, $x = 0.45$ or $x = 1.80$

EXERCISE 32 (page 123)

1 $x = -1.7$, $y = 5$; $x = 1.7$, $y = 5$
3 $x = -3$, $y = -5$; $x = 1$, $y = 3$
5 $x = 2$, $y = 7$; $x = -1$, $y = -2$
7 $x = 2$, $y = 2$; $x = 4$, $y = 6$
9 $x = -1.46$ and $y = 1.37$; or
  $x = 1.93$ and $y = 0.52$
11 $x = -1.56$ and $y = -2.56$; or
  $x = 2.56$ and $y = 1.56$
13 $x = -2$ and $y = 0$; or $x = -0.71$ and $y = 0.65$;
  or $x = 0.71$ and $y = 1.35$
15 a $x^2 + y^2 = 16$
   b $y = -3$
   c $x = -2.65$ and $y = -3$; or $x = 2.65$ and
     $y = -3$; diameter 5.30 cm
17 $x = 23.7$ and $y = 21.8$

EXERCISE 32★ (page 125)

1 $x = 1$, $y = 3$; $x = -2$, $y = 3$
3 $x = 2$, $y = -3$; $x = -3$, $y = 7$
5 $x = -2$, $y = 8$; $x = 2.5$, $y = 3.5$
7 $x = -0.5$, $y = -3$; $x = 0.4$, $y = -1.2$
9 $x = -1.93$ and $y = -0.86$; or $x = 0.73$ and
  $y = 4.46$
11 $x = -0.48$ and $y = 3.96$; or $x = 1.31$ and
  $y = 0.38$; or $x = 3.17$ and $y = 3.34$
13 $x = -1.23$ and $y = -4.14$; or $x = 1.63$ and
  $y = 10.1$
15 a $(x - 4)^2 + (y - 3)^2 = 4$
   b $(2.54, 1.64)$, $(5.93, 2.48)$
   c 3.5 s

Shape and space 2

EXERCISE 34 (page 130)

1 $x = 170°$
3 $x = 340°$
5 $x = 220°$

7 $x = 330°$

9 $x = 340°$

11 $x = 17.5°, 163°$

13 $x = 72.5°, 288°$

15 $x = 71.6°, 252°$

17 $x = 107°, 253°$

19 $x = 198°, 343°$

21 $x = 108°, 288°$

EXERCISE 34★ (page 131)

1 $x = 154°$

3 $x = -140°, -40°, 320°$

5 $x = -45°, 315°$

7 $x = 95°, 265°$

9 $x = -133°, 227°$

11 $x = 130°, 310°$

13 $x = 27.2°, 153°$

15 $x = -153°, -27.2°, 207°, 333°$

17 $x = -75.7°, 75.7°, 284°$

19 $x = -112°, 112°, 248°$

21 $x = -112°, 67.9°, 248$

23 $x = -55.5°, 125°, 305°$

EXERCISE 35 (page 134)

1 $x = 15°, 75°$

3 $x = -41°, 41°$

5 $x = 36°$

EXERCISE 35★ (page 134)

1 **a** $x = 19°, 71°, 200°, 250°$

c $180°$

5 **a** $y = -1.4, x = 220°$

b $x = 110°, 340°$

EXERCISE 36 (page 138)

1 $x = 5.94$

3 $MN = 39.0 \, cm$

5 $AC = 37.8 \, cm$

7 $x = 37.3°$

9 $\angle ABC = 38.8°$

11 $\angle ACB = 62.2°$

13 $13.5 \, km$

EXERCISE 36★ (page 139)

1 $x = 29.7$

3 $\angle LMN = 67.4°, 113°$

5 $EF = 10.4 \, cm, \angle DEF = 47.5°, \angle FDE = 79.0°$

7 $BC = 261 \, m$

9 $PR = 115 \, m; 112°$

EXERCISE 37 (page 143)

1 $x = 7.26$

3 $AB = 39.1 \, cm$

5 $RT = 24.2 \, cm$

7 $X = 73.4°$

9 $\angle ABC = 92.9°$

11 $\angle BAC = 81.8°$

13 $11.6 \, km$

EXERCISE 37★ (page 144)

1 $x = 9.34$

3 $\angle XYZ = 95.5°$

5 $QR = 4.18 \, cm, \angle PQR = 39.2°, \angle QRP = 62.8°$

7 $8.72 \, cm, 5.29 \, cm$

9 $BC = 23.4 \, km; 186°$

11 $\angle XZY = 38.1°; WX = 29.3 \, cm$

EXERCISE 38 (page 148)

1 $NW = 5 \, cm; 58.0°$ **3** $NA = 6.40 \, cm; 51.3°$

5 $53.1°$ **7** $39.1°$

9 **a** $18.4°$ **b** $AE = 500 \, m$ **c** $11.3°$

11 **a** $RT = 8.49 \, m$ **b** $62.1°$

c $VT = 9.06 \, m$

EXERCISE 38★ (page 149)

1 $NA = 4.72 \, cm; 5.17 \, cm$

3 $AN = 6.52 \, cm; 46.7°$

5 $58.5°$

7 **a** $127 \, m$ **b** $CA = 490$ **c** $AD = 387 \, m$

9 $61.9°$

11 **a** $54.7°$ **b** $35.3°$ **c** $70.5°$

13 **a** $53.1°$ **b** $62.6°$

EXERCISE 39 (page 152)

1 $O(0, 0, 0), E(5, 0, 3); (5, 0, 1.5); (2.5, 1.5, 0)$

3 $B(5, 3, 0), G(0, 3, 3); (2.5, 3, 0); (2.5, 3, 1.5)$

5 **a** $OB = 5.83 \, units$ **b** $27.2°$

7 $P(0, -3, 0), Q(-4, -3, 0), S(0, -3, 2);$
$OS = 3.61 \, units; 33.7°$

9 $(0, -1.5, 2); OQ = 5 \, units; 21.8°$

EXERCISE 39★ (page 153)

1 $P(-5, 0, 0), Q(-5, 0, -4); LP = 5 \, units; 25.1°$

3 $(-5, 0, -2); OX = 3.20 \, units; 38.7°$

5 $X(-2.5, 0, -2); JX = 4.39 \, units; 43.1°$

7 **a** $3.61 \, units$

b $7 \, units$

EXERCISE 40★ (page 154)

1 $EG = 20 \, cm; \angle JEG = 43.5°$

3 $EG = 17.1 \, m; EP = 13.7 \, m$

5 $BD = 10 \, cm; \angle DXB = 32.4°$

7 $\angle GED = 37.5°$

Handling data 2

EXERCISE 42 (page 161)

1 f.d.: 0.20, 0.40, 0.90, 0.60, 0.45, 0.05

3 **a** f.d.: 1.75, 3.5, 5.0, 12, 19, 8.0, 4.5

b 13–14 lbs

c 55%

5 **a** f.d.: 3.5, 9.5, 12, 13.6, 10.4, 2.5

c $\bar{x} = 26.8 \, years$

EXERCISE 42★ (page 163)

1 a f.d.: 0.04, 0.07, 0.087, 0.113, 0.024, 0.012
  b 51.4% **c** $\bar{x} = 368.5$

3 a f.d.: 10, 13, 15, 15, 13, 7, 7
  b $\bar{x} = 9.77$ yrs
  c 6.5 cm, 7.5 cm, 7.5 cm, 6.5 cm, 3.5 cm, 3.5 cm

5 a 522 customers
  b £1566
  c $\bar{x} = 52.5$ customers per hour. Not a useful statistic
  d 10.00–12.00, 1 staff; 12.00–14.00, 4 staff; 14.00–18.00, 2 staff; 18.00–20.00, 3 staff

7 a 6, 8
  b f.d.: 36, 17, 6, 1
  c $\bar{x} = 97.7$ min

Numeracy practice 2

Number (page 168)

1 0.067	**3** 0.453	**5** −55.2
7 259	**9** 60.32	**11** 0.36
13 5	**15** 45	**17** 216
19 0.391	**21** 33	**23** 60
25 50	**27** 1	

Algebra (page 168)

1 $\dfrac{2a}{b}$ **3** $\dfrac{y^3}{z}$ **5** $\dfrac{3+x}{2}$

7 $\dfrac{5y}{2x}$ **9** $(x-2)(x-3)$

11 $3ab^2(2a^2 - 9b)$ **13** $x = \dfrac{c-b}{a}$

15 $x = \dfrac{c}{a} + b$ **17** $x = \dfrac{by}{a+c}$

19 8   **21** 1

23 7   **25** 4

UNIT 3

Number 3

EXERCISE 44 (page 185)

1 £226, £11 752
3 £6.08
5 £3176.70; £1401.94
7 £8668.40; £2610.97
9 a £111.30 **b** £61.10 **c** £34.90
11 a £17.87 **b** £2.09 **c** £256.91

EXERCISE 44★ (page 186)

1 a £67 331.60 **b** £1294.84 **c** 32.67%
3 a £7068.40; £2410.97 **b** 31.6%

EXERCISE 45 (page 189)

1 a £270
  b £1815.48
3 12.68%
5 26.82%
7 34.49%
9 1.17%
11 1.53%
13 2.21%
15 £9.74
17 a £297.17 **b** £14 483.10 **c** £3323.10

EXERCISE 45★ (page 190)

1 a £4.85 **b** £4.63
3 a £40.91 **b** 4.99% **c** £231.47
5 Net = 4.485%, less than inflation. He can buy less!
7 £25 000 **a** $36 250 **b** $43 750
9 a 8.25% **b** £278.95

Algebra 3

EXERCISE 47 (page 196)

1 $x = -5$ or $x = -2$ **3** $x = -3$ or $x = 5$
5 $x = 3$ **7** $x = -6$ or $x = 2$
9 $x = 0$ or $x = 4$ **11** $x = -6$ or $x = 6$

EXERCISE 47★ (page 196)

1 $x = -8$ or $x = -7$
3 $x = -5$ or $x = 9$
5 $x = 7$
7 $x = -5$ or $x = 8$
9 $x = 0$ or $x = -17$
11 $x = -11$ or $x = 11$

EXERCISE 48 (page 197)

1 $x = 2$ or $x = 3$
3 $x = 0.5$ or $x = 2$
5 $x = -1.5$ or $x = -1$
7 $x = -2$ or $x = -1$
9 $x = -3$ or $x = 3$
11 $x = 0$ or $x = 2$
13 $x = -2$ or $x = -\frac{1}{3}$
15 $x = -\frac{1}{3}$ or $x = 2$
17 $x = -2$ or $x = 3$
19 $x = -2$ or $x = -\frac{2}{3}$
21 $x = -3$ or $x = -\frac{1}{4}$
23 $x = -\frac{1}{3}$ or $x = 1.5$
25 $x = -\frac{1}{2}$ or $x = -\frac{1}{4}$
27 $x = \frac{2}{5}$ or $x = 5$
29 $x = 0.8$ or $x = 1.5$

EXERCISE 48★ (page 197)

1 $x = 1$ or $x = 2$
3 $x = 1.5$ or $x = 2$
5 $x = -9$ or $x = -\frac{4}{3}$
7 $x = -\frac{4}{3}$ or $x = 7$
9 $x = -4$ or $x = 4$
11 $x = 0$ or $x = 3$
13 $x = -5$ (repeated root)
15 $x = 0.25$ or $x = 7$
17 $x = \frac{2}{3}$ or $x = 1.5$
19 $x = \frac{5}{3}$ (repeated root)

EXERCISE 49 (page 199)

1 $x = -3.45$ or $x = 1.45$
3 $x = -1.65$ or $x = 3.65$
5 $x = -5.46$ or $x = 1.46$
7 $x = 1.84$ or $x = 8.16$
9 $x = -14.2$ or $x = 0.211$
11 $x = -1.53$ or $x = 21.5$

EXERCISE 49★ (page 200)

1 $x = 0.171$ or $x = 5.83$
3 $x = 0.190$ or $x = 15.8$
5 $x = -7.58$ or $x = 1.58$
7 $x = -1.69$ or $x = 7.69$
9 $x = -0.414$ or $x = 2.41$
11 $x = 0.258$ or $x = 7.74$
13 $x = -1$ or $x = 3.5$
15 $x = -1.86$ or $x = -0.537$
17 $x = -2.77$ or $x = 0.271$
19 $x = -0.522$ or $x = 1.09$

EXERCISE 50 (page 201)

1 $x = -3.37$ or $x = 2.37$
3 $x = -1.83$ or $x = 3.83$
5 $x = -1.58$ or $x = -0.423$
7 $x = -1.13$ or $x = 0.883$
9 $x = -2.79$ or $x = 1.79$
11 $x = 0.172$ or $x = 5.83$
13 $x = 1.30$ or $x = -0.876$
15 $x = 0.310$ or $x = 1.29$
17 4.61 cm
19 At 1.55 seconds and 6.45 seconds

EXERCISE 50★ (page 201)

1 $x = -12.7$ or $x = 0.315$
3 $x = 1.59$ or $x = 4.41$
5 $x = -\frac{1}{3}$ or $x = 2$
7 $x = 0.137$ or $x = 1.46$
9 $x = -0.257$ or $x = 2.59$
11 $x = 3.11$ or $x = -1.61$

13 $x = 0.105$ or $x = 5.37$
15 $x = -2.16$ or $x = 1.16$
17 2.32 m by 4.43 m
19 1414 numbers

EXERCISE 51 (page 203)

1 1   3 0   5 0   7 2   9 0

EXERCISE 51★ (page 204)

1 2   3 2   5 1   7 2   9 2

EXERCISE 52 (page 206)

1 $x = 1, y = 2$ or $x = 2, y = 3$
3 $x = -3.45, y = -7.90$ or $x = 1.45, y = 1.90$
5 $x = -0.2, y = 1.4$ or $x = 1, y = -1$
7 $x = -2, y = -1.5$ or $x = 3, y = 1$
9 $x = -2.87, y = 4.87$ or $x = 0.871, y = 1.13$
11 $x = 1, y = -1$
13 $x = 2.17, y = 0.172$ or $x = 7.83, y = 5.83$
15 a $x^2 + y^2 = 30^2$
　 b $y = 3$
　 c $x = 29.85$ and $y = 3$
　 d 29.85 cm

EXERCISE 52★ (page 207)

1 $x = -1.54, y = -4.17$ or $x = 4.54, y = 20.2$
3 $x = 1, y = 0$ or $x = 7, y = -12$
5 $x = -2, y = 2$ or $x = -1, y = 3$
7 $x = \frac{2}{3}, y = \frac{1}{3}$ or $x = \frac{1}{3}, y = \frac{2}{3}$
9 $(6, -6)$; tangent

Graphs 3

EXERCISE 54 (page 210)

1 a $f(3) = 7$　b $f(-2) = -3$
　 c $f(x+2) = 2x+5$　d $f(x) + 2 = 2x + 3$
3 a $f(1) = 1$　b $f(-4) = -19$
　 c $f(2x) = 8x - 3$　d $2f(x) = 8x - 6$
5 a $f(-3) = 6$　b $f(-x) = 3 + x$
　 c $f(-3x) = 3 = 3x$　d $-3f(x) = 3x - 9$
7 a $f(-1) = -1$
　 b $f(x-1) = x^2 - 1$
　 c $f(x-1) + 1 = x^2$
　 d $1 - f(x-1) = 2 - x^2$

EXERCISE 54★ (page 211)

1 a $f(-2) = 5$
　 b $f(x+2) = x^2 + 4x + 5$
　 c $f(x) + 2 = x^2 + 3$
　 d $f(x+2) + 2 = x^2 + 4x + 7$
3 a $f(-x) = 2x^2 - 2$
　 b $-f(x) = 2 - 2x^2$
　 c $f(2x) = 8x^2 - 2$
　 d $2f(x) = 4x^2 - 4$

5 a $f(3x) = 9x - 9x^2$
  b $3f(x) = 9x - 3x^2$
  c $3f(-x) = -9x - 3x^2$
  d $f(-3x) = -9x - 9x^2$

7 a $\dfrac{1}{f(x)} = x^2$ **b** $f\left(\dfrac{1}{x}\right) = x^2$

  c $\dfrac{1}{f(1/x)} = \dfrac{1}{x^2}$

EXERCISE 55★   (page 214)

1

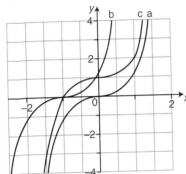

3

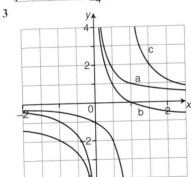

5

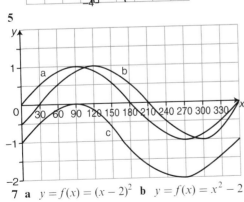

7 a $y = f(x) = (x-2)^2$ **b** $y = f(x) = x^2 - 2$

EXERCISE 56   (page 218)

1 a Reflection in x-axis
  b Reflection in y-axis
3 a Stretch with scale factor $\frac{1}{2}$ parallel to x-axis
  b Stretch with scale factor $\frac{1}{2}$ parallel to y-axis

5

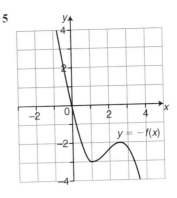

7

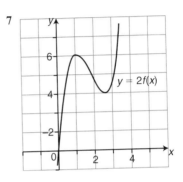

9

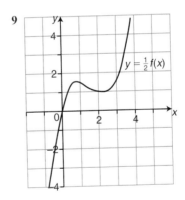

11

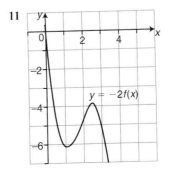

13

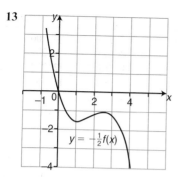

$y = -\frac{1}{2}f(x)$

EXERCISE 56★ (page 219)

1 a Stretch with scale factor 2 parallel to y-axis
 b Stretch with scale factor 2 parallel to x-axis
3 a $(3, 0), (0, 4), (-1, 3)$
 b $(6, 0), (0, 2), \left(-2, 1\frac{1}{2}\right)$
5 a $f(x) = -x^3$ b $f(x) = -x^3$
7 a $g(x) = -f(x)$ b $h(x) = f(-x)$
 c $j(x) = 2f(x)$

Shape and space 3

EXERCISE 58 (page 226)

1 a $\overrightarrow{XY} = \mathbf{x}$ b $\overrightarrow{EO} = 4\mathbf{y}$
 c $\overrightarrow{WC} = -8\mathbf{y}$ d $\overrightarrow{TP} = -4\mathbf{x}$
3 a $\overrightarrow{HJ}$ b $\overrightarrow{HN}$ c $\overrightarrow{HL}$ d $\overrightarrow{HO}$
5 a $\overrightarrow{DC} = \mathbf{x}$ b $\overrightarrow{DB} = \mathbf{x} + \mathbf{y}$
 c $\overrightarrow{BC} = -\mathbf{y}$ d $\overrightarrow{AC} = \mathbf{x} - \mathbf{y}$
7 a $\overrightarrow{DC} = \mathbf{x}$ b $\overrightarrow{AC} = \mathbf{x} + \mathbf{y}$
 c $\overrightarrow{BD} = \mathbf{y} - \mathbf{x}$ d $\overrightarrow{AE} = \frac{1}{2}(\mathbf{x} + \mathbf{y})$
9 a $\overrightarrow{AB} = \mathbf{x} - \mathbf{y}$ b $\overrightarrow{AD} = 3\mathbf{x}$
 c $\overrightarrow{CF} = 2\mathbf{y} - 3\mathbf{x}$ d $\overrightarrow{CA} = \mathbf{y} - 3\mathbf{x}$
11 a $2\mathbf{x} + 4\mathbf{y}$ b $4\mathbf{y} - 2\mathbf{x}$
 c $2\mathbf{y} - 2\mathbf{x}$ d $3\mathbf{x} - 4\mathbf{y}$

EXERCISE 58★ (page 229)

1 a $\overrightarrow{AB} = \mathbf{y} - \mathbf{x}$ b $\overrightarrow{AM} = \frac{1}{2}(\mathbf{y} - \mathbf{x})$
 c $\overrightarrow{OM} = \frac{1}{2}(\mathbf{x} + \mathbf{y})$
3 $\overrightarrow{AB} = \mathbf{y} - \mathbf{x}$; $\overrightarrow{OD} = 2\mathbf{x}$; $\overrightarrow{DC} = 2\mathbf{y} - 2\mathbf{x}$
 d $DC = 2AB$ and they are parallel lines
5 a $\overrightarrow{AB} = \mathbf{y} - \mathbf{x}$; $\overrightarrow{OC} = -2\mathbf{x}$; $\overrightarrow{OD} = -2\mathbf{y}$;
 $\overrightarrow{DC} = 2\mathbf{y} - 2\mathbf{x}$
 b $DC = 2AB$ and they are parallel lines
7 $\overrightarrow{AB} = \mathbf{y} - \mathbf{x}$; $\overrightarrow{BC} = \mathbf{y} - 2\mathbf{x}$; $\overrightarrow{AD} = 2\mathbf{y} - 4\mathbf{x}$;
 $\overrightarrow{BD} = \mathbf{y} - 3\mathbf{x}$
9 a $\overrightarrow{MA} = \frac{3}{5}\mathbf{x}$; $\overrightarrow{AB} = \mathbf{y} - \mathbf{x}$; $\overrightarrow{AN} = \frac{3}{5}(\mathbf{y} - \mathbf{x})$;
 $\overrightarrow{MN} = \frac{3}{5}\mathbf{y}$
 b OB and MN are parallel; $\overrightarrow{MN} = \frac{3}{5}\overrightarrow{OB}$

EXERCISE 59 (page 232)

1 $\mathbf{p} + \mathbf{q} = \begin{pmatrix} 6 \\ 8 \end{pmatrix}$; $\mathbf{p} - \mathbf{q} = \begin{pmatrix} -2 \\ -2 \end{pmatrix}$; $2\mathbf{p} + 3\mathbf{q}\begin{pmatrix} 16 \\ 21 \end{pmatrix}$
3 $\mathbf{p} + \mathbf{q} = \begin{pmatrix} 4 \\ 6 \end{pmatrix}$; $\mathbf{p} - \mathbf{q} = \begin{pmatrix} -2 \\ -2 \end{pmatrix}$
 $2\mathbf{p} + 5\mathbf{q} = \begin{pmatrix} 17 \\ 24 \end{pmatrix}$
5 $\mathbf{v} + \mathbf{w} = \begin{pmatrix} 4 \\ 5 \end{pmatrix}$, $\sqrt{41}$; $2\mathbf{v} - \mathbf{w} = \begin{pmatrix} 5 \\ -2 \end{pmatrix}$, $\sqrt{29}$
 $\mathbf{v} - 2\mathbf{w} = \begin{pmatrix} 1 \\ -7 \end{pmatrix}$, $\sqrt{50}$
7 a Chloe $\begin{pmatrix} 5 \\ 7 \end{pmatrix}$; Leo $\begin{pmatrix} 4 \\ 5 \end{pmatrix}$; Max $\begin{pmatrix} 3 \\ 2 \end{pmatrix}$
 b Chloe: $\sqrt{74}$ km, 2.9 km/hour
 Leo: $\sqrt{41}$ km, 2.1 km/hour
 Max: $\sqrt{13}$ km, 1.2 km/hour

EXERCISE 59★ (page 233)

1 $\mathbf{p} + \mathbf{q} = \begin{pmatrix} 5 \\ 0 \end{pmatrix}$, 5, 090°
 $\mathbf{p} - \mathbf{q} = \begin{pmatrix} -1 \\ 2 \end{pmatrix}$, $\sqrt{5}$, 333°
 $2\mathbf{p} - 3\mathbf{q} = \begin{pmatrix} -5 \\ 5 \end{pmatrix}$, $\sqrt{50}$, 315°
3 $m = -1, n = -2$
5 a $\begin{pmatrix} 10.4 \\ 6 \end{pmatrix}$ km   b $\begin{pmatrix} 13 \\ -7.5 \end{pmatrix}$ km

Handling data 3

EXERCISE 61 (page 241)

1 a $\frac{1}{36}$ b $\frac{5}{18}$
3 a 0.655   b 0.345
5 a $\frac{2}{9}$ b $\frac{5}{9}$ c $\frac{1}{9}$

EXERCISE 61★ (page 242)

1 a $\frac{1}{11}$ b $\frac{1}{3}$ c $\frac{3}{11}$ d $\frac{9}{55}$
3 a $\frac{1}{16}$ b $\frac{1}{4}$ c $\frac{15}{16}$

Numeracy practice 3

Number (page 248)

1 1.869   3 29
5 49.84   7 3.4
9 44.99   11 162
13 1.2   15 10^{-1}
17 24   19 2
21 9.6   23 16
25 3.6×10^2 27 1.5×10^7

Algebra (page 248)

1 $-x^2$ **3** $8x^3y^3$ **5** $\dfrac{2a}{b}$

7 $x+2$ **9** $\dfrac{5a}{6}$ **11** $\dfrac{xy}{6}$

13 5 **15** 0.45 **17** 6.2 **19** ± 5
21 $7, -2$ **23** 4 **25** 64

UNIT 4

Numeracy practice 4

Number (page 300)

1 3028.5 **3** 7.9 **5** 4.2 **7** 1.69
9 31 **11** -2.99 **13** 0.5 **15** 800
17 62 000 **19** 6 **21** 0.997 **23** 0.375
25 $\dfrac{38}{99}$ **27** 4 **29** 2 **31** 0.08

Algebra (page 300)

1 $\dfrac{1}{ab}$ **3** $\dfrac{1}{3}$
5 a^{-4} **7** a^{-2}
9 4 **11** $2(x-1)(x+3)$
13 $(2x+y)(2x-y)$ **15** $a(a-b)(a+b)$
17 $x=3$ **19** $x=-2$ or $x=4$
21 $x > -2\frac{2}{3}$

Examination practice 4

Answers are not supplied for these papers but if
you need help, turn to the pages given.

Paper 4A (page 305)

1 266 **2** 286 **3** 286 **4** 280
5 293 **6** 264 **7** 285 **8** 270
9 53 **10** 294 **11** 158 **12** 266
13 84 **14** 33 **15** 210 **16** 111
17 74 **18** 44 **19** 206 **20** 198

Paper 4B (page 308)

1 265 **2** 273 **3** 294 **4** 272
5 273 **6** 55 **7** 266 **8** 224
9 264 **10** 279 **11** 25 **12** 279
13 132 **14** 273 **15** 293 **16** 95
17 280 **18** 152, 146 **19** 113 **20** 204

Paper 4C (page 313)

1 266 **2** 264 **3** 272 **4** 285
5 266 **6** 286 **7** 224 **8** 286
9 263 **10** 285 **11** 278 **12** 278
13 270 **14** 272 **15** 88, 96 **16** *Book 1*
17 240 **18** 44 **19** 271 **20** 280

Paper 4D (page 317)

1 183 **2** 264 **3** 265 **4** 100
5 278 **6** 272 **7** 293 **8** 272
9 272 **10** 292 **11** 264, 270 **12** 272
13 285 **14** 270 **15** 285 **16** 188
17 240 **18** 270, 272 **19** 271, 266 **20** 113

Paper 4E (page 321)

1 74 **2** 265 **3** 12 **4** 285
5 294 **6** 285 **7** 264 **8** 292
9 293 **10** 95 **11** 39 **12** 113, 278
13 285 **14** 78 **15** 4 **16** 272
17 273 **18** 231 **19** 270 **20** 213

Paper 4F (page 325)

1 271 **2** 265 **3** 292 **4** 279
5 286 **6** 285 **7** 280 **8** 278
9 55 **10** 128 **11** 270 **12** 158
13 265 **14** 15 **15** 25 **16** 264
17 272 **18** 111 **19** 88 **20** 132

UNIT 5

Modelling 5

EXERCISE 68 (page 330)

1

x	-3	-2	-1	0	1	2	3
y	$0.0\dot{3}\dot{7}$	$0.\dot{1}$	$0.\dot{3}$	1	3	9	27

3

x	-3	-2	-1	0	1	2	3
y	27	9	3	1	$0.\dot{3}$	$0.\dot{1}$	$0.0\dot{3}\dot{7}$

5 a 60.6 million, 61.2 million, 66.3 million

c

n (years after 2000)	0	10	20	30	40	50
p (millions)	60	66.3	73.2	80.9	89.3	98.7

d 76.9 million approx.; $p = 75$ million in
2022.4

EXERCISE 68★ (page 330)

1

x	0	0.5	1	1.5	2
y	1	1.2	2	4.8	16

3 a

t (years)	0	10	20	30	40	50
A (m^2)	100	**200**	**400**	800	**1600**	**3200**

c 566 m^2; 35.8 years

5 a

t (min)	0	4	8	12	16	20
T (°C)	90	67.3	50.4	37.7	28.2	21.1

b At $t = 14$, $T = 32.6$, so she will complain.

EXERCISE 69 (page 335)

1 $y = x^2 + 3$; $a = 1$, $b = 3$
3 $y = 2x^2 - 3$; $a = 2$, $b = -3$
5 **a** $y = 3x^2 + 2$; $a = 3$, $b = 2$
　　　b $y = 14$; $x = 1.2$

EXERCISE 69★ (page 336)

1 $y = x^3 - 10$; $a = 1$, $b = -10$
3 $\sqrt{y} = 1.5\sqrt{x} + 4$; $a = 1.5$, $b = 4$

Algebra 5

EXERCISE 71 (page 340)

1 $x^3 + x^2 - 5x + 3$
3 $x^3 - 13x - 12$
5 $2x^3 + 7x^2 - 29x + 21$
7 $x^3 + 7x^2 + 14x + 8$
9 $x^3 + 2x^2 - 13x + 10$
11 $3x^3 + 7x^2 - 103x - 35$

EXERCISE 71★ (page 340)

1 $2x^3 + 5x^2 - x - 1$
3 $3x^3 + 14x^2 + x - 28$
5 $6x^4 + 7x^3 - 7x^2 - 21x - 10$
7 $6x^3 + 9x^2 - 33x - 18$
9 $6x^3 - 31x^2 - 73x - 28$
11 $2x^4 + 19x^3 + 37x^2 - 55x - 75$

EXERCISE 72 (page 341)

1 5　　**3** 0　　**5** -1　　**7** 0　　**9** 2

EXERCISE 72★ (page 342)

1 8　　　　**3** -13　　**5** -17
7 8　　　　**9** 0

EXERCISE 73 (page 342)

1 $x^2 + 2x + 3$
3 $x^2 + 5x + 2$
5 $x^2 - 4x - 1$
7 $x^3 + 2x^2 - 3x + 1$
9 $x^2 + 4x + 1$

EXERCISE 73★ (page 343)

1 $x^2 + 3x - 1$
3 $x^3 - 2x^2 + 4x - 3$
5 $3x^2 + 5x - 2$
7 $4x^3 + 12x - 5$

EXERCISE 74 (page 344)

1 $(1 + x)^2(5 + x)$　　**3** $2(x + 3)(2 - x)^3$
5 $3(x + 1)(x - 2)$　　**7** $(x + 3)^2$
9 $-\frac{1}{2}(x + 2)(x + 5)$

EXERCISE 74★ (page 344)

1 $(5 - 4x)(4x - 3)^2$　　　　**3** $4(2x - 1)(x - 2)^2$
5 $(2x + 3)(x - 1)(x + 1)$　**7** $5(2x - 1)$
9 $(7x - 4)(5x - 7)$　　　　**11** $-\frac{1}{4}(x + 1)^3(3x + 2)$

EXERCISE 75 (page 345)

1 $\dfrac{3}{2}$　　　　**3** $\dfrac{r}{s}$　　　　**5** $t + 2$

7 $\dfrac{(a + b)}{(a - b)}$　　**9** $\dfrac{(x + 1)}{(x - 3)}$

EXERCISE 75★ (page 345)

1 $\dfrac{3}{5}$　　　　**3** $\dfrac{y}{x}$　　　　**5** $\dfrac{(r - 3)}{(r + 1)}$

7 $\dfrac{(a - b)}{(a + b)}$　　**9** $\dfrac{2(x + 8)}{y}$

EXERCISE 76 (page 346)

1 $2x$　　　　**3** $\dfrac{y}{x}$　　　　**5** $\dfrac{(p - 1)}{(p - 2)}$

7 $\dfrac{(x - 2)}{(x - 4)}$　　**9** $\dfrac{(x + 3)}{(x + 4)}$

EXERCISE 76★ (page 346)

1 $\dfrac{2(x - 3)}{(x + 2)}$　　**3** $\dfrac{1}{(x + 1)}$　　**5** $\dfrac{(x + 2)}{(x - 2)}$

7 $\dfrac{(p + 4)}{(p - 5)}$　　**9** $\dfrac{y}{(x + 3y)}$

EXERCISE 77 (page 348)

1 $\dfrac{(2y + 3x)}{xy}$　　　　**3** $\dfrac{-1}{4x}$

5 $\dfrac{2x}{(x - 1)(x + 1)}$　　**7** $\dfrac{1}{(x + 1)}$

9 $\dfrac{17}{15x}$　　　　　　**11** $\dfrac{1}{(x + 1)}$

EXERCISE 77★ (page 348)

1 $\dfrac{x - 1}{(x + 3)(x + 2)}$　　**3** $\dfrac{x^2 + x + 1}{1 + x}$

5 $\dfrac{x + 2}{(x + 1)^2}$　　　　**7** $\dfrac{2x + 3}{(x + 1)(x + 2)}$

9 $\dfrac{8}{(x - 3)(x + 1)}$

EXERCISE 78 (page 349)

1 $x = 6$ **3** $x = -\frac{2}{3}$

5 $x = -4$ or $x = 5$ **7** $x = 0$ or $x = 6$

9 $x = -1$ or $x = 4$

EXERCISE 78★ (page 349)

1 $x = 4$ **3** $x = -6$ or $x = 6$

5 $x = -\frac{7}{3}$ or $x = 2$ **7** $x = -\frac{1}{3}$ or $x = 2$

9 $x = -2$ or $x = 6$

EXERCISE 79 (page 352)

1 Yes   **3** No   **5** Yes

7 Yes   **9** 401   **11** 609

13 $a = 1, d = 3, S = 15\,251$

15 $d = 6, S = 4800$

17 a £33 000   **b** £336 000

EXERCISE 79★ (page 353)

1 −534

3 770

5 $a = 8, d = 3, S = 10\,120$

7 25 terms

9 $x = -1$

11 3367

EXERCISE 80 (page 356)

1 Yes   **3** No

5 Yes   **7** Yes

9 29 524.5   **11** $S = 3495$ (4 s.f.)

13 $r = 6$ **15** $a = 1, r = 4$

EXERCISE 80★ (page 356)

1 61.6 (3 s.f.)

3 $S = 65\,535$

5 $r = 4$, 10th term is 12 288

7 $x = \frac{5}{4}$

9 $S = 14\,043$

11 a $r = 1.1$ **b** £336.37   **c** £3200.12

EXERCISE 81 (page 358)

1 $S = 1.25$

3 $r = 0.5$

5 57 m

EXERCISE 81★ (page 359)

1 $S = 40.5$

3 $r = 0.8$ or $r = 0.2$

5 No, he walks 100 km

Graphs 5

EXERCISE 83 (page 363)

1 a 52.5 units^2 **b** 91.6 units^2

    c 344 units^2 **d** 83 units^2

3 a 126 m^2 **b** 35 m^3/s

EXERCISE 83★ (page 365)

1 a 370 units^2 **b** 103.9 units^2

    c 903.8 units^2

3 a 365 000 joules   **b** 3650 joules/second

Rates of change 5

EXERCISE 85 (page 369)

1 a 6; 2; −4   **b** At $x = 3$

3 a 1.4; 5.5   **b** At $x \simeq 4$

EXERCISE 85★ (page 371)

1 b −10 °C/min; −4.7 °C/min

    Rate of temperature change decreases as time increases

3 a

t (h)	0	2	4	6	8	10	12
y (m)	5	8	5	2	5	8	5

    b Approx 10.27am

    c 1.7 m/h = 2.8 cm/min

      −1.7 m/h = −2.8 cm/min

      1.7 m/h = 2.8 cm/min

Measures of spread 5

EXERCISE 87 (page 380)

1 2010–2190 g

3 34.5 cm; 1.75 cm

5 $\Sigma x = 72, \Sigma x^2 = 848, \Sigma(x - \bar{x})^2 = 200,$
    $\bar{x} = 9, \sigma = 5$

7 $\Sigma x = 60, \Sigma x^2 = 450, \Sigma(x - \bar{x})^2 = 90,$
    $\bar{x} = 6, \sigma = 3$

9 $\bar{x} = 6.36, \sigma = 2.46$

11 $\bar{x} = 75.7, \sigma = 0.286$

13 a $\bar{x} = 64.6, \sigma = 12.9; \bar{x} = 66, \sigma = 31.9$

EXERCISE 87★ (page 383)

1 $\bar{x} = £30, \sigma = £14.14$

3 $\bar{x} = £3900, \sigma = £258.20$

5 $\bar{x} = 1.5, \sigma = 1.1$

7 $\bar{x} = 7, \sigma = 1.59$

INDEX

◆ Index

Index